Merrill

Advanced Mathematical Concepts

Precalculus with Applications

EVALUATION MASTERS

GLENCOE

McGraw-Hill

New York, New York
Columbus, Ohio
Woodland Hills, California
Peoria, Illinois

Send all inquiries to:
Glencoe/McGraw-Hill
8787 Orion Place
Columbus, OH 43240

ISBN: 0-02-824294-7

Printed in the United States of America.

6 7 8 9 10 11 12   009   02 01 00 99

CONTENTS

Glencoe Division, Macmillan/McGraw-Hill

CONTENTS

Glencoe Division, Macmillan/McGraw-Hill

Chapter 1 Test, Form 1A

Write the letter for the correct answer in the blank at the right of each problem.

1. Given that x is an integer and $-1 \le x < 4$, state the relation represented by $y = |2x| + 1$ by listing a set of ordered pairs. Then state whether the relation is a function.
   A. $(-1, 3), (0, 1), (1, 3), (2, 5), (3, 7)$; yes
   B. $(-1, 3), (0, 1), (1, 3), (2, 5), (3, 7), (4, 9)$; yes
   C. $(-1, 3), (0, 1), (1, 3), (2, 5), (3, 7)$; no
   D. $(-1, 3), (0, 1), (1, 3), (2, 5), (3, 7), (4, 9)$; no

   1. _____

2. Given $f(x) = x^2 - 4$, find $f(-3)$.
   A. -13 B. 5 C. 13 D. -10

   2. _____

3. Name all values of x that are not in the domain of the function $f(x) = \dfrac{2x + 1}{x^2 - 1}$.
   A. $x \le 1$ B. $x = \pm \dfrac{1}{2}$ C. $-1 \le x \le 1$ D. $x = \pm 1$

   3. _____

4. Given $f(x) = \dfrac{x^2}{x + 3}$ and $g(x) = 3x - 2$, find $(f + g)(x)$.

   A. $\dfrac{4x^2 - 2x}{x + 3}$ B. $\dfrac{4x^2 + 7x - 6}{x + 3}$

   C. $\dfrac{6x^2 + 5x + 9}{x + 3}$ D. $\dfrac{x^3 + 6x^2 + 7x - 6}{x + 3}$

   4. _____

5. If $f(x) = 2x - 5$ and $g(x) = \dfrac{2}{x + 3}$, find $[g \circ f](x)$.

   A. $-\dfrac{5x + 11}{x + 3}$ B. $\dfrac{1}{x - 4}$ C. $\dfrac{5x + 13}{x + 3}$ D. $\dfrac{1}{x - 1}$

   5. _____

6. Given $f(x) = x^2 - 4$, find $f^{-1}(x)$. Then state whether the inverse is a function.
   A. $\pm\sqrt{x - 4}$; yes   B. $\pm\sqrt{x + 4}$; yes   C. $\pm\sqrt{x + 4}$; no   D. $\pm\sqrt{x^2 + 4}$; no

   6. _____

7. Which equation is shown by the graph?
   A. $13x - 20y + 40 = 0$
   B. $3x + 2y - 1 = 0$
   C. $4x - 3y + 6 = 0$
   D. $6x - 3y = 0$

   7. _____

8. Which inequality describes the graph?
   A. $2x + y < 1$
   B. $1 - y < 2x$
   C. $x + y \le 2$
   D. $y > \dfrac{1}{2}x + 1$

   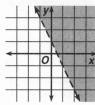

   8. _____

9. Find the zero of the function $f(x) = 7x - 8$.
   A. $-\dfrac{7}{8}$ B. $-\dfrac{8}{7}$ C. $\dfrac{7}{8}$ D. $\dfrac{8}{7}$

   9. _____

10. Find the distance between $(2, -1)$ and $(6, 9)$.
    A. $4\sqrt{5}$ B. 11 C. $2\sqrt{29}$ D. $8\sqrt{2}$

    10. _____

11. Find the slope of the line passing through $(-3, 8)$ and $(-2, 4)$.
    A. $-\dfrac{1}{4}$ B. 4 C. -4 D. $\dfrac{1}{4}$

    11. _____

Glencoe Division, Macmillan/McGraw-Hill

～ Chapter 1 Test, Form 1A (continued)

12. Find the slope and the y-intercept of the line passing through $(6, 5)$ and $(6, -4)$.

    A. 0; 6   **B.** undefined; 6

    C. 0; none   **D.** undefined; none   **12.** _____

13. Write the slope-intercept form of the equation of the line passing through $(4, -3)$ and having slope $\frac{1}{2}$.

    A. $y = \frac{1}{2}x + \frac{11}{2}$ **B.** $y = \frac{1}{2}x - 1$ **C.** $y = \frac{1}{2}x - 7$ **D.** $y = \frac{1}{2}x - 5$ **13.** _____

14. Write the slope-intercept form of the equation of the line passing through $(-5, 0)$ and $(1, -4)$.

    A. $y = -\frac{2}{3}x - \frac{10}{3}$ **B.** $y = \frac{2}{3}x + \frac{10}{3}$ **C.** $y = \frac{3}{2}x + \frac{15}{2}$ **D.** $y = -\frac{3}{2}x - \frac{15}{2}$ **14.** _____

15. Write the standard form of the equation of the line parallel to $3x - y + 1 = 0$ and passing through $(-3, 4)$.

    A. $3x - y + 15 = 0$ **B.** $3x - y + 13 = 0$

    C. $x + 3y - 9 = 0$ **D.** $x + 3y + 5 = 0$ **15.** _____

16. Write the standard form of the equation of the line perpendicular to $y = 2x - 4$ and passing through the point $(1, -5)$.

    A. $x + 2y + 9 = 0$ **B.** $x + 2y + 11 = 0$

    C. $2x - y - 3 = 0$ **D.** $2x - y + 11 = 0$ **16.** _____

17. Find the slope and the y-intercept of the line $4x + 3y - 12 = 0$.

    A. $\frac{3}{4}; -\frac{1}{3}$ **B.** $-\frac{3}{4}; \frac{1}{3}$ **C.** $\frac{4}{3}; -4$ **D.** $-\frac{4}{3}; 4$ **17.** _____

18. Why is the relation whose graph is shown at the right *not* a function?

    A. There are no values for $x < -4$.

    B. There are two values for $x = 3$.

    C. There are two values for $x = -2$.

    D. There are two values for $y = -1$.   **18.** _____

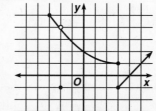

19. During one week, the Washington Senior High School Bookstore made a profit of \$546 when 91 students bought something from the store. The next week, the store made a profit of \$496 when 86 students purchased something. Write a linear equation relating profit, y, to the number of students, x.

    A. $y = \frac{1}{10}x + 36.4$ **B.** $y = \frac{1}{5}x + 45$

    C. $y = 10x - 364$ **D.** $y = 5x + 50$ **19.** _____

20. Which is a true statement about using analytic geometry to prove theorems?

    A. Analytic proofs do not use a coordinate system.

    B. Analytic proofs do not use algebraic operations.

    C. Analytic proofs often use formulas.

    D. All of the above.   **20.** _____

Bonus

For what value of k will the graph of $kx + 6y - 2 = 0$ be the same line as the graph of $y = \frac{2}{5}x + \frac{1}{3}$?

    A. $-\frac{6}{5}$ **B.** $-\frac{12}{5}$ **C.** $-\frac{1}{15}$ **D.** 5   **Bonus:** _____

Chapter 1 Test, Form 1B

Write the letter for the correct answer in the blank at the right of each problem.

1. Given that x is an integer and $-2 < x < 2$, state the relation represented by $y = |-4x| - 6$ by listing a set of ordered pairs. Then state whether the relation is a function.
   A. $(-2, 2), (-1, -2), (0, -6), (1, -2), (2, 2)$; yes
   B. $(-1, -2), (0, -6), (1, -2)$; yes
   C. $(-1, -2), (0, -6), (1, -10)$; yes
   D. $(-2, 2), (-1, -2), (0, -6), (1, -10), (2, -14)$; no

   1. _____

2. Given $f(x) = x^3 - 7$, find $f(-2)$.
   A. -15 B. 1 C. -1 D. -13

   2. _____

3. Name all values of x that are not in the domain of the function $f(x) = \sqrt{x^2 - 36}$.
   A. $x = \pm 6$ B. $-6 \le x \le 6$ C. $-6 < x < 6$ D. $x = 36$

   3. _____

4. Given $f(x) = \dfrac{x - 4}{x - 3}$ and $g(x) = 2 - 7x$, find $(f - g)(x)$.

   A. $\dfrac{-7x^2 + 24x - 10}{x - 3}$ B. $\dfrac{-6x - 2}{x - 3}$

   C. $\dfrac{7x^2 - 22x + 2}{x - 3}$ D. $\dfrac{7x + 2}{7x + 1}$

   4. _____

5. If $f(x) = 3x - 1$ and $g(x) = \dfrac{1}{2x - 1}$, find $[f \circ g](x)$.

   A. $\dfrac{2 - 2x}{2x - 1}$ B. $\dfrac{1}{6x - 3}$ C. $\dfrac{2 - x}{x - 1}$ D. $\dfrac{4 - 2x}{2x - 1}$

   5. _____

6. Given $f(x) = x^2 + 6$, find $f^{-1}(x)$. Then state whether the inverse is a function.
   A. $\pm\sqrt{x - 6}$; no B. $\pm\sqrt{x - 6}$; yes C. $\pm\sqrt{x + 6}$; no D. $\pm\sqrt{x + 6}$; yes

   6. _____

7. Which equation is shown by the graph?
   A. $5x - 2y - 8 = 0$
   B. $1.7x - 4y = 0$
   C. $2x - y - 4 = 0$
   D. $2x - 5y - 20 = 0$

   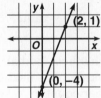

   7. _____

8. Which inequality describes the graph?
   A. $-1 < -x + y < 3$
   B. $-1 \le -x + y < 3$
   C. $-1 \le -x + y \le 3$
   D. $-1 < -x + y \le 3$

   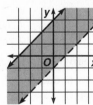

   8. _____

9. Find the zero of the function $f(x) = 11 - \dfrac{2}{5}x$.

   A. $-\dfrac{55}{2}$ B. $\dfrac{55}{2}$ C. $\dfrac{2}{55}$ D. $-\dfrac{2}{55}$

   9. _____

10. Find the distance between $(-2, -2)$ and $(-4, 1)$.
    A. $2\sqrt{17}$ B. $3\sqrt{5}$ C. $\sqrt{5}$ D. $\sqrt{13}$

    10. _____

11. Find the slope of the line passing through $(2, 6)$ and $(-3, 9)$.
    A. $-\dfrac{3}{5}$ B. $\dfrac{3}{5}$ C. -3 D. $-\dfrac{5}{3}$

    11. _____

~ Chapter 1 Test, Form 1B (continued)

12. Find the slope and the y-intercept of the line passing through $(-8, 11)$ and $(4, 11)$.
    A. undefined; none
    B. 0; 11
    C. 0; none
    D. undefined; 11

12. _____

13. Write the slope-intercept form of the equation of the line passing through $(-4, 0)$ and having slope $\frac{2}{3}$.

    A. $y = \frac{2}{3}x - 4$ B. $y = \frac{2}{3}x + \frac{8}{3}$ C. $y = \frac{2}{3}x - \frac{8}{3}$ D. $y = \frac{2}{3}x + 4$

13. _____

14. Write the slope-intercept form of the equation of the line passing through $(4, -4)$ and $(5, -10)$.
    A. $y = 14x - 60$ B. $y = -6x + 20$ C. $y = -\frac{1}{6}x + \frac{10}{3}$ D. $y = -\frac{1}{14}x + \frac{26}{7}$

14. _____

15. Write the standard form of the equation of the line parallel to $3x - 15y + 35 = 0$ and passing through $(-4, -1)$.
    A. $x - 5y - 1 = 0$
    B. $4x + y + 40 = 0$
    C. $x - 5y + 15 = 0$
    D. $x - 5y + 19 = 0$

15. _____

16. Write the standard form of the equation of the line perpendicular to $y = -\frac{1}{3}x + \frac{7}{2}$ and passing through $(2, 5)$.

    A. $3x + y - 1 = 0$
    B. $x + 3y + 17 = 0$
    C. $3x - y - 1 = 0$
    D. $2x - 6y + 13 = 0$

16. _____

17. Find the slope and the y-intercept of the line $5x - 3y + 2 = 0$.
    A. $\frac{3}{5}; -\frac{3}{2}$ B. $-\frac{5}{3}; -\frac{2}{3}$ C. $\frac{5}{3}; \frac{2}{3}$ D. $-\frac{3}{5}; -\frac{3}{2}$

17. _____

18. Why is the relation whose graph is shown at the right a function?
    A. There are opened and closed circles on the graph.
    B. For every y-value, there is only one x-value.
    C. There are two y-values at $x = 2$.
    D. For every x-value, there is only one y-value.

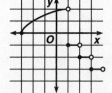

18. _____

19. Tyrone plays fullback for his high school football team. During one game, he carried the ball 16 times for 76 yards. The next game, he carried the ball 24 times for 114 yards. Write a linear equation relating yards, y, to the number of carries, x.
    A. $y = 4.75x$
    B. $y = 4.75x + 8$
    C. $y = 1.5x + 52$
    D. $y = 1.5x + 78$

19. _____

20. Which is a true statement about using analytic geometry to prove theorems?
    A. The formula for distance is often used.
    B. The formula for slope is often used.
    C. The formula for midpoint is often used.
    D. All of the above.

20. _____

Bonus

For what value of k will the graph of $3x + ky - 10 = 0$ be the same line as the graph of $y = \frac{6}{5}x - 4$?

    A. $-\frac{2}{5}$ B. $-\frac{4}{15}$ C. $-\frac{5}{2}$ D. -5

Bonus: _____

Chapter 1 Test, Form 2A

1. State the domain and range of the relation {(4, 12), (3, 6), (−1, 6), (2, 4)}.
   Then state whether the relation is a function.

   1. _____

2. Given $f(x) = |-x^2 + 4|$, find $f(-2)$.

   2. _____

3. Name all values of x that are not in the domain of the function
   $f(x) = \dfrac{6x + 5}{25 - x^2}$.

   3. _____

Given $f(x) = \dfrac{10}{x}$ and $g(x) = \dfrac{x}{x + 1}$, find each function.

4. $(f \circ g)(x)$

   4. _____

5. $[f \circ g](x)$ and $[g \circ f](x)$

   5. _____

6. Determine if the functions $f(x) = \dfrac{-4}{7 - x}$ and $g(x) = -\dfrac{4 + 7x}{x}$

   are inverses of each other. Write *yes* or *no*. Show your work.

   6. _____

7. Find the inverse of the function $f(x) = \pm\sqrt{x - 3}$. Then state whether
   the inverse is a function.

   7. _____

Graph each equation or inequality.

8. $y = -2x - 5$

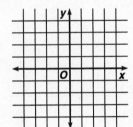

9. $y \geq \dfrac{1}{3}x + 1$

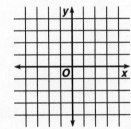

   8. _____

   9. _____

10. $2x - 3y = 6$

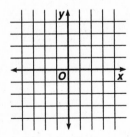

11. $2 < y < 3$

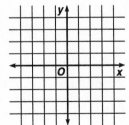

   10. _____

   11. _____

12. Find the zero of the function $f(x) = 2x - 7$.

   12. _____

13. Find the distance between $(1, 9)$ and $(-5, 6)$.

   13. _____

Glencoe Division, Macmillan/McGraw-Hill

Chapter 1 Test, Form 2A (continued)

14. Find the slope of the line passing through $(4, 2)$ and $(6, -7)$.

14. _____

15. Find the slope and y-intercept of the equation of the line passing through $(7, 0)$ and $(-5, 0)$.

15. _____

16. Write the slope-intercept form of the equation of the line passing through $(1, 7)$ and having slope -3.

16. _____

17. Write the slope-intercept form of the equation of the line passing through $(4, -3)$ and $(1, 4)$.

17. _____

18. Write the standard form of the equation of the line perpendicular to $-x + 2y = 6$ and passing through $(-6, 3)$.

18. _____

19. Write the standard form of the equation of the line parallel to $y = \frac{1}{2}x + 3$ and passing through $(0, 4)$.

19. _____

20. Find the slope and the y-intercept of the line with equation $10x - 3y + 12 = 0$.

20. _____

21. Find the slope and the y-intercept of the line with equation $-px - my + q = 0$.

21. _____

22. Is the graph below that of a function? Why or why not?

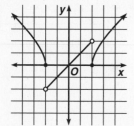

22. _____

23. Write an inequality that describes the graph shown below.

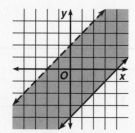

23. _____

24. In practice, Leslie ran 5 miles in 24 minutes. The next day in practice, she ran 15 miles in 1 hour and 12 minutes. Assuming that Leslie ran at about the same rate each day, write a linear equation relating miles, x, to minutes, y.

24. _____

25. Prove analytically that the diagonals of a square are congruent.

25. _____

Bonus

Find the inverse of the function $f(x) = \left(\sqrt[4]{x^3}\right)^{\frac{1}{5}}$.

Bonus: _____

Chapter 1 Test, Form 2B

1. State the domain and range of the relation {(6, 3), (1, 1), (−8, 9), (9, −8), (6, 4)}. Then state whether the relation is a function.

    1. _____

2. Given $f(x) = \sqrt{9 + (-x)^3}$, find $f(-3)$.

    2. _____

3. Name all values of x that are not in the domain of the function $f(x) = \dfrac{11}{8 - |4x|}$.

    3. _____

Given $f(x) = x^2 - x - 6$ and $g(x) = x + 2$, find each function.

4. $\left(\dfrac{f}{g}\right)(x)$

    4. _____

5. $[f \circ g](x)$ and $[g \circ f](x)$

    5. _____

6. Determine if the functions $f(x) = \pm\sqrt{x^2 - 4}$ and $g(x) = \pm\sqrt{x^2 + 4}$ are inverses of each other. Write *yes* or *no*. Show your work.

    6. _____

7. Find the inverse of the function $f(x) = \dfrac{5}{x - 3}$. Then state whether the inverse is a function.

    7. _____

Graph each equation or inequality.

8. $y = \dfrac{2}{3}x - 3$

9. $y > -6x + 2$

    8. _____

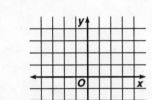
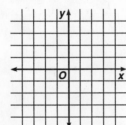

    9. _____

10. $-4x - y = 2$

11. $-2 \le x \le 3$

    10. _____

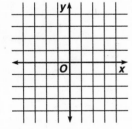
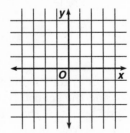

    11. _____

12. Find the zero of the function $f(x) = -4x - 1$.

    12. _____

13. Find the distance between $(-8, 5)$ and $(-1, -2)$.

    13. _____

Glencoe Division, Macmillan/McGraw-Hill

Chapter 1 Test, Form 2B (continued)

14. Find the slope of the line passing through $(-9, 4)$ and $(6, 1)$.

14. _____

15. Find the slope and y-intercept of the equation of the line passing through $(1, 4)$ and $(1, -3)$.

15. _____

16. Write the slope-intercept form of the equation of the line passing through $(4, -2)$ and having slope $\frac{1}{3}$.

16. _____

17. Write the slope-intercept form of the equation of the line passing through $(1, -5)$ and $(-2, 6)$.

17. _____

18. Write the standard form of the equation of the line perpendicular to $2x + y = -2$ and passing through $(7, 4)$.

18. _____

19. Write the standard form of the equation of the line parallel to $y = 4x + 5$ and passing through $(3, 0)$.

19. _____

20. Find the slope and the y-intercept of the line with equation $-9x - 4y + 1 = 0$.

20. _____

21. Find the slope and the y-intercept of the line with equation $kx - hy + d = 0$.

21. _____

22. Is the graph below that of a function? Why or why not?

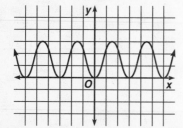

22. _____

23. Write an inequality that describes the graph shown below.

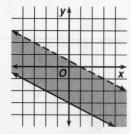

23. _____

24. Jason is selling candy bars to raise money for his high school band. He sold 22 candy bars on Saturday and the school made a profit of $17.16. On Sunday, he sold 43 candy bars and the school made a profit of $33.54. Write a linear equation relating candy bars sold, x, to profit made for the school, y.

24. _____

25. Prove analytically that the opposite sides of a parallelogram are congruent.

25. _____

Bonus

Find the inverse of the function $f(x) = \left(\sqrt[3]{x^2}\right)^{\frac{1}{5}}$.

Bonus: _____

Chapter 1, Quiz A (Lessons 1-1 through 1-2)

Use the relation {(9, 3), (−2, 2), (6, 5), (−2, 4), (7, 1)} for Exercises 1 and 2.

1. State the domain and range of the relation.

2. Is the relation a function?

3. Given that x is an integer and $-2 \leq x < 1$, state the relation represented by $y = -3x + 8$ by listing a set of ordered pairs. Then state whether the relation is a function.

Given $f(x) = \dfrac{4x}{2x + 3}$, find each value.

4. $f(4)$

5. $f(n - 2)$

Given $f(x) = \dfrac{x + 2}{6}$ and $g(x) = 7x - 1$, find each function.

6. $(f + g)(x)$

7. $\left(\dfrac{f}{g}\right)(x)$

8. $[f \circ g](x)$

9. $[g \circ f](x)$

10. Determine if the functions $f(x) = 3x + 4$ and $g(x) = \dfrac{1}{3}x - \dfrac{4}{3}$ are inverses of each other. Write *yes* or *no*. Show your work.

1. _____

2. _____

3. _____

4. _____

5. _____

6. _____

7. _____

8. _____

9. _____

10. _____

Chapter 1, Quiz B (Lesson 1-3)

1. Write an inequality that describes the graph.

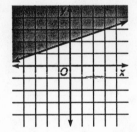

2. Find the zero of the function $f(x) = -4x - 6$.

Graph each equation or inequality.

3. $y = 0.75x + 2.5$ 4. $2x + y = -4$ 5. $4x - 2y < 16$

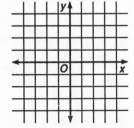 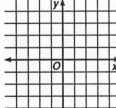 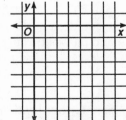

1. _____

2. _____

3. _____

4. _____

5. _____

NAME _____ DATE _____

~ Chapter 1, Quiz C (Lesson 1-4)

1. Find the distance between $(-3, 4)$ and $(8, -7)$.

   1. _____

2. Find the slope of the line passing through $(c - 1, d + 3)$ and $(c, d + 4)$.

   2. _____

3. Determine whether the figure with vertices at $(3, 13)$, $(6, 2)$, $(4, 0)$ and $(1, 10)$ is a parallelogram.

   3. _____

4. Find the value of k for which points with the set of coordinates $\{(-2, 1), (1, k), (4, 9)\}$ are collinear.

   4. _____

5. Prove analytically that quadrilateral $ABCD$ with vertices at $A(0, 0)$, $B(1, 2)$, $C(5, 5)$, and $D(4, 3)$ is a parallelogram.

   5. _____

NAME _____ DATE _____

Chapter 1, Quiz D (Lessons 1-5 through 1-6)

1. Write the slope-intercept form of the equation of the line passing through $(-6, 6)$ and having slope -1.

   1. _____

2. Write the slope-intercept form of the equation of the line passing through $(9, 2)$ and $(-3, 1)$.

   2. _____

3. Write the standard form of the equation of the line that is parallel to $y = \frac{1}{4}x + \frac{1}{3}$ and passes through $(1, -2)$.

   3. _____

4. Write the standard form of the equation of the line that is perpendicular to $3x - 2y = 5$ and passes through $(2, 4)$.

   4. _____

5. When Olivia delivers newspapers for her brother John, he pays her $1.00 for helping and $0.50 for each hour that she helps. Write an equation that relates the money she makes, y, to the number of hours she helps, x.

   5. _____

Glencoe Division, Macmillan/McGraw-Hill

NAME _____ DATE _____

Consider the relation {(0, 1), (6, 3), (−4, 9), (6, 1), (1, 5), (2, −2)}.

1. State the domain and range of the relation.

2. Name the two ordered pairs in the relation that show the relation is not a function.

1. _____

2. _____

Given f(x) = 6x² − 4x + 3, find each value.

3. $f(-2)$

4. $f(k + 1)$

3. _____

4. _____

Name all values of x that are not in the domain of the given function.

5. $f(x) = \dfrac{2x}{3x - 1}$

6. $f(x) = \sqrt{x^2 - 2}$

5. _____

6. _____

Given f(x) = −x² + 3x + 4 and g(x) = x + 2, find each function.

7. $[f \circ g](x)$

8. $(f - g)(x)$

7. _____

8. _____

9. Are the functions $f(x) = \dfrac{x + 7}{4}$ and $g(x) = \dfrac{4 + 7x}{x}$ inverses

of each other? Write *yes* or *no*. Show your work.

9. _____

10. Find the inverse of the function $f(x) = \dfrac{2}{x}$.

10. _____

11. Find the inverse of the function $g(x) = \dfrac{3x - 7}{6}$.

11. _____

12. Write an inequality that describes the graph.

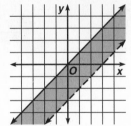

13. Find the zero of the function $f(x) = \dfrac{1}{3}x - 5$.

12. _____

13. _____

Graph each equation or inequality.

14. $2x + 4y = 8$

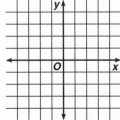

15. $y \geq |x + 3|$

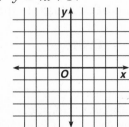

14. _____

15. _____

11

Standardized Test Questions (Chapter 1)

Choose the best answer. Write A, B, C, or D.

1. The perimeter of a quadrilateral with sides of lengths 8, 4, 6, and x is equal to the perimeter of a square with sides of length 7. What is the value of x?
   A. 2   B. 7   C. 10   D. 12   1. _____

2. If $\frac{6}{x} = 9$, then $\frac{8}{x} = \underline{\ ?\ }$.

   A. 12   B. $\frac{2}{3}$ C. $\frac{4}{3}$ D. $\frac{16}{3}$ 2. _____

3. To dilute a concentrated liquid fabric softener, the directions state to mix 3 cups of water with 1 cup of concentrated liquid. How many gallons of water will you need to make 6 gallons of diluted fabric softener?
   A. $1\frac{1}{2}$ gallons   B. 3 gallons   C. 4 gallons   D. $4\frac{1}{2}$ gallons   3. _____

4. A long-distance telephone call costs $1.25 a minute for the first 2 minutes and $0.50 for each minute thereafter. At these rates, how much will a 12-minute telephone call cost?
   A. $6.25   B. $7.25   C. $7.50   D. $8.50   4. _____

5. Which of the following *CANNOT* be the values for x and y if $m = \sqrt{x^2 - y^2}$ and m is a real number?
   A. $x = 5, y = 0$ B. $x = -2, y = 1$ C. $x = 5, y = -5$ D. $x = 3, y = -4$ 5. _____

6. On line LO below, $LM = 4$, $MN = \frac{3}{2}LM$, and $NO = \frac{1}{2}MN$. What is the length of line segment LO?

   A. 5   B. 10   C. 12   D. 13   6. _____

7. In a bookstore, 40 books were sold in one day to 24 different customers. Which of the following statements must be true?
   A. Some of the customers purchased exactly 1 book.
   B. One of the customers purchased more than 2 books.
   C. Sixteen customers purchased 2 books.
   D. Each of the customers purchased at most 1 book.   7. _____

8. The picture at the right shows a circle inscribed in a square. Find the area of the shaded region.

   A. $3\sqrt{3}$ sq. units B. 6 sq. units   C. $6\sqrt{3}$ sq. units D. 12 sq. units   8. _____

9. If $x = \frac{4}{5}$, then $3(x - 1) + 4x$ is how many fifths?

   A. 13   B. 15   C. 23   D. 25   9. _____

10. Mr. Jones spent 25% of the money he had on groceries and 80% of the remaining money on clothes. If he had $6.00 left in his pocket, how much did he spend on groceries?
    A. $2.70   B. $10.00   C. $10.80   D. $7.50   10. _____

Chapter 2 Test, Form 1A

Write the letter for the correct answer in the blank at the right of each problem.

1. Which term(s) describe(s) this system? $3x - 2y = -5$
   $4x + y = 8$

   A. dependent
   B. consistent and dependent
   C. consistent and independent
   D. inconsistent

   1. _____

2. Solve by graphing. $x - 2y = 5$
   $x + y = -1$

   A.   **B.**   **C.**   **D.**

   2. _____

   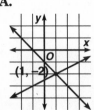 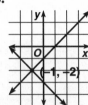 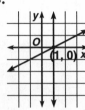 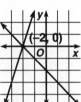

3. Solve algebraically. $y = -2x + 3$
   $3x + 4y = 12$

   A. $(3, 0)$ **B.** $(0, -3)$ **C.** $(-3, 0)$ **D.** $(0, 3)$

   3. _____

4. Find $A - B$ if $A = \begin{bmatrix} -5 & 0 \\ 1 & 1 \\ 4 & -7 \end{bmatrix}$ and $B = \begin{bmatrix} 6 & -2 \\ -3 & -3 \\ 0 & 1 \end{bmatrix}$.

   A. $\begin{bmatrix} -11 & 2 \\ 4 & 4 \\ 4 & -8 \end{bmatrix}$ **B.** $\begin{bmatrix} -1 & -2 \\ -2 & -2 \\ 4 & 6 \end{bmatrix}$ **C.** $\begin{bmatrix} 1 & -2 \\ -2 & -2 \\ 4 & -6 \end{bmatrix}$ **D.** $\begin{bmatrix} -1 & -2 \\ 4 & 4 \\ 4 & -6 \end{bmatrix}$

   4. _____

5. Find the values of x and y for which $\begin{bmatrix} 3y \\ x \\ 6y \end{bmatrix} = \begin{bmatrix} x + 5 \\ 0 \\ 10 \end{bmatrix}$ is true.

   A. $\left(0, \frac{3}{5}\right)$ **B.** $\left(0, \frac{5}{3}\right)$ **C.** $\left(0, -\frac{3}{5}\right)$ **D.** $\left(0, -\frac{5}{3}\right)$

   5. _____

6. Find DE if $D = [5 \quad 2]$ and $E = \begin{bmatrix} 9 \\ -6 \end{bmatrix}$.

   A. $[45 \quad -12]$ **B.** $[33]$ **C.** $\begin{bmatrix} 45 \\ -12 \end{bmatrix}$ **D.** $[57]$

   6. _____

7. Find the value of $\begin{vmatrix} 5 & -1 \\ 2 & 7 \end{vmatrix}$.

   A. 33   **B.** -37 **C.** 37   **D.** 39

   7. _____

8. Find the inverse of $\begin{bmatrix} 3 & -6 \\ 1 & -2 \end{bmatrix}$, if it exists.

   A. does not exist   **B.** $\begin{bmatrix} \frac{1}{6} & -\frac{1}{2} \\ \frac{1}{12} & -\frac{1}{4} \end{bmatrix}$ **C.** $\begin{bmatrix} -\frac{1}{6} & \frac{1}{2} \\ -\frac{1}{12} & \frac{1}{4} \end{bmatrix}$ **D.** $\begin{bmatrix} -\frac{1}{2} & \frac{1}{6} \\ -\frac{1}{4} & \frac{1}{12} \end{bmatrix}$

   8. _____

9. Solve using matrix equations. $4x - 3y = 2$
   $7x + y = 6$

   A. $\left(\frac{4}{5}, \frac{2}{5}\right)$ **B.** $\left(-\frac{4}{5}, \frac{2}{5}\right)$ **C.** $\left(\frac{5}{4}, 1\right)$ **D.** $\left(1, \frac{2}{3}\right)$

   9. _____

~ Chapter 2 Test, Form 1A (continued)

10. State the row operation you would use to get a zero in the second column of row 2: $\begin{bmatrix} 2 & 1 & 5 \\ 3 & -4 & 1 \end{bmatrix}$

    A. Interchange rows 1 and 2.

    B. Multiply row 2 by $-\frac{1}{4}$.

    C. Replace row 2 with the sum of row 1 and row 2.

    D. Replace row 2 with the sum of row 2 and four times row 1.

10. _____

11. Solve by using an augmented matrix.

$$x - 3y - 3z = 0$$
$$2x + 5y - 5z = 1$$
$$-x + 5y - 6z = -9$$

    A. $(1, 1, -2)$ **B.** $(3, 0, 1)$ **C.** $(0, -3, 3)$ **D.** $(-2, 4, 3)$

11. _____

12. Which is the graph of this system? $y \leq 0$ $x \geq y$

                                           $x \leq 0$ $x + y \geq -4$

A. 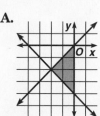   **B.** 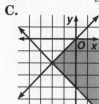   **C.**   **D.**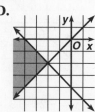

12. _____

13. Find the maximum and minimum values of $f(x,y) = x + y$ for the polygonal convex set determined by this system of inequalities.

$$x \geq 1$$
$$y \geq 0$$
$$x \leq 4 - y$$

    A. minimum: 1; maximum: 8   **B.** minimum: 0; maximum: 4

    C. minimum: 0; maximum: 8   **D.** minimum: 1; maximum: 4

13. _____

14. Which term best describes the linear programming system represented by the graph?

    A. infeasible

    B. unbounded

    C. an optimal solution

    D. alternate optimal solutions

14. _____

15. A farm supply store carries 50-lb bags of both grain pellets and grain mash for pig feed. They can store 600 bags of pig feed. At least twice as many of their customers prefer the mash to the pellets. The store buys the pellets for $3.75 per bag and sells them for $6.00. It buys the mash for $2.50 per bag and sells it for $4.00. If the store orders no more than $1400 worth of pig feed, how many bags of mash should the store order to make the most profit?

    A. 160 bags   **B.** 200 bags   **C.** 320 bags   **D.** 400 bags

15. _____

Bonus

Solve the system by graphing. $|y| \geq 2$

                                          $|x| \leq 1$

    A. no solution   **B.**   **C.** 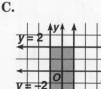   **D.**

Bonus: _____

Chapter 2 Test, Form 1B

Write the letter for the correct answer in the blank at the right of each problem.

1. Which system is inconsistent?

   A. $4x + y = 5$ **B.** $x - 2y = 1$ **C.** $2x = y$ **D.** $x = 2$

       $2x - y = 8$ $y = 0.5x$ $x + y = 0$ $y = -1$ **1.** _____

2. Which system of equations is shown by the graph?

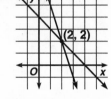

   A. $x + y = 4$ **B.** $y = 2x - 1$

       $3x + y = 8$ $x + y = 4$

   C. $y = x$ **D.** $x = 1$

       $3x = -4y$ $3x + y = 8$ **2.** _____

3. Solve algebraically. $y + 2x = 7$

                           $y = 5 - x$

   A. $(8, -3)$ **B.** $(-2, 3)$ **C.** $(4, 1)$ **D.** $(2, 3)$ **3.** _____

4. Find $A + B$ if $A = \begin{bmatrix} 2 & 3 & 1 \\ -1 & 0 & -4 \end{bmatrix}$ and $B = \begin{bmatrix} -5 & 2 & -1 \\ 8 & 4 & -3 \end{bmatrix}$.

   A. $\begin{bmatrix} -3 & 7 \\ 6 & 4 \\ 0 & -7 \end{bmatrix}$ **B.** $\begin{bmatrix} -3 & 5 & 0 \\ 7 & 4 & -7 \end{bmatrix}$ **C.** $\begin{bmatrix} 3 & 6 & 0 \\ -7 & 4 & 7 \end{bmatrix}$ **D.** $\begin{bmatrix} 3 & -7 \\ 6 & 4 \\ 0 & 7 \end{bmatrix}$ **4.** _____

5. Find the values of x and y for which $\begin{bmatrix} y \\ 3x \end{bmatrix} = \begin{bmatrix} 5 - x \\ 2y - 5 \end{bmatrix}$ is true.

   A. $(4, 1)$ **B.** $(1, 4)$ **C.** $(-1, 12)$ **D.** $(2, 4)$ **5.** _____

6. Find $-2D$ if $D = \begin{bmatrix} -4 & 1 & 0 \\ 3 & -5 & -2 \end{bmatrix}$.

   A. $\begin{bmatrix} 8 & -6 \\ -2 & 10 \\ 0 & 4 \end{bmatrix}$ **B.** $\begin{bmatrix} 8 & -2 & 0 \\ -6 & 10 & 4 \end{bmatrix}$ **C.** $\begin{bmatrix} -8 & -2 & 2 \\ -6 & -10 & 4 \end{bmatrix}$ **D.** $\begin{bmatrix} -8 & -6 \\ -2 & -10 \\ 2 & 4 \end{bmatrix}$ **6.** _____

7. Find the value of $\begin{vmatrix} 3 & 4 \\ 1 & 5 \end{vmatrix}$.

   A. 9   **B.** 7   **C.** 11   **D.** -9 **7.** _____

8. Find the inverse of $\begin{bmatrix} 7 & 1 \\ 3 & 0 \end{bmatrix}$, if it exists.

   A. does not exist   **B.** $\begin{bmatrix} -1 & 0 \\ 3 & 2 \end{bmatrix}$ **C.** $\begin{bmatrix} 0 & \frac{1}{3} \\ 1 & -\frac{7}{3} \end{bmatrix}$ **D.** $\begin{bmatrix} 0 & \frac{1}{4} \\ 1 & -\frac{7}{4} \end{bmatrix}$ **8.** _____

9. Sarah Cordwell wants to make 40 gallons of buttermilk with a 4.5% fat content by mixing a batch of 7% buttermilk with a batch of 3% buttermilk. Use matrix equations to find how many gallons of the 7% butter-milk she should use.

   A. 20.25 gal   **B.** 19.75 gal   **C.** 25 gal   **D.** 15 gal   **9.** _____

~ **Chapter 2 Test, Form 1B (continued)**

10. Simplify the augmented matrix $\begin{bmatrix} 6 & 1 & -1 & \vdots & -2 \\ 2 & 5 & -1 & \vdots & 2 \\ 1 & 2 & 1 & \vdots & 5 \end{bmatrix}$

    A. $\begin{bmatrix} 0 & 0 & 1 & \vdots & 0 \\ 0 & 1 & 0 & \vdots & 1 \\ 1 & 0 & 0 & \vdots & 3 \end{bmatrix}$ **B.** $\begin{bmatrix} 1 & 0 & 0 & \vdots & 0 \\ 0 & 1 & 0 & \vdots & 1 \\ 0 & 0 & 1 & \vdots & 3 \end{bmatrix}$ **C.** $\begin{bmatrix} 1 & 0 & 0 & \vdots & 0 \\ 0 & 1 & 0 & \vdots & -1 \\ 0 & 0 & 1 & \vdots & -3 \end{bmatrix}$ **D.** $\begin{bmatrix} 0 & 0 & 1 & \vdots & 0 \\ 0 & 1 & 0 & \vdots & -1 \\ 1 & 0 & 0 & \vdots & -3 \end{bmatrix}$ 10. _____

11. Solve the system of equations by using an augmented matrix. $x - y + z = 5$
    $$-2x - y - z = -6$$
    $$3x + 3y - 2z = -5$$

    A. $(1, 0, 4)$ **B.** $(0, -1, 6)$ **C.** $(-1, -2, 4)$ **D.** $(-3, 0, 2)$ 11. _____

12. Which is the graph of the system? $x \geq 0$
    $$y \geq 0$$
    $$x + 3y \leq 6$$

    A.   **B.**   **C.**   **D.**

                    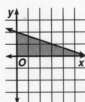   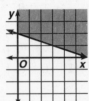

    12. _____

13. Find the minimum value of $f(x, y) = 2x - y + 2$ for the polygonal convex set
    determined by this system of inequalities. $0 \leq x \leq 3$
    $$y \geq 0$$
    $$x + y \leq 5$$

    A. -2 **B.** 0 **C.** -3 **D.** 5 13. _____

14. Marion Schaeffer wants to expand her cut-flower business. She has 12
    additional acres where she intends to plant lilies and gladioli. She can plant
    at most 7 acres of gladiolus bulbs, and no more than 11 acres of lilies. In
    addition, the number of acres planted to gladioli can be no more than twice
    the number of acres planted to lilies. The inequality $L + 2G \geq 10$ represents
    her labor restrictions. If her profits are represented by the function
    $f(L, G) = 300L + 200G$, how many acres of lilies should she plant to maximize
    her profit?

    A. 0 acres   **B.** 11 acres   **C.** 1 acre   **D.** 9.5 acres   14. _____

15. Describe the linear programming situation for this system of inequalities.
    $x \leq 1$
    $y \geq 0$
    $3x + y \leq 5$

    A. infeasible   **B.** two optimal solutions
    C. an optimal solution   **D.** unbounded   15. _____

Bonus

Find the value of c for which $3x + y = 5$
the system is consistent and dependent. $-4.5y = c + 9x$

    A. -8 **B.** no value   **C.** -7.5 **D.** 9.5   Bonus: _____

Chapter 2 Test, Form 2A

1. Determine whether the system shown by the graph is consistent and independent, consistent and dependent, or inconsistent.

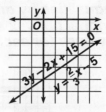

1. _____

2. Solve by graphing.

   $5x + 2y = 8$
   $x - y = 3$

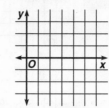

2. _____

3. Solve algebraically. $4x - 3y = 5$
                         $4x - 3y = 10$

3. _____

Use matrices D, E, and F to find the difference and product.

$$D = \begin{bmatrix} -2 & 1 \\ 7 & 5 \\ 3 & -4 \end{bmatrix} \quad E = \begin{bmatrix} -3 & -4 \\ 0 & 1 \\ 2 & 6 \end{bmatrix} \quad F = \begin{bmatrix} -2 & 5 & 1 \\ 3 & 4 & -6 \end{bmatrix}$$

4. _____

4. $E - D$ 5. $3F$

5. _____

6. For what values of x and y is the matrix equation
   $$\begin{bmatrix} x \\ y + 3 \end{bmatrix} = \begin{bmatrix} 5y \\ x + 7 \end{bmatrix}$$ true?

6. _____

7. Find the value of $\begin{vmatrix} -3 & 2 \\ 5 & -7 \end{vmatrix}$.

7. _____

8. If it exists, find A^{-1} if $A = \begin{bmatrix} 2 & 0 \\ 1 & 3 \end{bmatrix}$.

8. _____

9. Solve using matrix equations. $x - y = 5$
                                   $2x + 3y = 10$

9. _____

10. Lucien can buy 1 pound of Columbian coffee beans for $4.25. He can buy 1 pound of French roast coffee beans for $3.75. If he buys a one-pound mixture of the two kinds of beans for $4.00, how much of each kind of coffee bean does he buy? Write a system of equations and solve by using augmented matrices.

10. _____

11. Solve this system by using augmented matrices. $x - 2y + z = -5$
                                                     $3x - 2y + z = 3$
                                                     $2x - y + 2z = -7$

11. _____

~ Chapter 2 Test, Form 2A (continued)

Solve each system of inequalities by graphing and name the vertices of each polygonal convex set. Then, find the maximum and minimum values for each function.

12. $x \geq 0$
    $y \geq 0$
    $x + y \leq 6$
    $f(x, y) = 5x + 3y$

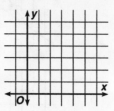

12. _____

13. $x \leq 0$
    $y \leq 0$
    $2x + y \leq 3$
    $f(x, y) = 2x + 2y$

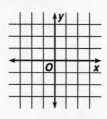

13. _____

Solve each problem, if possible. If not possible, state whether the problem is infeasible, has alternate optimal solutions, or is unbounded.

14. The members of the junior class at White Mountain High School are selling ice cream cones in the school cafeteria to raise money for their prom. A local ice cream shop has donated the ice cream. The students have enough Heath Bar Crunch ice cream for 50 cones and enough frozen yogurt for 80 cones. They have 100 cones available. If they plan to sell each Heath Bar Crunch cone for $2.00 and each frozen yogurt cone for $1, and they sell all 100 cones, what is the maximum amount they can expect to make?

14. _____

15. Ginny Dettore custom sews bridal gowns and bridesmaid dresses on a part-time basis. Each dress sells for $200 and each gown sells for $650. It takes her 2 weeks to produce a bridesmaid dress and 5 weeks to produce a bridal gown. She accepts orders for at least 3 times as many bridesmaid dresses as she does bridal gowns. In the next 22 weeks, what is the maximum amount of money she can expect to earn?

15. _____

Bonus

Use matrix equations to find the value of x for the system $\begin{array}{l} ax + by = c. \\ dx + ey = f \end{array}$

Bonus: _____

Chapter 2 Test, Form 2B

1. Identify the system shown by the graph as consistent and independent, consistent and dependent, or inconsistent.

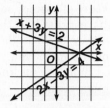

1. _____

2. Graph the system to find the solution set.
$y = 3 - x$
$y - x = -1$

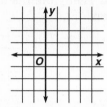

2. _____

3. Solve algebraically. $4x - y = -3$
$5x + 2y = 1$

3. _____

Use matrices A, B, and C to find the sum or product.

$A = \begin{bmatrix} -3 & -2 \\ 0 & 5 \\ 6 & -1 \end{bmatrix}$ $B = \begin{bmatrix} 8 & 6 \\ -5 & 4 \\ 3 & -1 \end{bmatrix}$ $C = \begin{bmatrix} -3 & 2 & 1 \\ 0 & 5 & -6 \end{bmatrix}$

4. _____

4. $A + B$

5. AC

5. _____

6. Find the value of x and y for which $[5 \quad -3x] = [-4x \quad 5y]$ is true.

6. _____

7. Find the value of $\begin{vmatrix} 4 & -3 & 1 \\ 7 & 2 & -5 \\ -1 & 1 & 3 \end{vmatrix}$.

7. _____

8. Given $A = \begin{bmatrix} -3 & 7 \\ 5 & 1 \end{bmatrix}$, find A^{-1}, if it exists.

8. _____

9. Solve by using matrix equations. $3x + 2y = 1$
$2x - 3y = 18$

9. _____

Solve each system of equations by using augmented matrices.

10. $3x + 2y = 7$
$6x + 4y = 14$

11. $2x - y + z = -3$
$y + z - 1 = 0$
$x + y - z = 9$

10. _____

11. _____

～ Chapter 2 Test, Form 2B (continued)

12. A seed company sells a mixture of cosmos seeds and larkspur seeds in a 2-oz package. By weight, at least half the mixture should contain cosmos seeds. There are 3500 seeds per ounce of cosmos and 9000 seeds per ounce of larkspur. How many ounces of each kind of seed should the seed company package in its mix in order to package the maximum number of seeds?

12. _____

13. Solve the system of inequalities by graphing and name the vertices of the polygonal convex set. Then, find the maximum and minimum values for the given function.

$x \leq y$

$y \leq 0$

$x \geq -4$

$f(x, y) = 7x + y$

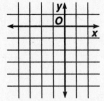

13. _____

Solve each problem, if possible. If not possible, state whether the problem is infeasible, has alternate optimal solutions, or is unbounded.

14. A manufacturer of garden furniture makes a Giverny bench and a Kensington bench. The company needs to produce at least 15 Giverny benches a day and at least 20 Kensington benches a day. They must also meet their demand for at least twice as many Kensington benches as Giverny benches. They can produce no more than 60 benches a day. If each Kensington sells for $250 and each Giverny sells for $325, how many of each kind of bench should be produced for maximum daily income?

14. _____

15. André Gagné caters small dinner parties on weekends. Because of an increase in demand for his work, he needs to hire more chefs and waiters. He will have to pay each chef $120 per weekend and each waiter $70 per weekend. He needs at least 2 waiters for each chef he hires. Find the maximum amount André will need to spend to hire extra help for one weekend.

15. _____

Bonus

Find an equation of the line that passes through $P(2, 1)$ and through the intersection of $\frac{3x}{2} + \frac{y}{4} = 7$ and $\frac{x}{5} - \frac{2y}{3} = \frac{7}{3}$.

Bonus: _____

Chapter 2, Quiz A (Lessons 2-1 through 2-2)

1. State the number of solutions to the system.
   $3x - 2y = -16$
   $2x + y = -9$

   1. _____

2. Solve by graphing. $4x + 3y = 0$
   $2x - 6y = 5$

   2. _____

3. Solve algebraically. $2x + y = -2$
   $4x + 2y = -4$

   3. _____

4. If $A = \begin{bmatrix} 2 & -3 \\ 4 & 2 \end{bmatrix}$ and $B = \begin{bmatrix} -6 & 9 \\ 4 & -8 \end{bmatrix}$, find $-A + B$.

   4. _____

5. If $D = \begin{bmatrix} 3 & -4 \\ 5 & 2 \\ -8 & 6 \end{bmatrix}$ and $E = \begin{bmatrix} -4 & 4 & 3 \\ 5 & -6 & 2 \end{bmatrix}$, find DE.

   5. _____

Chapter 2, Quiz B (Lesson 2-3)

Find the value of each determinant.

1. $\begin{vmatrix} -3 & 5 \\ 2 & 6 \end{vmatrix}$

2. $\begin{vmatrix} 4 & -1 & 6 \\ -3 & 0 & 1 \\ 5 & -2 & 2 \end{vmatrix}$

   1. _____

   2. _____

3. Find the inverse of $\begin{bmatrix} -6 & -8 \\ 4 & 3 \end{bmatrix}$, if it exists.

   3. _____

Solve each system by using matrix equations.

4. $6x + 4y = 0$
   $3x - y = 1$

5. $2x - 3y = -8$
   $-3x + 5y = 13$

   4. _____

   5. _____

Chapter 2, Quiz C (Lesson 2-4)

1. Write the augmented matrix for this system of equations.
   $2x - y + z = 6$
   $x + 3y + 5z = 10$
   $4x - 4y + 2z = -3$

1. _____

Solve each system of equations by using augmented matrices.

2. $3x + 5y = 21$

   $x + y = 5$

3. $2x + y + 3z - 8 = 0$

   $x + 2y - 2z - 3 = 0$

   $5x + y + z - 1 = 0$

2. _____

3. _____

4. $x + 2y + z = 3$

   $2x + y - 2z = -4$

   $4y + 7 = x - z$

4. _____

5. In a triangle, the measure of the largest angle is twice the measure of the smallest angle. The sum of the two smaller angles is 30° more than the measure of the largest angle. Find the measure of each angle.

5. _____

Chapter 2, Quiz D (Lessons 2-5 through 2-6)

1. Given $f(x,y) = -2x - 5y + 1$, find $f(0.5, -4.2)$.

1. _____

Use the system $x \geq 0$, $y \geq 0$, $y \leq 3$, $3x + y \leq 6$ and the function $f(x,y) = 3x - 2y$ for Exercises 2, 3, and 4.

2. Solve the system by graphing and name the vertices of the polygonal convex set.

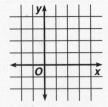

2. _____

3. Find the maximum value of the function.

3. _____

4. Find the minimum value of the function.

4. _____

5. Describe the situation that is graphed as infeasible, having alternate optimal solutions, or as unbounded.

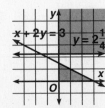

5. _____

~Chapter 2 Mid-Chapter Test (Lessons 2-1 through 2-3)

1. Solve by graphing. $x = 2y + 7$
$$y = -x - 2$$

1. _____

2. Solve algebraically. $4x + 2y = 6$
$$3x - 4y = 10$$

2. _____

3. If $A = \begin{bmatrix} 3 & -2 & 5 \\ 1 & 0 & 9 \\ -4 & -6 & -1 \end{bmatrix}$ and $B = \begin{bmatrix} 3 & -2 & 8 \\ 0 & -3 & 4 \\ 6 & -3 & -9 \end{bmatrix}$,

find $A + (-B)$.

3. _____

Find the values of x and y for which each matrix equation is true.

4. $\begin{bmatrix} -3x \\ 1 \\ -15 \end{bmatrix} \begin{bmatrix} y + 2 \\ x \\ 3y \end{bmatrix}$

5. $[-10 \quad 3y] = [2x \quad 4x]$

4. _____

5. _____

Use matrices D, E, and F to find each product.

$D = \begin{bmatrix} -3 & 0 \\ 6 & 2 \end{bmatrix}$ $E = \begin{bmatrix} 1 & 5 \\ -9 & 2 \\ 4 & -3 \end{bmatrix}$ $F = \begin{bmatrix} -2 & -3 & 5 \\ 6 & 1 & -4 \end{bmatrix}$

6. _____

6. $-2D$

7. EF

7. _____

Find the value of each determinant.

8. $\begin{vmatrix} 8 & -9 \\ 3 & 10 \end{vmatrix}$

9. $\begin{vmatrix} 3 & -2 & 5 \\ 7 & 1 & -4 \\ 0 & 1 & 1 \end{vmatrix}$

8. _____

9. _____

10. Solve by using matrix equations.
$$2x + 3y = 4$$
$$x + 2y = -7$$

10. _____

Standardized Test Questions (Chapters 1-2)

Choose the best answer. Write A, B, C, or D.

1. Find $[f \circ g](x)$ if $f(x) = \dfrac{1}{x^2}$ and $g(x) = 3x^2 + 1$.

 A. $\dfrac{9}{x^4} + 1$ **B.** $\dfrac{3}{x^4 + 1}$ **C.** $\dfrac{1}{9x^2} + 1$ **D.** $\dfrac{1}{9x^4 + 6x^2 + 1}$

1. _____

2. For which value of k are the points $A(0, -5)$, $B(6, k)$, and $C(-4, -13)$ collinear?

 A. 7   **B.** -3 **C.** 1   **D.** $\dfrac{3}{2}$

2. _____

3. Find the slope of a line perpendicular to $2y - 3x = 7$.

 A. $\dfrac{2}{3}$ **B.** $\dfrac{3}{2}$ **C.** $-\dfrac{3}{2}$ **D.** $-\dfrac{2}{3}$

3. _____

4. Which system of equations is consistent?

 A. $x - 2y = 7$
     $6y = 3x + 21$

 B. $x - 2y = 7$
     $3x + 5y = -2$

 C. $x - 2y = 7$
     $6y = 3x + 5$

 D. $x - 2y = 7$
     $3y = 1.5x + 10$

4. _____

The questions below involve comparing two quantities, one in Column A and one in Column B. In certain questions, information related to one or both quantities is centered above them. All variables used stand for real numbers.

Directions:
Write A if the quantity in column A is greater.
Write B if the quantity in column B is greater.
Write C if the two quantities are equal.
Write D if there is not enough information to determine the relationship.

Column A	Column B	
5. $[-3]$	$[-3.5]$	5. _____
6. the zero of $f(x) = \dfrac{5}{9}(x - 32)$	the zero of $f(x) = \dfrac{9}{5}x + 32$	6. _____
7. $\begin{aligned} x + y + z &= 4 \\ 2x - y + 2z &= 5 \\ x - 2y - z &= -3 \end{aligned}$ the x-value in the solution	the y-value in the solution	7. _____
8. $x \geq 0,\ 0 \leq y \leq 3,\ y \geq x$ the maximum value at the vertices of the graph	the minimum value at the vertices of the graph	8. _____

Chapter 3 Test, Form 1A

Write the letter for the correct answer in the blank at the right of each problem.

1. The graph of $\dfrac{x^2}{25} + \dfrac{y^2}{9} = 1$ is symmetric with respect to

   A. the x-axis.　　**B.** the y-axis.　　**C.** neither axis.　　**D.** both axes.

   1. _____

2. The graph of $y = x^3$ is symmetric with respect to the origin and passes through the points $(-1, -1)$, $(-2, -8)$, and $(-3, -27)$. Choose the graph of the function.

   A. 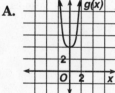　**B.** 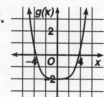　**C.** 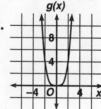　**D.**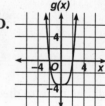

   2. _____

3. Which function is an even function?
   A. $y = 2x^3 + 1$　　　　　　　**B.** $y = -x^4 - 1$
   C. $y = x^3 - 4x^2 + x + 6$　　**D.** $x = -0.25y^2 + 9$

   3. _____

4. The graph of $f(x) = x^4$ is shown at the right. Which graph below is the graph of $g(x) = 0.25f(x)$?

   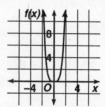

   A. 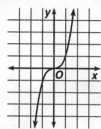　**B.** 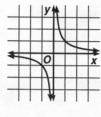　**C.** 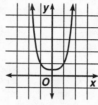　**D.**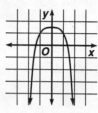

   4. _____

5. Describe the transformation that relates the graph of $y = (-x)^3$ to the parent graph $y = x^3$.
   A. The parent graph is reflected over the line $y = x$.
   B. The parent graph is reflected over the y-axis.
   C. The parent graph stretches vertically.
   D. The parent graph shrinks horizontally.

   5. _____

6. Find the inverse of $y = (x + 2)^3$.
   A. $y = 3x - 2$　　　　　　**B.** $y = \sqrt[3]{x} - 2$
   C. $y = \sqrt[3]{x} + 2$　　　　**D.** $y = \sqrt[3]{x - 2}$

   6. _____

7. Choose the graph of $f(x) = x^3 - 1$ and its inverse.

   A. 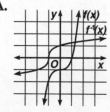　**B.** 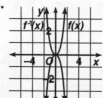　**C.** 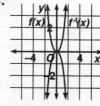　**D.**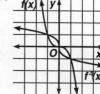

   7. _____

Glencoe Division, Macmillan/McGraw-Hill

8. Choose the graph of the function $y = \dfrac{x - 4}{x^2 - 5x + 4}$.

A. 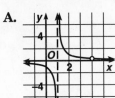 **B.** 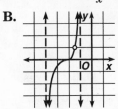 **C.** 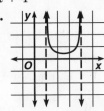 **D.**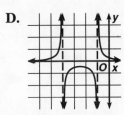

8. _____

9. Choose the graph of $y \geq -|x| - 5$.

A. 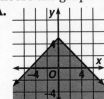 **B.** 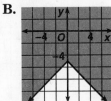 **C.** 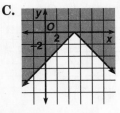 **D.**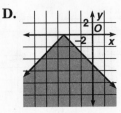

9. _____

10. Find the equation of the line tangent to the graph of $y = -2x^2 - 3x + 4$ at the point $(-1, 5)$.

A. $y = 7x - 2$ **B.** $y = x - 6$ **C.** $y = x + 6$ **D.** $y = 7x + 2$

10. _____

11. Which graph has a maximum point?

A. $y = x^2 + 6x + 11$ **B.** $y = x^2 + 8x + 21$
C. $y = -5x^2 - 30x + 51$ **D.** $y = 8x^2 + 40x + 37$

11. _____

12. Which point is the maximum point of the graph of $y = -x^2 - x + 3$?

A. $(-0.5, 3.25)$ **B.** $(0, 3)$ **C.** $(-2.5, 0)$ **D.** $(1.5, 0)$

12. _____

13. Find the x- and y-intercepts of the graph of $y = x^2 + 6x + 11$.

A. x: -3; **B.** x: none; **C.** x: -1; **D.** x: 11;
 y: 2 y: 11 y: 11 y: none

13. _____

14. Describe the graph of $f(x) = \dfrac{x^3 + 27}{x + 3}$.

A. The graph has infinite discontinuity.
B. The graph has jump discontinuity.
C. The graph has point discontinuity.
D. The graph is continuous.

14. _____

15. Without graphing, describe the end behavior of the graph of $f(x) = 3x^4 - 2x^2 - x + 5$.

A. As $x \to \infty$, $f(x) \to \infty$.
 As $x \to -\infty$, $f(x) \to \infty$.
B. As $x \to \infty$, $f(x) \to \infty$.
 As $x \to -\infty$, $f(x) \to -\infty$.
C. As $x \to \infty$, $f(x) \to -\infty$.
 As $x \to -\infty$, $f(x) \to \infty$.
D. As $x \to \infty$, $f(x) \to -\infty$.
 As $x \to -\infty$, $f(x) \to -\infty$.

15. _____

Bonus

Which is the graph of $|x| > x$?

Bonus: _____

A. 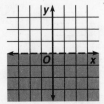 **B.** 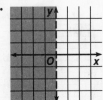 **C.** 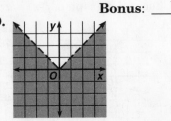 **D.**

Chapter 3 Test, Form 1B

Write the letter for the correct answer in the blank at the right of each problem.

1. The graph of $f(x) = x^2 - 6x$ is symmetric with respect to

   A. the x-axis.   **B.** the y-axis.   **C.** neither axis.   **D.** both axes.

   1. _____

2. The graph of $\dfrac{x^2}{16} - \dfrac{y^2}{9} = 1$ is symmetric to both the x- and y-axes, and passes

   through the points $(4, 0)$, and $\left(5, 2\frac{1}{4}\right)$. Choose the graph of the function.

   A. 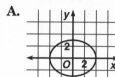   **B.** 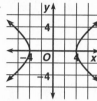   **C.** 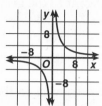   **D.**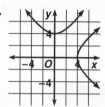

   2. _____

3. Which function is an odd function?

   A. 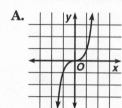   **B.**   **C.** 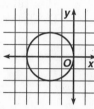   **D.**

   3. _____

4. The vertex of the graph of $f(x) = -4x^2$ is $(0, 0)$. Find the vertex of the graph of $f(x) = -4x^2 + 36$.

   A. $(0, 36)$ **B.** $(0, -36)$ **C.** $(36, 0)$ **D.** $(-36, 0)$

   4. _____

5. Describe the transformation that relates the graph of

   $y = \dfrac{1}{x} - 5$ to the parent graph $y = \dfrac{1}{x}$.

   A. The parent graph stretches vertically.
   B. The parent graph is translated 5 units left.
   C. The parent graph is translated 5 units right.
   D. The parent graph is translated 5 units down.

   5. _____

6. Find the inverse of $f(x) = (3x - 4)^2$.

   A. $f^{-1}(x) = \sqrt{\dfrac{x+4}{3}}$ **B.** $f^{-1}(x) = \dfrac{4 \pm \sqrt{x}}{3}$ **C.** $f^{-1}(x) = \dfrac{\sqrt{4-x}}{3}$ **D.** $f^{-1}(x) = \sqrt[3]{x^2 - 4}$

   6. _____

7. Choose the graph of $f(x) = x^3 + 1$ and its inverse.

   A. 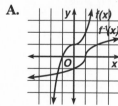   **B.** 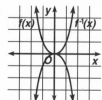   **C.** 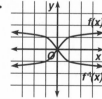   **D.**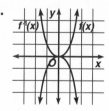

   7. _____

8. Choose the graph of the function $y = \dfrac{x^2 - 1}{x^2 + 2x - 3}$.

   A. 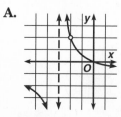   **B.** 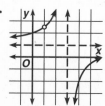   **C.** 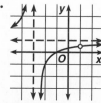   **D.**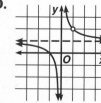

   8. _____

~ Chapter 3 Test, Form 1B (continued)

9. Choose the graph of $-\sqrt{x-3} < y < \sqrt{x-3}$.

A. 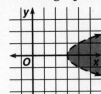 **B.** 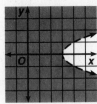 **C.** 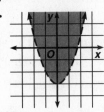 **D.**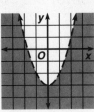

9. _____

10. Find the equation of the line tangent to the graph of $y = x^2 + \frac{2}{3}x$ at the point $(-3, 7)$.

A. $y = -8x - 14$ **B.** $y = -8x + 53$
C. $y = -\frac{16}{3}x - 9$ **D.** $y = -\frac{16}{3}x + \frac{103}{3}$.

10. _____

11. Determine which critical points are found on the graph of
$f(x) = x^3 - 4x^2 + 2x + 7$.

A. a relative minimum point   **B.** a relative maximum point
C. a point of inflection   **D.** all three types

11. _____

12. Which point is a relative minimum of the graph of $f(x) = x^3 - 4x^2 - 3x + 8$?

A. $(3, -10)$ **B.** $(-2, 0)$ **C.** $(0, 14)$ **D.** $(-1, 14)$

12. _____

13. Find the x- and y-intercepts of $y = x^2 - 6x + 8$.

A. x: 2, 4; y: 8   **B.** x: 4; y: 8
C. x: $-4, -2$; y: 0, 8   **D.** x: $-4, -2$; y: 8

13. _____

14. Describe the graph of $y = \begin{cases} x^2 - x + 1, \text{ if } x > 1 \\ x^3, \text{ if } x \le 1 \end{cases}$.

A. The graph has infinite discontinuity.
B. The graph has jump discontinuity.
C. The graph has point discontinuity.
D. The graph is continuous.

14. _____

15. Without graphing, choose the function for which as $x \to \infty$, $f(x) \to -\infty$.

A. $f(x) = 3x^5 + 4x^3 - x^2 + 1$
B. $f(x) = -3x^5 + 4x^3 - x^2 + 1$
C. $f(x) = 3x^4 - 4x^3 + x^2 - 1$
D. $f(x) = 3x^5 - 4x^3 - x^2 + 1$

15. _____

Bonus

If $f(f^{-1}(x)) = x$, find $f^{-1}(f(x))$.

A. $\frac{1}{x}$ **B.** x **C.** $-\frac{1}{x}$ **D.** $-x$

Bonus: _____

Chapter 3 Test, Form 2A

1. To which axis is the graph of $y = 2x^2 - 4$ symmetric?

1. _____

2. Complete the graph if the graph is symmetric with respect to the origin.

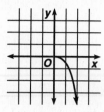

2. _____

3. Is the function graphed at the right, odd, even, or neither?

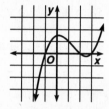

3. _____

4. If $f(x) = x^2$ has its vertex at $(0, 0)$, what is the vertex of $f(x) = -5x^2 + 2$?

4. _____

5. The graph of $f(x) = [x]$ is shown below. Sketch the graph of $h(x) = [x - 1]$.

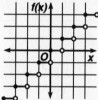

5. _____

6. Find the inverse of $y = (x + 1)^2 - 2$.

6. _____

7. Is the inverse of $f(x) = (x - 3)^2$ a function?

7. _____

8. If $f(x) = (x + 2)^2$, sketch $f(x)$ and $f^{-1}(x)$.

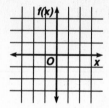

8. _____

9. Determine any horizontal, vertical, or slant asymptotes in the graph of $f(x) = \dfrac{2x^3 - 5x^2 + 2}{2x^2}$.

9. _____

10. Graph the function $y = \dfrac{1}{x - 2}$.

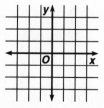

10. _____

~ Chapter 3 Test, Form 2A (continued)

11. Graph the function $y > |2x + 1| - 3$.

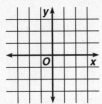

11. _____

12. Solve $|x + 1| > 6$.

12. _____

13. Find the derivative of $f(x) = 1.2x^3 - 0.7x^2 + 5x - 1$.

13. _____

14. Write the equation, in slope-intercept form, of the line tangent to the graph of $y = -2x^2 + x - 7$ at the point $(-3, -28)$.

14. _____

15. Find the critical points for $f(x) = x^4 - x^3 - 5x^2 - 1$, and tell whether each point is a maximum, a minimum, or a point of inflection.

15. _____

16. Find the critical point(s) for $f(x) = x^3$.

16. _____

17. Find the x- and y-intercepts of the graph of $y = x^3 + 2x^2 + x$.

17. _____

18. Determine whether the graph of $y = \dfrac{3}{x^2} + 2x$ has infinite

discontinuity, jump discontinuity, point discontinuity, or is continuous.

18. _____

19. Graph $y = \dfrac{1}{x^2}$. Then determine the interval(s) over which the graph

is decreasing.

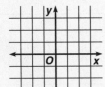

19. _____

20. Without graphing, describe the end behavior of the graph of $f(x) = -10x^3 - 5$.

20. _____

Bonus

For which intervals is the graph of
$y = x^3 + 3x^2 - 9x - 10$ increasing?

Bonus: _____

~ Chapter 3 Test, Form 2B

1. To which axis is the graph of $x^2 + y^2 - 4x = 0$ symmetric?

1. _____

2. Complete the graph if the graph is symmetric to the y-axis.

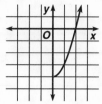

2. _____

3. Is the function $y = x^4 + 8x^2 + 9$ odd, even, or neither?

3. _____

4. If $f(x) = |x|$ has its vertex at $(0, 0)$, what is the vertex of $g(x) = -3|x| + 1$?

4. _____

5. The graph of $f(x)$ is shown below. Sketch the graph of $h(x) = 0.25f(x) + 3$.

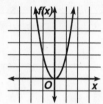 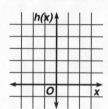

5. _____

6. Find the inverse of $y = x^2 + 2$.

6. _____

7. Is the inverse of $f(x) = 2x + 3$ a function?

7. _____

8. Sketch the graph of $f(x) = \sqrt{x^2 + 4}$ and its inverse.

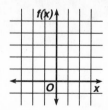

8. _____

9. Determine any horizontal, vertical, or slant asymptotes in the graph of $y = \dfrac{1}{x + 5} - 2$.

9. _____

10. Graph the function $y = \dfrac{x - 2}{x^2 + x - 6}$.

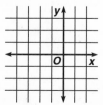

10. _____

~ Chapter 3 Test, Form 2B (continued)

11. Graph $y > x^2 - 4x + 2$.

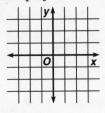

11. _____

12. Solve $|2x - 9| \leq 1$.

12. _____

13. Find the derivative of $f(x) = 2x^3 - 3x^2 - \dfrac{6}{7}$.

13. _____

14. Write the equation, in slope-intercept form, of the line tangent to the graph of $y = x^2 + 4x - 2$ at the point $(3, 19)$.

14. _____

15. Find the critical points for $f(x) = x^3 - 3x - 1$, and tell whether each point is a maximum, a minimum, or a point of inflection.

15. _____

16. How many inflection points does the graph of $y = x^3 - 3x + 1$ have? Name the coordinates of any such point(s).

16. _____

17. Find the x- and y-intercepts of the graph of $y = x^3 - x^2 - 6x$.

17. _____

18. Determine whether the graph of $y = \begin{cases} 3x - 2, \text{ if } x > 2 \\ 3x + 2, \text{ if } x < 2 \end{cases}$

has infinite discontinuity, jump discontinuity, jump point discontinuity, or is continuous.

18. _____

19. For the interval $-1 < x < 1$, does the graph of $y = x^3 + 1$ increase or decrease?

19. _____

20. Without graphing, describe the end behavior of
$y = 5x^4 + 3x^3 - 7x^2 - 10x + 4$.

20. _____

Bonus

Sketch the graph of $|y| = x^2$.

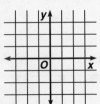

Bonus _____

Chapter 3, Quiz A (Lessons 3-1 through 3-2)

1. Determine whether the graph of $f(x) = \dfrac{1}{-3x}$ is symmetric

   with respect to the line $y = x$ and/or the line $y = -x$.   1. _____

2. Is the function $y = -7x^5 + 3x^3$ even, odd, or neither?   2. _____

3. Is the graph of $y = x^3 + 3x^2 - 9x - 10$ symmetric with
   respect to the origin?   3. _____

4. Graph $f(x) = x^3$ and $g(x) = x^3 - 2$. Then describe how the graph
   of $g(x)$ is related to the graph of $f(x)$, its parent graph.

   4. _____

5. Describe the transformation(s) that relate the graph of
   $y = -(x - 1)^2$ to the graph of $y = x^2$, its parent graph.   5. _____

Chapter 3, Quiz B (Lessons 3-3 through 3-4)

1. Is the inverse of $y = 2x^2 + 1$ a function?   1. _____

2. Sketch the function $f(x) = (x + 1)^3$ and its inverse.
   Is the inverse a function?

   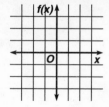

   2. _____

3. Determine any horizontal, vertical, or slant asymptotes

   in the graph of $y = \dfrac{x}{x^2 - 36}$.   3. _____

4. Describe the transformation(s) that relate the graph of

   $y = \dfrac{5}{x}$ to the graph of $y = \dfrac{1}{x}$, its parent graph.   4. _____

5. Identify any asymptotes and/or holes in the graph of

   $f(x) = \dfrac{x - 4}{(x - 4)(x - 1)}$.   5. _____

Glencoe Division, Macmillan/McGraw-Hill

Chapter 3, Quiz C (Lessons 3-5 through 3-6)

1. Graph $-\sqrt{x+4} \le y \le \sqrt{x+4}$.

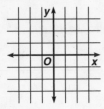

1. _____

2. Solve $|3 - 2x| > 4$.

2. _____

3. Find the derivative of $f(x) = 4x^3 - 2x^2 - x + 1$.

3. _____

4. Find the slope of the line tangent to the
   graph of $y = \frac{1}{4}x^2 - 3x + 5$ at the point $(2, 0)$.

4. _____

5. Write the equation, in slope-intercept form, of the line
   tangent to the graph of $y = 3x^2 + 6x + 1$ at the point $(-2, 1)$.

5. _____

Chapter 3, Quiz D (Lessons 3-7 through 3-8)

1. Find the critical point(s) for $f(x) = x(x^2 - 3)$. Then tell whether
   each point is a maximum, a minimum, or a point of inflection.

1. _____

2. Find the x-and y-intercepts of the graph of $y = x^4 - x^2$.

2. _____

3. For which interval(s) is the graph of $f(x) = \dfrac{-2}{x}$ increasing?

3. _____

4. Determine whether the graph of

   $$f(x) = \begin{cases} x + 1, \text{ if } x > 0 \\ 0, \text{ if } x = 0 \\ x - 1, \text{ if } x < 0 \end{cases} \quad \text{has infinite}$$

   discontinuity, jump discontinuity,
   point discontinuity, or is continuous.

4. _____

5. Graph the function $f(x) = \frac{4}{x}$ for $x > 0$. Then

   describe its end behavior.

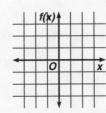

5. _____

Chapter 3 Mid-Chapter Test (Lessons 3-1 through 3-4)

Determine whether the graph of each relation is symmetric with respect to the x-axis, the y-axis, the line y = x, the line y = −x, and/or the origin.

1. $y = x^3 + 6x$

2. $y = x^4 + x^2$

Determine whether each function is even, odd, or neither.

3. $y = -4x^4 - 2x^2 + 7$

4. $y = 10x^3 - 6x^2 + x + 4$

Describe the transformations that have taken place in each family of graphs.

5. $f(x) = |x|$;
    $y = \frac{1}{4}|x + 5|$

6. $f(x) = x^4$;
    $y = (2x)^4 - 1$

7. Is the inverse of $y = 4x + 3$ a function?

Find the inverse of each function.

8. $y = x^2 - 3$

9. $y = 5 + 2x^3$

Sketch each function and its inverse. Is the inverse a function?

10. $y = \frac{3}{x}$

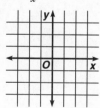

11. $y = (x - 2)^2$

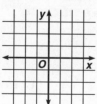

Determine the asymptotes for the graph of each function

12. $y = \dfrac{x^2 + x - 2}{x}$

13. $y = \dfrac{x - 4}{x^2 - 5x + 4}$

Graph each rational function.

14. $y = \dfrac{-2}{x - 3}$

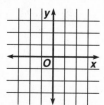

15. $y = \dfrac{x - 3}{x^2 - 9}$

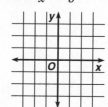

1. _____

2. _____

3. _____

4. _____

5. _____

6. _____

7. _____

8. _____

9. _____

10. _____

11. _____

12. _____

13. _____

14. _____

15. _____

Standardized Test Questions (Chapters 1-3)

Choose the best answer. Write A, B, C, or D.

1. For which equation is the graph symmetric with respect to the origin?
   A. $y = \pm \sqrt{x + 2}$ **B.** $y = 4x$
   C. $y = 2x^4 - 6x^2$ **D.** $y = 7x^5 - 3x^3 + 1$

   1. _____

2. Which value of x is not in the domain of $f(x) = \dfrac{x}{20 - x^2}$?

   A. 10.5   **B.** ± 10 **C.** $\pm 2\sqrt{5}$ **D.** 0

   2. _____

3. Find the midpoint of the segment with endpoints at $(a + b, c)$ and $(2a, -3c)$.

   A. $\left(\dfrac{3a + b}{2}, -c \right)$ **B.** $\left(\dfrac{3a + b}{2}, 2c \right)$

   C. $(a - b, -2c)$ **D.** $(4c, b - a)$

   3. _____

4. Solve $\begin{bmatrix} -5 & 1 \\ 2 & 1 \end{bmatrix} \begin{bmatrix} x \\ y \end{bmatrix} = \begin{bmatrix} -2 \\ 5 \end{bmatrix}$.

   A. $(-1, -7)$ **B.** $(1, 3)$ **C.** all reals   **D.** $\varnothing$

   4. _____

The questions below involve comparing two quantities, one in Column A and one in Column B. In certain questions, information related to one or both quantities is centered above them. All variables used stand for real numbers.

Directions:
Write A if the quantity in column A is greater.
Write B if the quantity in column B is greater.
Write C if the two quantities are equal.
Write D if there is not enough information to determine the relationship.

Column A	Column B	
5. $4x + 8y = 7$ $2x - 3y = 0$		
x	y	5. _____
6. the value of x at the minimum point of $f(x) = x^4 + 5$	the value of x at the maximum point of $f(x) = 5 - x^2$	6. _____
7. the zero of $f(x) = -2x + 7$	the zero of $f(x) = 0.2x - 8$	7. _____
8. the slope of the tangent to the graph of $y = 0.5x^2 + x + 1$	the slope of the tangent to the graph of $y = 2x^2 + 5x - 3$	8. _____
9. $f(x) = |\sqrt[3]{x} - 10|$		
$f(-8)$	$f(8)$	9. _____

Chapter 4 Test, Form 1A

Write the letter for the correct answer in the blank at the right of each problem.

1. Find the complex roots of $x^3 + x^2 - 10x + 8 = 0$.
   A. 1, 2, 4   **B.** −1, −2, −4   **C.** 1, 2, −4   **D.** −1, 2, −4

   1. _____

2. Write the polynomial equation of least degree for the roots $2i$, $-2i$, -4.
   A. $x^3 - 4x^2 + 4x - 16$ **B.** $x^3 + 4x^2 - 4x - 16$
   C. $x^3 + 4x^2 + 4x + 16$ **D.** $x^3 - 4x^2 - 4x + 16$

   2. _____

3. Find the discriminant of $3m^2 - 4m + 1 = 0$ and describe the nature of the roots.
   A. 4; real   **B.** 1; real   **C.** −4; imaginary   **D.** −28; imaginary

   3. _____

4. Which inequality represents the graph?
   A. $y \geq x^2 - 6x - 1$
   B. $y \geq x^2 + 7x + 6$
   C. $y \geq x^2 - 6x - 3.5$
   D. $y > x^2 + 6x - 6$

   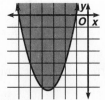

   4. _____

5. Solve $x^2 - 4x - 9 = 0$ by completing the square.
   A. $2 \pm \sqrt{13}$ **B.** $2 \pm \sqrt{5}$ **C.** $-2 \pm \sqrt{13}$ **D.** $-2 \pm \sqrt{5}$

   5. _____

6. Solve $-3x^2 + 4 = 0$ by using the quadratic formula.
   A. $\pm\dfrac{\sqrt{3}}{6}$ **B.** $\dfrac{2 \pm 2i}{3}$ **C.** $\pm\dfrac{2\sqrt{3}}{3}$ **D.** $0, \dfrac{4}{3}$

   6. _____

7. Divide $(x^3 - 4x^2 + 12x - 9)$ by $(x - 2)$ using synthetic division.
   A. $x^2 - 2x + 8$ R 7   **B.** $-x^2 - 2x + 15$ R −41
   C. $3x^2 + 2x + 16$ R 23   **D.** $x^2 - 6x$ R 9

   7. _____

8. Use the remainder theorem to find the remainder of $(2x^3 - 4x^2 + 5x) \div (x + 2)$.
   A. 10   **B.** 5   **C.** −11   **D.** −42

   8. _____

9. List all possible rational zeros of $f(x) = 2x^3 - x^2 + 3x - 4$.
   A. $\pm 1, \pm 4$ **B.** $\pm 1, \pm 2, \pm 4, \pm 0.5, \pm 0.25$
   C. $\pm 1, \pm 2, \pm 4, \pm 0.5$ **D.** $\pm 1, \pm 2, \pm 4$

   9. _____

10. Which of the following is a rational zero of $f(x) = 2x^4 - 3x^2 + 1$?
    A. $-\dfrac{1}{2}$ **B.** $\dfrac{1}{2}$ **C.** 2   **D.** −1

    10. _____

11. Find the number of possible positive real zeros of $f(x) = 6 + x^4 + 2x^2 - 5x^3 - 12x$.
    A. 4, 2 or 0   **B.** 3 or 1   **C.** 4   **D.** 1

    11. _____

12. Determine between which consecutive integers the real zeros of $f(x) = 3x^4 + x^3 - 2x^2 + 4$ are located.
    A. −1 and 0   **B.** 0 and 1   **C.** −2 and −3   **D.** no real zeros

    12. _____

13. Find the greatest integral lower bound of the zeros of
$f(x) = 4x^3 - 2x^2 - 12x + 1$.

    A. -1 **B.** -2 **C.** 1   **D.** 2   **13.** _____

14. Solve $\dfrac{2x-5}{x} + \dfrac{4x-1}{x+2} = -\dfrac{3x+8}{x(x+2)}$.

    A. ± 1 **B.** $-\dfrac{2}{9}$ **C.** $-\dfrac{2}{3}, \dfrac{1}{2}$ **D.** $\dfrac{-1 \pm \sqrt{433}}{12}$ **14.** _____

15. Solve $2 + \dfrac{6}{a-4} > \dfrac{1}{3}$.

    A. $a > 4$ **B.** $a < \dfrac{2}{5}$ or $a > 4$

    C. $\dfrac{2}{5} < a < 4$ **D.** $\dfrac{2}{5} < a$ **15.** _____

16. Decompose $\dfrac{5x+1}{x^2 - x - 12}$ into partial fractions.

    A. $\dfrac{3}{x+3} + \dfrac{-2}{x-4}$ **B.** $\dfrac{3}{x+3} + \dfrac{2}{x-4}$

    C. $\dfrac{2}{x+3} + \dfrac{3}{x-4}$ **D.** $\dfrac{-2}{x+3} + \dfrac{3}{x-4}$ **16.** _____

17. Solve $\sqrt[3]{6x-1} - 4 = -2$.

    A. $\dfrac{1}{3}$ **B.** $\dfrac{5}{6}$ **C.** 9   **D.** $\dfrac{3}{2}$ **17.** _____

18. Solve $\sqrt{7x+2} < 4$.

    A. $x > 2$ **B.** $x > 1$ **C.** $-\dfrac{2}{7} \le x < 2$ **D.** $x < 1$ **18.** _____

19. Gretchen's garden measured 10 feet long by 12 feet wide. Gretchen decreased the length of each side by the same amount and this reduced the area of her garden by one third. By how much did Gretchen reduce each side of her garden?

    A. 2 feet   **B.** 3 feet   **C.** 4 feet   **D.** 20 feet   **19.** _____

20. Which equation represents the graph of the function?

    A. $y = x^2 + 1$
    B. $y = x^2 + x + 4$
    C. $y = x^2 - 2x - 3$
    D. $y = x^2 - 4x + 1$

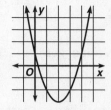

    20. _____

Bonus

Find the discriminant of $(2 + \sqrt{3})x^2 - (4 - \sqrt{3})x = 1$.

    A. $11 - 12\sqrt{3}$ **B.** $-16 - 9\sqrt{3}$ **C.** $-2 + 2\sqrt{3}$ **D.** $27 - 4\sqrt{3}$ **Bonus:** _____

Chapter 4 Test, Form 1B

Write the letter for the correct answer in the blank at the right of each problem.

1. Find the complex roots of $x^3 + x^2 - 8x - 12 = 0$.
   A. $2, 2, 3$ **B.** $2, 2, -3$ **C.** $-2, -2, 3$ **D.** $2, -2, -3$ 1. _____

2. Write the polynomial equation of least degree for the roots $i, -i, 1$.
   A. $x^3 - x^2 + x - 1$ **B.** $x^3 + x^2 + x + 1$
   C. $x^3 + x^2 - x - 1$ **D.** $x^3 - x^2 - x + 1$ 2. _____

3. Find the discriminant of $2w^2 - w + 1 = 0$ and describe the nature of the roots.
   A. -7; imaginary   **B.** 9; real   **C.** 1; real   **D.** -5; imaginary   3. _____

4. Which inequality represents the graph?
   A. $y < x^2 + 2x + 1$
   B. $y < x^2 + 3x + 1$
   C. $y \leq -x^2 + 4x - 3$
   D. $y \leq -x^2 - 3x + 2$ 4. _____

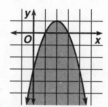

5. Solve $2x^2 + 4x = 4$ by completing the square.
   A. 2   **B.** $1 \pm \sqrt{5}$ **C.** $-1 \pm \sqrt{3}$ **D.** $1 \pm \sqrt{3}$ 5. _____

6. Solve $3x^2 - x - 2 = 0$ by using the quadratic formula.
   A. $\dfrac{1 \pm i\sqrt{23}}{6}$ **B.** $\dfrac{1 \pm \sqrt{13}}{6}$ **C.** $1; 0$ **D.** $1; -\dfrac{2}{3}$ 6. _____

7. Divide $(x^3 - 3x + 2)$ by $(x + 4)$ using synthetic division.
   A. $x + 1$ R 6   **B.** $x^2 + 4x + 13$ R 54
   C. $x - 7$ R 30   **D.** $x^2 - 4x + 13$ R-50 7. _____

8. Use the remainder theorem to find the remainder of $(x^2 - 2x - 4) \div (x + 1)$.
   A. -5 **B.** -1 **C.** -4 **D.** -2 8. _____

9. List all possible rational zeros of $f(x) = x^4 - 3x^3 + 5x^2 + x - 4$.
   A. $\pm 1, \pm 4, \pm 0.25$ **B.** $\pm 1, \pm 4$
   C. $\pm 1, \pm 2, \pm 4$ **D.** $\pm 1, \pm 2, \pm 4, \pm 0.5, \pm 0.25$ 9. _____

10. Which of the following is a rational zero of $f(x) = -3x^3 + 6x^2 + x - 4$?
    A. -1 **B.** 1   **C.** $\dfrac{4}{3}$ **D.** $-\dfrac{2}{3}$ 10. _____

11. Find the number of possible negative real zeros of $f(x) = x^5 - 2x^4 + x^2 - 6x - 6$.

    A. 4 or 2   **B.** 3 or 1   **C.** 3   **D.** 2 or 0   11. _____

Glencoe Division, Macmillan/McGraw-Hill

Chapter 4 Test, Form 1B (continued)

12. Determine between which consecutive integers the real zeros of
$f(x) = 7x^2 - 4x - 2$ are located.

    A. −1 and 0   **B.** −1 and −2   **C.** 1 and 2   **D.** −3 and −4   12. _____

13. Find the least integral upper bound of the zeros of $f(x) = x^4 - 6x^3 + 2x - 1$.

    A. 4   **B.** 5   **C.** 6   **D.** 7   13. _____

14. Solve $\dfrac{2}{5n} + \dfrac{3n-4}{2n} = \dfrac{n-2}{3n}$.

    A. $\dfrac{4}{5}$ **B.** 0   **C.** $\dfrac{1}{2}$ **D.** 1 and −1   14. _____

15. Solve $-x^3 + 9x^2 - 18x \geq 0$.

    A. $0 \leq x \leq 6$ **B.** $3 \leq x \leq 6$

    C. $x \leq 0, 3 \leq x \leq 6$ **D.** $0 \leq x \leq 3, x \geq 6$ 15. _____

16. Decompose $\dfrac{5p+3}{p^2 - 3p}$ into partial fractions.

    A. $\dfrac{1}{p} + \dfrac{-6}{p-3}$ **B.** $\dfrac{1}{p-3} + \dfrac{-6}{p}$ **C.** $\dfrac{-1}{p} + \dfrac{6}{p-3}$ **D.** $\dfrac{-1}{p-3} + \dfrac{6}{p}$ 16. _____

17. Solve $\sqrt{4x-3} + \sqrt{x+1} = 5$.

    A. $3, \dfrac{274}{9}$ **B.** 3   **C.** $\dfrac{274}{9}$ **D.** $\dfrac{1}{2}$ 17. _____

18. Solve $\sqrt[3]{2x-5} \geq 3$.

    A. $x \geq 7$ **B.** $x \leq 7$ **C.** $x \leq 16$ **D.** $x \geq 16$ 18. _____

19. Mr. and Mrs. Appleby are building a rectangular garden with a sidewalk
surrounding it all around the outer edge. They have a 16-foot by 20-foot area
to build both the garden and the sidewalk, but they only have enough topsoil
for 192 square feet of garden. What should the width of the sidewalk around
the garden be so that they use all of the topsoil?

    A. 1 foot   **B.** 2 feet   **C.** 3 feet   **D.** 4 feet   19. _____

20. Which equation represents the
graph of the function?

    A. $y = x^2 - 3x - 4$

    B. $y = x^2 + 3x - 6$

    C. $y = x^2 + 2x - 6$

    D. $y = x^2 + 2x - 4$ 20. _____

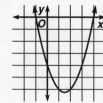

Bonus

Find the discriminant of $(3 - \sqrt{5})x^2 - (1 + 2\sqrt{5})x = 1$.

    A. $21 + 4\sqrt{5}$ **B.** 33   **C.** $11 + 8\sqrt{5}$ **D.** $11 + 4\sqrt{5}$ Bonus: _____

Chapter 4 Test, Form 2A

Solve each equation or inequality.

1. $2x^2 - 11x - 156 = 0$

1. _____

2. $\dfrac{3}{d+3} - \dfrac{4}{d} = \dfrac{-d}{d+3}$

2. _____

3. $4x^2 + 5x - 4 = 0$

3. _____

4. $\sqrt{k+4} - \sqrt{k} = \sqrt{2}$

4. _____

5. $x^4 - 3x^2 + 2x^3 \le 0$

5. _____

6. $x^2 + \dfrac{11}{2}x = -\dfrac{15}{2}$

6. _____

7. $\sqrt{3x+4} + 7 = 5$

7. _____

8. $4 + \dfrac{4}{a+2} \ge \dfrac{4}{5}$

8. _____

9. $-2x^2 - 3x + 9 = 0$

9. _____

10. $\sqrt{x-1} < 8$

10. _____

11. Find all complex roots of $x^3 - 3x^2 + 2x = 0$.

11. _____

12. Write the polynomial equation of least degree having the roots -1, 4, and -2.

12. _____

13. Graph $y = x^2 - 6x + 9$.

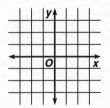

13. _____

14. Graph $y \le 10 - 3x - x^2$.

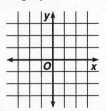

14. _____

Chapter 4 Test, Form 2A (continued)

15. Divide $(x^4 - 4x^2 + 4)$ by $(x - 2)$ using synthetic division.

15. _____

16. Use the remainder theorem to find the remainder of $(x^3 + 5x^2 - 2x - 4) \div (x - 1)$. State whether the binomial is a factor of the polynomial.

16. _____

17. Find the discriminant of $x^2 + 3 = 0$ and describe the nature of the roots.

17. _____

18. List all possible rational zeros of $f(x) = 2x^4 + x^3 - 8x^2 - 5x + 6$.

18. _____

19. Determine the rational zeros of $f(x) = 3x^3 - 2x^2 + 5x + 4$.

19. _____

20. Find the number of possible positive real zeros and the number of possible negative real zeros of $f(x) = -x^5 + 4x^4 - 3x^3 - 4x + 2$.

20. _____

21. Determine between which consecutive integers the real zeros of $f(x) = 2x^3 + 2x^2 + 3x + 1$ are located.

21. _____

22. Approximate the real zeros of $f(x) = -x^3 - x^2 - 5x + 6$ to the nearest tenth.

22. _____

23. Use the upper bound theorem to find the least integral upper bound of the zeros of $f(x) = 3x^3 - 4x - 2$.

23. _____

24. Decompose $\dfrac{6x^2 - 11x - 8}{x^3 - x^2 - 2x}$ into partial fractions.

24. _____

25. The volume of a cereal box must be 280 cubic inches. The box is 5 times wider than it is long and 4 inches taller than it is wide. What are the dimensions of the box?

25. _____

Bonus

Determine the value of k such that $f(x) = kx^3 + 3x^2 - 5x + 6$ has possible rational roots of $\pm 1, \pm 2, \pm 3, \pm 6, \pm \dfrac{1}{2}, \pm \dfrac{1}{4}, \pm \dfrac{3}{2}, \pm \dfrac{3}{4}$.

Bonus: _____

Chapter 4 Test, Form 2B

Solve each equation or inequality.

1. $8x^2 + 5x - 13 = 0$

1. _____

2. $6x^2 - 1 = 0$

2. _____

3. $3 = \dfrac{7}{3 + y} + \dfrac{y - 1}{y - 3}$

3. _____

4. $\sqrt{x - 7} + 3 = \sqrt{x + 2}$

4. _____

5. $x^2 - 4x + 13 = 0$

5. _____

6. $\dfrac{6}{q} + 4 \geq \dfrac{3}{q}$

6. _____

7. $\sqrt[3]{10x + 2} - 3 = -5$

7. _____

8. $x^3 - 8x^2 + 12x > 0$

8. _____

9. $-x^2 + 6x - 3 = 0$

9. _____

10. $\sqrt{2x + 5} + 4 \leq 9$

10. _____

11. Find the complex roots of $x^3 + 3x^2 - 4x = 0$.

11. _____

12. Write the polynomial equation of least degree having the roots -1, 5, and -3.

12. _____

13. Graph $y = 2x^2 - 3x - 2$.

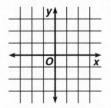

13. _____

14. Graph $y \geq 3x^2 - 7x + 2$.

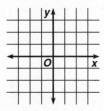

14. _____

~ Chapter 4 Test, Form 2B (continued)

15. Divide $(x^3 - x - 5)$ by $(x + 4)$ using synthetic division.

15. _____

16. Use the remainder theorem to find the remainder of $(x^3 - 5x^2 + 6x - 3) \div (x - 1)$. State whether the binomial is a factor of the polynomial.

16. _____

17. Find the discriminant of $4x^2 + 12x + 9 = 0$ and describe the nature of the roots.

17. _____

18. List all possible rational zeros of $f(x) = 4x^3 + 5x^2 - x + 2$.

18. _____

19. Determine the rational zeros of $f(x) = x^3 + 4x^2 + 6x + 9$.

19. _____

20. Find the number of possible positive real zeros and the number of possible negative real zeros of $f(x) = x^3 - 4x^2 - 3x - 9$.

20. _____

21. Determine between which consecutive integers the real zeros of $f(x) = x^3 + x^2 - 5$ are located.

21. _____

22. Approximate the real zeros of $f(x) = x^3 - 2x^2 - 4x - 5$ to the nearest tenth.

22. _____

23. Use the upper bound theorem to find the greatest integral lower bound of the zeros of $f(x) = -2x^3 + 4x^2 + 1$.

23. _____

24. Decompose $\dfrac{3x^2 - 20x - 24}{x^3 - x^2 - 12x}$ into partial fractions.

24. _____

25. Three times the multiplicative inverse of a number is added to twice the number. The result is 7. What is the number?

25. _____

Bonus

Determine the value of k such that $f(x) = kx^3 - x^2 + 7x + 9$ has possible rational roots of $\pm 1, \pm 3, \pm 9, \pm \dfrac{1}{6}, \pm \dfrac{1}{3}, \pm \dfrac{1}{2}, \pm \dfrac{3}{2}, \pm \dfrac{9}{2}$.

Bonus: _____

Chapter 4, Quiz A (Lessons 4-1 through 4-2)

Find the roots of each equation.

1. $x^2 + 36 = 0$
2. $4x^3 - 10x^2 - 24x = 0$

3. Write the polynomial equation of least degree having the roots
   $1, -1$, and 0.5.

Solve each equation by completing the square.

4. $x^2 - 5x - 84 = 0$
5. $x^2 - \frac{7}{12}x + \frac{1}{12} = 0$

6. Find the discriminant of $2x^2 - 8 + 3x = 0$ and describe the nature
   of the roots.

Solve each equation by using the quadratic formula.

7. $2x^2 - 5x + 2 = 0$
8. $3x^2 - x + 10 = 0$

Graph each equation or inequality.

9. $y < 4 - x - x^2$
10. $y = x^2 + 4x + 4$

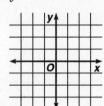
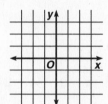

1. _____

2. _____

3. _____

4. _____

5. _____

6. _____

7. _____

8. _____

9. _____

10. _____

Chapter 4, Quiz B (Lessons 4-3 through 4-4)

1. Use synthetic division to divide $(x^3 - 5x^2 - 17x - 6)$ by $(x + 2)$.

   1. _____

Find the remainder for each division. Then state whether the binomial is a factor of the polynomial.

2. $(x^3 - 14x) \div (x - 5)$
3. $(x^3 - 6x + 9) \div (x - 3)$

2. _____

3. _____

4. List all possible rational zeros of $f(x) = 2x^3 - 4x^2 + 5x - 3$.
   Then determine the rational zeros.

   4. _____

5. Find the number of possible positive real zeros and the number of
   possible negative real zeros of $f(x) = x^3 - x^2 + 6x + 1$.

   5. _____

Chapter 4, Quiz C (Lessons 4-5 through 4-6)

Determine between which consecutive integers the real zeros of each function are located.

1. $f(x) = x^3 + 4x^2 - 3x - 5$

2. $f(x) = -3x^4 - 5x^3 + x - 2$

1. _____

2. _____

Approximate the real zeros of each function to the nearest tenth.

3. $f(x) = -x^3 - 2x + 4$

4. $f(x) = x^4 - 3x^3 + 2x - 1$

3. _____

4. _____

5. Use the upper bound theorem to find the least integral upper bound and the greatest integral lower bound of zeros of
$f(x) = x^3 - 3x^2 - 2x - 1.$

5. _____

Solve each equation or inequality.

6. $b - \dfrac{10}{b} = -3$

7. $\dfrac{3y + 1}{4} + \dfrac{2 + 4y}{3} \le -\dfrac{5}{6}$

6. _____

7. _____

8. $\dfrac{2}{w} + \dfrac{6}{w - 1} \le -5$

9. $\dfrac{a}{a - 2} + \dfrac{6}{a + 2} = 2$

8. _____

9. _____

10. Decompose $\dfrac{4p^2 + 13p - 12}{p^3 - p^2 - 2p}$ into partial fractions.

10. _____

Chapter 4, Quiz D (Lesson 4-7)

Solve each equation or inequality.

1. $\sqrt{x - 3} + 4 = 6$

1. _____

2. $\sqrt{2x - 3} = \sqrt{5x + 4}$

2. _____

3. $\sqrt{k - 7} + \sqrt{k - 3} = 2$

3. _____

4. $\sqrt[3]{2m - 1} + 6 = 3$

4. _____

5. $\sqrt{3t + 7} > 7$

5. _____

NAME _____ DATE _____

Chapter 4 Mid-Chapter Test (Lessons 4-1 through 4-4)

Find the complex roots of each equation.

1. $x^2 - 20 = 0$

1. _____

2. $x^3 - 2x^2 + x = 0$

2. _____

3. Write the polynomial equation of least degree having the roots 4, $3i$, and $-3i$.

3. _____

Solve each equation by completing the square.

4. $x^2 + 8x - 84 = 0$

4. _____

5. $x^2 + \dfrac{1}{3}x - \dfrac{2}{3} = 0$

5. _____

6. Find the discriminant of $3x^2 + 4 - 5x = 0$ and describe the nature of the roots.

6. _____

Solve each equation by using the quadratic formula.

7. $10x^2 - 2x + 3 = 0$

7. _____

8. $-6x^2 - 5x + 6 = 0$

8. _____

Graph each equation or inequality.

9. $y > 3x^2 - 3x + 4$

10. $y = x^2 + 3x + 6$

9. _____

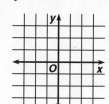
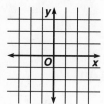

10. _____

11. Use synthetic division to divide $(x^3 - 4x^2 - 5x + 12)$ by $(x - 3)$.

11. _____

Find the remainder for each division. Then state whether the binomial is a factor of the polynomial.

12. $(x^3 - x^2 + 4x - 8) \div (x - 3)$

12. _____

13. $(x^3 + 3x^2 - 4) \div (x + 2)$

13. _____

14. List all possible rational zeros of $f(x) = 2x^3 - 3x^2 - 8x - 6$. Then determine the rational zeros.

14. _____

15. Find the number of possible positive real zeros and the number of possible negative real zeros of $f(x) = 3x^3 - 2x^2 + x - 7$.

15. _____

Standardized Test Questions (Chapters 1-4)

The questions on this page involve comparing two quantities, one in
Column A and one in Column B. In certain questions, information
related to one or both quantities is centered above them. All variables
used stand for real numbers.

Directions:

Write A if the quantity in Column A is greater.
Write B if the quantity in Column B is greater.
Write C if the quantities are equal.
Write D if there is not enough information to determine the
relationship.

	Column A	Column B	
1.	$\left(\dfrac{1}{2} + \dfrac{1}{3}\right) - \left(\dfrac{1}{3} + \dfrac{1}{4}\right) - \left(\dfrac{1}{4} + \dfrac{1}{5}\right)$	0.3	**1.** _____
2.	$7^3 \times 0.1$	$7^4 \times 0.01$	**2.** _____
3.	$\sqrt{169} + \sqrt{144}$	25	**3.** _____
4.	$0 < y < x < 1$ $x - y$	$\dfrac{1}{x} - \dfrac{1}{y}$	**4.** _____
5.	the number of seconds in 4 minutes and 200 seconds	the number of seconds in 5 minutes and 100 seconds	**5.** _____
6.	$\dfrac{n}{m} \neq 1$ n	m	**6.** _____
7.	$\overline{AC}$ and $\overline{BD}$ are the diagonals of square $ABCD$. length of $\overline{AB}$	length of $\overline{BD}$	**7.** _____
8.	$x + y = 3$ 2	y	**8.** _____
9.	the slope of the line $4x - 3y = 1$	the slope of the line $y = -\dfrac{4}{3}x + 6$	**9.** _____
10.	$4^2 + 4^2 + 4^2 + 4^2$	4^3	**10.** _____

~Unit Test, Chapters 1-4

1. Find the maximum and minimum values of $f(x, y) = 3x + y$ for
   the polygonal convex set determined by $x \geq 1$, $y \geq 0$, and $x + 0.5y \leq 2$.   1. _____

2. Write the polynomial equation of least degree that has
   roots $-3i$, $3i$, i, and $-i$.   2. _____

3. Divide $4x^3 + 3x^2 - 2x + 75$ by $x + 3$ by using synthetic division.   3. _____

4. Solve the system of   5. Sketch the
   equations by graphing.   missing part
   $3x - 5y = -8$ of the graph if
   $x + 2y = 1$ the graph is   4. _____
                                    symmetric to
                                    the y-axis.

   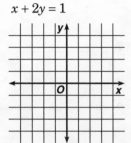   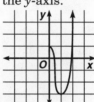   5. _____

6. Write the augmented matrix for the system of equations. Then solve.
   $x - y - z = 2$
   $x + 2y - 2z = 3$
   $3x - 2y - 4z = 5$ 6. _____

7. Decompose the expression $\dfrac{17n - 23}{4n^2 + 23n - 6}$ into partial fractions.   7. _____

8. Is the graph of $\dfrac{x^2}{9} - \dfrac{y^2}{25} = 1$ symmetric to the x-axis, the y-axis,

   neither axis, or both axes?   8. _____

9. Without graphing, describe the end behavior of the
   graph of $y = -5x^2 - 3x + 1$.   9. _____

10. How many solutions does a consistent and dependent system of
    linear equations have?   10. _____

11. Solve $3x^2 - 7x - 6 = 0$.   11. _____

12. Solve $3y^2 + 4y - 2 \leq 0$.   12. _____

Glencoe Division, Macmillan/McGraw-Hill

~ Unit Test, Chapters 1-4 (continued)

13. If $f(x) = -4x^2$ and $g(x) = \dfrac{2}{x}$, find $[g \circ f](x)$. 13. _____

14. Are $f(x) = \dfrac{1}{2}x + 5$ and $g(x) = 2x - 5$ inverses of each other? 14. _____

15. Find the inverse of $y = \dfrac{x^2}{10}$. Then state whether the

inverse is a function. 15. _____

16. Determine if the expression $4m^5 - 6m^8 + m + 3$ is a polynomial in one variable. If so, state the degree. 16. _____

17. Describe how the graph of $y = |x - 2|$ is related to its parent graph. 17. _____

18. Write the slope-intercept form of the equation of the line that passes through the point $(-5, 4)$ and has a slope of -1. 18. _____

19. Determine whether the figure with vertices at $(1, 2)$, $(3, 1)$, $(4, 3)$, and $(2, 4)$ is a parallelogram. 19. _____

20. A plane flies with a ground speed of 160 mph if there is no wind. It travels 350 miles with a headwind in the same time it takes to go 450 miles with a tailwind. Find the speed of the wind. 20. _____

21. Solve the system of equations algebraically.
$$\frac{1}{3}x + \frac{1}{3}y = 1$$
$$2x + 2y = 9$$ 21. _____

22. Find the value of $\begin{vmatrix} 5 & 3 & -2 \\ 1 & 0 & 4 \\ 4 & -1 & 2 \end{vmatrix}$ by using expansion by minors. 22. _____

23. Solve the system of equations by using augmented matrices.
$$y = 3x - 10$$
$$x = 12 - 4y$$ 23. _____

24. Approximate the greatest real zero of the function $g(x) = x^3 - 3x + 1$ to the nearest tenth. 24. _____

25. Graph $f(x) = \dfrac{1}{x - 1}$. 25. _____

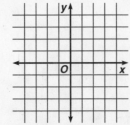

Unit Test, Chapters 1-4 (continued)

26. Write the slope-intercept form of the equation of the line tangent to the graph of $y = 3x^2 + 6x + 1$ at the point where $x = -2$. Graph the function and the tangent line.

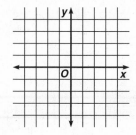

26. _____

27. Write the standard form of the equation of the line perpendicular to the line $y = 3x - 5$ that passes through $(-3, 7)$.

27. _____

28. Use the remainder theorem to find the remainder of $(x^3 - 5x^2 + 7x + 3) \div (x - 2)$. State whether the binomial is a factor of the polynomial.

28. _____

29. Solve $x - \sqrt{2x + 1} = 7$.

29. _____

30. Determine the value of w so that the line whose equation is $5x - 2y = -w$ passes through the point $(-1, 3)$.

30. _____

31. Determine the slant asymptote for $f(x) = \dfrac{x^2 - 5x - 3}{x}$.

31. _____

32. Find the value of $\begin{vmatrix} 3 & 5 \\ 7 & -2 \end{vmatrix}$.

32. _____

33. State the domain and range of $\{(-5, 2), (4, 3), (-2, 0), (-5, 1)\}$. Then state whether the relation is a function.

33. _____

34. Determine whether the relation $f(x) = [x + 1]$ is odd, even, or neither.

34. _____

35. Find the least integral upper bound of the zeros of the function $f(x) = x^3 - x^2 + 1$.

35. _____

36. Solve $|2 - 3x| \le 4$.

36. _____

37. If $A = \begin{bmatrix} 2 & 3 \\ 1 & 4 \end{bmatrix}$ and $B = \begin{bmatrix} 0 & -2 \\ 1 & 5 \end{bmatrix}$, find AB.

37. _____

38. Name all the values of x that are not in the domain of $f(x) = \dfrac{2 - x^2}{x + 5}$.

38. _____

39. Find the equation of the line tangent to the graph of $y = x^2 + 3x + 2$ at $(-2, 0)$. Write the equation in slope-intercept form.

39. _____

Glencoe Division, Macmillan/McGraw-Hill

~ **Unit Test, Chapters 1-4 (continued)**

40. Given that x is an integer between -2 and 2, state the relation represented by the equation $y = 2 - |x|$ by listing a set of ordered pairs. Then state whether the relation is a function. Write *yes* or *no*.

40. _____

41. Determine whether the system of inequalities graphed at the right is *infeasible*, has *alternate optimal solutions*, or is *unbounded* for the function $f(x, y) = 2x + y$.

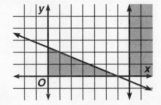

41. _____

42. Solve $1 = (y + 3)(2y - 2)$.

42. _____

43. Determine whether the relation $y = -\dfrac{3}{x^2}$ has *infinite discontinuity, jump discontinuity, point discontinuity,* or is *continuous*.

43. _____

44. Find the slope of the line passing through the points $(a, a + 3)$ and $(4a, a - 5)$.

44. _____

45. Together, two printers can print 7500 lines if the first printer prints for 2 minutes and the second printer prints for 1 minute. If the first printer prints for 1 minute and the second printer prints for 2 minutes, they can print 9000 lines together. Find the number of lines per minute that each printer prints.

45. _____

46. A box for packaging roofing nails must have a volume of 84 ft^3. If the box must be 3 feet wide and its height must be 3 feet less than its length, what should the dimensions of the box be?

46. _____

47. Solve the system of equations.
$-3x - 2y + 3z = -1$
$2x + 5y - 3z = -6$
$4x + 3y + 3z = 22$

47. _____

48. Solve $4x^2 + 12x - 7 = 0$ by completing the square.

48. _____

49. Find the critical point of the function $y = -2(x - 1)^2 - 3$. Then determine whether the point represents a *maximum*, a *minimum*, or a *point of inflection*.

49. _____

50. Solve $\begin{bmatrix} 1 & -3 \\ -1 & 1 \end{bmatrix} \cdot \begin{bmatrix} x \\ y \end{bmatrix} = \begin{bmatrix} -5 \\ 1 \end{bmatrix}$.

50. _____

Chapter 5 Test, Form 1A

Write the letter for the correct answer in the blank at the right of each problem.

1. Find one positive and one negative angle that are coterminal with an angle measuring $\frac{2\pi}{3}$.

   A. $\frac{5\pi}{3}, -\frac{2\pi}{3}$ **B.** $\frac{4\pi}{3}, -\frac{\pi}{3}$ **C.** $\frac{11\pi}{3}, -\frac{7\pi}{3}$ **D.** $\frac{8\pi}{3}, -\frac{4\pi}{3}$ 1. _____

2. Find the reference angle for an angle measuring 125°.
   A. 35°   **B.** 225°   **C.** 135°   **D.** 55°   2. _____

3. Change –62°11'45" to radian measure to the nearest thousandth.
   A. –1.084   **B.** –1.085   **C.** –1.086   **D.** –1.087   3. _____

4. Find the degree measure, to the nearest tenth, of the central angle whose intercepted arc measures 16 in. in a circle of radius 12 in.
   A. 76.4°   **B.** 270.0°   **C.** 283.6°   **D.** 43.0°   4. _____

5. Find the area, to the nearest tenth, of a sector of a circle defined by a central angle measuring 105° if the radius of the circle is 4.2 m.
   A. 7.7 m^2 **B.** 16.2 m^2 **C.** 32.3 m^2 **D.** 926.1 m^2 5. _____

For Exercises 6-8, suppose csc θ = –2 and the terminal side of the angle lies in Quadrant III. Find each value.

6. $\sin \theta$
   A. $-\frac{1}{2}$ **B.** $\frac{1}{2}$ **C.** $-\frac{\sqrt{3}}{2}$ **D.** $\frac{\sqrt{3}}{2}$ 6. _____

7. $\cos \theta$
   A. $-\frac{1}{2}$ **B.** $\frac{1}{2}$ **C.** $-\frac{\sqrt{3}}{2}$ **D.** $\frac{\sqrt{3}}{2}$ 7. _____

8. $\tan \theta$
   A. $-\frac{\sqrt{3}}{3}$ **B.** $\frac{\sqrt{3}}{3}$ **C.** $-\sqrt{3}$ **D.** $\sqrt{3}$ 8. _____

9. Find the exact value of $\tan \frac{9\pi}{3}$ without using a calculator.

   A. 1   **B.** –1   **C.** 0   **D.** undefined   9. _____

10. Find the exact value of csc 315° without using a calculator.
    A. $-\sqrt{2}$ **B.** –2   **C.** –1   **D.** $-\frac{2\sqrt{3}}{2}$ 10. _____

11. Use a calculator to approximate tan (–122°) to four decimal places.
    A. –0.5754   **B.** 0.5754   **C.** –1.6003   **D.** 1.6003   11. _____

12. State the number of possible solutions to ΔPQR if $P = 43°$, $p = 13.3$, and $q = 9.1$.
    A. no solutions   **B.** 1 solution   **C.** 2 solutions   **D.** 3 solutions   12. _____

13. There are 20 rollers under a conveyor belt and each roller has a radius of 8 cm. The rollers turn at a rate of 2 revolutions per second. What is the linear velocity of the belt driving the rollers in meters per second?
    A. 0.50 m/s   **B.** 50.26 m/s   **C.** 100.53 m/s   **D.** 1.005 m/s   13. _____

53

Chapter 5 Test, Form 1A (continued)

For Exercises 14-16, use right triangle ABC to find each value. Round angle measures to the nearest degree and side measures to the nearest tenth.

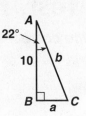

14. the measure of angle C

   A. 112°   **B.** 79°   **C.** 68°   **D.** 58°   **14.** _____

15. the measure of side b

   A. 10.8   **B.** 26.7   **C.** 3.7   **D.** 24.8   **15.** _____

16. the measure of side a

   A. 9.3   **B.** 4.0   **C.** 3.7   **D.** 24.8   **16.** _____

17. In $\triangle ABC$, $A = 55°14'$, $B = 27°19'$, and $c = 12.3$. Find C to the nearest minute.

   A. 98°   **B.** 98°27'   **C.** 97°5'   **D.** 97°27'   **17.** _____

18. In $\triangle ABC$, $A = 63°$, $B = 19°$, and $a = 2.4$. Find b to the nearest tenth.

   A. 0.9   **B.** 0.7   **C.** 6.6   **D.** 3.6   **18.** _____

19. In $\triangle ABC$, $B = 112°2'$, $C = 21°46'$, and $c = 18$. Find a to the nearest tenth.

   A. 35.0   **B.** 4.8   **C.** 9.2   **D.** 35.6   **19.** _____

For Exercises 20-22, find each value for $\triangle ABC$ if $a = 5$, $b = 6$, and $c = 8$.

20. the measure of angle A

   A. 141°   **B.** 124°   **C.** 39°   **D.** 20°   **20.** _____

21. the measure of angle B

   A. 131°   **B.** 160°   **C.** 28°   **D.** 49°   **21.** _____

22. the measure of angle C

   A. 87°   **B.** 93°   **C.** 152°   **D.** 160°   **22.** _____

23. Find the area of $\triangle ABC$ to the nearest tenth if $a = 8$, $b = 5$, and $c = 4$.

   A. 5.8 units^2 **B.** 8.2 units^2 **C.** 16.4 units^2 **D.** 13.1 units^2 **23.** _____

24. Find the area of $\triangle ABC$ to the nearest tenth if $b = 11.9$, $A = 44°30'$, and $B = 56°12'$.

   A. 58.7 units^2 **B.** 117.4 units^2 **C.** 42.0 units^2 **D.** 4.9 units^2 **24.** _____

25. Find the area of a circular segment to the nearest tenth if the measure of its central angle is 135° and the measure of its radius is 6.9 units.

   A. 39.3 units^2 **B.** 78.5 units^2 **C.** 5.7 units^2 **D.** 72.9 units^2 **25.** _____

Bonus

How many possible solutions are there for a triangle whose sides measure 1, 9, and 15?

   A. no solutions   **B.** 1 solution   **C.** 2 solutions   **D.** 3 solutions   **Bonus:** _____

Chapter 5 Test, Form 1B

Write the letter for the correct answer in the blank at the right of each problem.

1. Find one positive and one negative angle that are coterminal with an angle measuring $\frac{7\pi}{4}$.

    A. $\frac{15\pi}{4}, -\frac{9\pi}{4}$ B. $\frac{9\pi}{4}, -\frac{\pi}{4}$ C. $\frac{5\pi}{4}, -\frac{\pi}{4}$ D. $\frac{3\pi}{4}, -\frac{3\pi}{4}$

    1. _____

2. Find the reference angle for an angle measuring 215°.
    A. 145°   B. 35°   C. 70°   D. 215°

    2. _____

3. Change −149°51'21" to radian measure. Round to the nearest thousandth.
    A. −2.614   B. −2.615   C. −2.616   D. −2.609

    3. _____

4. Find the degree measure, to the nearest tenth, of a central angle whose intercepted arc measures 21 cm in a circle of radius 4 cm.
    A. 10.9°   B. 59.2°   C. 68.6°   D. 300.8°

    4. _____

5. Find the area, to the nearest tenth, of a sector of a circle defined by a central angle measuring 40° if the radius of the circle is 12.5 in.
    A. 54.5 in^2 B. 109.1 in^2 C. 8.7 in^2 D. 4.4 in^2

    5. _____

For Exercises 6-8, suppose sec θ = 2 and the terminal side of the angle lies in Quadrant IV. Find each value.

6. $\sin \theta$

    A. $\frac{1}{2}$ B. $-\frac{1}{2}$ C. $\frac{\sqrt{3}}{2}$ D. $-\frac{\sqrt{3}}{2}$

    6. _____

7. $\cos \theta$

    A. $\frac{1}{2}$ B. $-\frac{1}{2}$ C. $\frac{\sqrt{3}}{2}$ D. $-\frac{\sqrt{3}}{2}$

    7. _____

8. $\tan \theta$

    A. $\frac{\sqrt{3}}{3}$ B. $-\frac{\sqrt{3}}{3}$ C. $\sqrt{3}$ D. $-\sqrt{3}$

    8. _____

9. Find the exact value of $\cot \frac{15\pi}{4}$ without using a calculator.

    A. $-\frac{\sqrt{3}}{3}$ B. $-\sqrt{3}$ C. 0   D. −1

    9. _____

10. Find the exact value of sec 120° without using a calculator.

    A. $-\frac{2\sqrt{3}}{3}$ B. $-\sqrt{2}$ C. −2   D. −1

    10. _____

11. Use a calculator to approximate csc (−49°) to four decimal places.
    A. 1.3250   B. −1.3250   C. 1.0485   D. −1.0485

    11. _____

12. State the number of possible solutions to $\triangle STU$ if T = 71°, s = 5.2, and t = 3.8.
    A. no solutions   B. 1 solution   C. 2 solutions   D. 3 solutions

    12. _____

13. There are 3 large rollers under a conveyor belt and each roller has a radius of 0.5 meters. The rollers turn at a rate of 30 revolutions per minute. What is the linear velocity of the belt driving the rollers in meters per second?
    A. 94.25 m/s   B. 1.57 m/s   C. 6.28 m/s   D. 4.71 m/s

    13. _____

Glencoe Division, Macmillan/McGraw-Hill

Chapter 5 Test, Form 1B (continued)

For Exercises 14-16, use right triangle ABC to find each value. Round angle measures to the nearest degree and side measures to the nearest tenth.

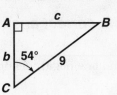

14. the measure of angle B
    A. 36°   **B.** 46°   **C.** 63°   **D.** 126°   14. _____

15. the measure of side b
    A. 12.4   **B.** 6.5   **C.** 5.3   **D.** 7.3   15. _____

16. the measure of side c
    A. 12.4   **B.** 6.5   **C.** 5.3   **D.** 7.3   16. _____

17. In $\triangle ABC$, $A = 104°50'$, $B = 37°25'$, and $c = 4.5$. Find C to the nearest minute.
    A. 37°45'   **B.** 39°25'   **C.** 39°45'   **D.** 37°25'   17. _____

18. In $\triangle ABC$, $B = 14°$, $C = 45°$, and $b = 5.2$. Find c to the nearest tenth.
    A. 1.8   **B.** 6.1   **C.** 15.2   **D.** 0.9   18. _____

19. In $\triangle ABC$, $A = 91°46'$, $C = 18°20'$, and $c = 12$. Find b to the nearest tenth.
    A. 4.0   **B.** 3.5   **C.** 33.2   **D.** 35.8   19. _____

For Exercises 20-22, find each value for $\triangle ABC$ if $a = 4$, $b = 3$, and $c = 6$.

20. the measure of angle A
    A. 144°   **B.** 72°   **C.** 36°   **D.** 53°   20. _____

21. the measure of angle B
    A. 154°   **B.** 26°   **C.** 127°   **D.** 144°   21. _____

22. the measure of angle C
    A. 63°   **B.** 127°   **C.** 154°   **D.** 118°   22. _____

23. Find the area of $\triangle ABC$ to the nearest tenth if $a = 11$, $b = 9$, and $c = 5$.
    A. 22.2 units²   **B.** 3.8 units²   **C.** 44.4 units²   **D.** 15.7 units²   23. _____

24. Find the area of $\triangle ABC$ to the nearest tenth if $a = 8.5$, $B = 61°15'$, and $C = 84°45'$.
    A. 17.8 units²   **B.** 56.4 units²   **C.** 112.8 units²   **D.** 6.6 units²   24. _____

25. Find the area of a circular segment to the nearest tenth if the measure of its central angle is 120° and the measure of its radius is 5.8 units.
    A. 41.3 units²   **B.** 3.6 units²   **C.** 49.8 units²   **D.** 20.7 units²   25. _____

Bonus

How many possible solutions are there for a triangle whose sides measure 3, 16, and 19?
    A. no solutions   **B.** 1 solution   **C.** 2 solutions   **D.** 3 solutions   **Bonus:** _____

Chapter 5 Test, Form 2A

1. Find the reference angle for the angle measuring –42°.

1. _____

2. Find the reference angle for the angle measuring $\frac{21\pi}{4}$ radians.

2. _____

3. If an angle in standard position measures $-\frac{12\pi}{5}$ radians, in which quadrant does its terminal side lie?

3. _____

4. Change 675° to radian measure in terms of π.

4. _____

5. Change $\frac{11\pi}{9}$ radians to degree measure.

5. _____

6. Change 246°19'24" to radian measure. Round your answer to the nearest thousandth.

6. _____

7. Find the degree measure, to the nearest tenth, of the central angle whose intercepted arc measures 14 in. in a circle of radius 12 in.

7. _____

8. Find the area, to the nearest tenth, of the sector of a circle defined by a central angle measuring 52° if the radius of the circle is 8 cm.

8. _____

9. Find the length of an arc that subtends an angle of 36° in a circle of diameter 10 in. Write your answer in terms of π.

9. _____

Suppose sin $\theta = -\frac{5}{13}$ and the terminal side of the angle lies in Quadrant IV. Find each value.

10. $\cos \theta$

10. _____

11. $\tan \theta$

11. _____

12. $\cot \theta$

12. _____

13. $\sec \theta$

13. _____

14. $\csc \theta$

14. _____

Find the exact value of each function without using a calculator.

15. $\cot \frac{24\pi}{6}$

15. _____

16. $\sec 150°$

16. _____

Use a calculator to approximate each value to four decimal places.

17. $\sin 725°$

17. _____

18. $\sec 12$

18. _____

For Exercises 19-21, use right triangle ABC to find each value. Round angle measures to the nearest degree and side measures to the nearest tenth.

19. the measure of angle B

19. _____

20. the length of side b

20. _____

21. the length of side c

21. _____

22. State the number of possible solutions to $\triangle DEF$ if $F = 121°$, $d = 12$, and $f = 12$.

22. _____

Find each value for $\triangle ABC$ if $a = 3.6$, $A = 7°34'$, $B = 74°6'$, and $C = 98°20'$. Round the measures to the nearest tenth.

23. the measure of side b

23. _____

24. the measure of side c

24. _____

For Exercises 25-27, find each value for $\triangle ABC$ if $a = 13$, $b = 10$, and $C = 56°$. Round angle measures to the nearest degree and side measures to the nearest tenth.

25. the measure of side c

25. _____

26. the measure of angle A

26. _____

27. the measure of angle B

27. _____

28. Find the area of $\triangle ABC$, to the nearest tenth, if $a = 12$, $b = 10$, and $c = 4$.

28. _____

29. Find the area of a circular segment, to the nearest tenth, if its central angle measures $60°$ and the radius of the circle is 10.6 units.

29. _____

30. Mr. Allen needs to rent a ladder to paint the outside of his house. The painted part of his house is 20 feet high, and the ladder must reach the top of the painted part. How long must the ladder be if the angle formed by the ladder and level ground is $75°$?

30. _____

Bonus

The terminal side of an angle θ in standard position coincides with the line $2x + y = 0$ in Quadrant II. Find $\sec \theta$.

Bonus: _____

Chapter 5 Test, Form 2B

1. Find the reference angle for the angle measuring $-196°$.

    1. _____

2. Find the reference angle for the angle measuring $\frac{14\pi}{6}$ radians.

    2. _____

3. If an angle in standard position measures $-\frac{19\pi}{5}$ radians, in which quadrant does its terminal side lie?

    3. _____

4. Change $585°$ to radian measure in terms of π.

    4. _____

5. Change $-\frac{23\pi}{6}$ radians to degree measure.

    5. _____

6. Change $203°41'2''$ to radian measure. Round your answer to the nearest thousandth.

    6. _____

7. Find the degree measure, to the nearest tenth, of the central angle whose intercepted arc measures 9 m in a circle of radius 14 m.

    7. _____

8. Find the area, to the nearest tenth, of the sector of a circle defined by a central angle measuring $70°$ if the radius of the circle is 12 yd.

    8. _____

9. Find the length of an arc that subtends an angle of $90°$ in a circle of diameter 15 cm. Write your answer in terms of π.

    9. _____

Suppose $\cos\theta = -\frac{8}{17}$ and the terminal side of the angle lies in Quadrant III. Find each value.

10. $\sin\theta$

    10. _____

11. $\tan\theta$

    11. _____

12. $\cot\theta$

    12. _____

13. $\sec\theta$

    13. _____

14. $\csc\theta$

    14. _____

Find the exact value of each function without using a calculator.

15. $\csc\frac{11\pi}{3}$

    15. _____

16. $\tan 225°$

    16. _____

~ Chapter 5 Test, Form 2B (continued)

**Use a calculator to approximate each value to
four decimal places.**

17. cot 498°

17. _____

18. sin 5

18. _____

**For Exercises 19-21, use right triangle
ABC to find each value. Round angle
measures to the nearest degree and side
measures to the nearest tenth.**

18°

B

c / 12

A *b* *C*

19. the measure of angle *A*

19. _____

20. the measure of side *b*

20. _____

21. the measure of side *c*

21. _____

22. State the number of possible solutions to $\triangle GHI$ if $H = 97°$,
$g = 3.2$, and $h = 4$.

22. _____

**Find each value for $\triangle ABC$ if $b = 6.3$, $A = 46°36'$,
$B = 63°30'$, and $C = 69°54'$. Round the measures to
the nearest tenth.**

23. the measure of side *a*

23. _____

24. the measure of side *c*

24. _____

**For Exercises 25-27, find each value for $\triangle ABC$ if
$b = 8$, $c = 5$, and $A = 98°$. Round angle measures to the
nearest degree and side measures to the nearest tenth.**

25. the measure of side *a*

25. _____

26. the measure of angle *B*

26. _____

27. the measure of angle *C*

27. _____

28. Find the area of $\triangle ABC$, to the nearest tenth, if $a = 8$, $b = 7$, and $c = 3$.

28. _____

29. Find the area of a circular segment, to the nearest tenth, if its
central angle measures 45° and the radius of the circle is 12.5 units.

29. _____

30. Alyssa is leaning a 25-foot ladder onto the outside of her house.
If the angle formed by the ladder and level ground is 60°, how far
up the side of Alyssa's house does the ladder reach?

30. _____

Bonus

The terminal side of an angle θ in standard position coincides with
the line $3x + y = 0$ in Quadrant IV. Find sec θ.

Bonus: _____

Chapter 5, Quiz A (Lessons 5-1 through 5-2)

1. Find the reference angle for an angle measuring $-510°$.

1. _____

2. Find the reference angle for an angle measuring $\dfrac{11\pi}{3}$ radians.

2. _____

3. If an angle in standard position measures $-\dfrac{10\pi}{3}$ radians, in which quadrant does its terminal side lie?

3. _____

4. Change $700°$ to radian measure in terms of π.

4. _____

5. Change $-\dfrac{\pi}{12}$ radians to degree measure.

5. _____

6. Change $50°4'52''$ to radian measure. Round your answer to the nearest thousandth.

6. _____

7. Find the degree measure, to the nearest tenth, of the central angle whose intercepted arc measures 8 cm in a circle of radius 6 cm.

7. _____

8. Find the area, to the nearest tenth, of the sector of a circle defined by the central angle measuring $\dfrac{7\pi}{12}$ radians if the radius of the circle is 2.6 m.

8. _____

9. Find the area, to the nearest tenth, of the sector of a circle defined by the central angle measuring $66°$ if the radius of the circle is 12.1 yd.

9. _____

10. Find the length of an arc that subtends an angle of $12°$ in a circle of diameter 16 m. Write your answer in terms of π.

10. _____

Chapter 5, Quiz B (Lessons 5-3 through 5-4)

Suppose tan $\theta = \sqrt{2}$ and the terminal side of the angle lies in Quadrant III. Find each value.

1. _____

1. $\sin \theta$

2. _____

2. $\cos \theta$

3. $\cot \theta$

3. _____

4. $\sec \theta$

5. $\csc \theta$

4. _____

Find the exact value of each function without using a calculator.

5. _____

6. $\sin \dfrac{12\pi}{4}$

6. _____

7. $\cot 600°$

8. $\sec\left(-\dfrac{\pi}{3}\right)$

7. _____

Use a calculator to approximate each value to four decimal places.

8. _____

9. $\cos 294°$

9. _____

10. $\tan 11$

10. _____

Chapter 5, Quiz C (Lessons 5-5 through 5-6)

**Use the triangle at the right
for Exercises 1 and 2.**

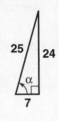

1. Find tan α.

1. _____

2. Find csc α.

2. _____

**For Exercises 3-5, use right triangle
ABC to find each value. Round angle
measures to the nearest degree and
side measures to the nearest tenth.**

3. the measure of angle A

3. _____

4. the measure of side a

4. _____

5. the measure of side b

5. _____

6. State the number of possible solutions to $\triangle JKL$ if $L = 24°$,
   $j = 14$, and $l = 6$.

6. _____

**For Exercises 7-9, find each value for $\triangle ABC$ if $a = 5.4$,
$B = 42°26'$, and $C = 71°44'$. Round angle measures to
the nearest minute and side measures to the nearest tenth.**

7. the measure of angle A

7. _____

8. the measure of side b

8. _____

9. the measure of side c

9. _____

10. Jerome wants to fly his rocket over a tree that is 53 feet high. If the
    rocket travels in a straight line when Jerome launches it off level
    ground at an angle of 60°, how far away from the tree should he
    stand to launch his rocket over the top of the tree?

10. _____

Chapter 5, Quiz D (Lessons 5-7 through 5-8)

**For Exercises 1-3, find each value for $\triangle ABC$ if
$a = 8.2$, $b = 5.5$, and $c = 12.1$. Round angle measures
to the nearest minute.**

1. the measure of angle A

1. _____

2. the measure of angle B

2. _____

3. the measure of angle C

3. _____

4. Find the area of $\triangle ABC$, to the nearest tenth, if $a = 14$, $b = 9$,
   and $c = 8$.

4. _____

5. Find the area of a circular segment, to the nearest tenth,
   if its central angle measures 30° and the radius of the
   circle is 18.2 units.

5. _____

Chapter 5 Mid-Chapter Test (Lessons 5-1 through 5-3)

1. Find the reference angle for an angle measuring 620°.

1. _____

2. Find the reference angle for an angle measuring $-\dfrac{31\pi}{6}$ radians.

2. _____

3. If an angle in standard position measures $\dfrac{11\pi}{4}$ radians, in which quadrant does its terminal side lie?

3. _____

4. Change −42° to radian measure in terms of π.

4. _____

5. Change 75° to radian measure in terms of π.

5. _____

6. Change $\dfrac{4\pi}{15}$ radians to degree measure.

6. _____

7. Change $-\dfrac{9\pi}{10}$ radians to degree measure.

7. _____

8. Change 14°5'1" to radian measure. Round your answer to the nearest thousandth.

8. _____

9. Find the degree measure of the central angle whose intercepted arc measures 17 in. in a circle of radius 10 in.

9. _____

10. Find the area, to the nearest tenth, of the sector of a circle defined by a central angle measuring $\dfrac{4\pi}{9}$ radians if the radius of the circle is 4.7 cm.

10. _____

11. Find the area, to the nearest tenth, of the sector of a circle defined by a central angle measuring 92° if the radius of the circle is 18 m.

11. _____

12. Find the length of an arc that subtends an angle of 120° in a circle of diameter 6 yd. Write your answer in terms of π.

12. _____

13. Find one positive and one negative angle between −360° and 720° that is coterminal with an angle measuring 160°.

13. _____

Use the figure at the right to find each value. Round your answers to the nearest tenth.

14. the length of the intercepted arc

14. _____

15. the area of the sector

15. _____

Suppose sec θ = 3 and the terminal side of the angle lies in Quadrant IV. Find each value.

16. _____

16. sin θ

17. cos θ

17. _____

18. tan θ

18. _____

19. cot θ

19. _____

20. csc θ

20. _____

~~~ Standardized Test Questions (Chapters 1-5)

Choose the best answer. Write A, B, C, or D.

1. Which of the following *cannot* be the measures of the sides of a right triangle?
   A. 5, 7, 13   **B.** 3, 4, 5   **C.** 8, 15, 17   **D.** 7, 24, 25   1. _____

2. What number is $\frac{4}{5}$ of $\frac{3}{4}$ of 10?
   A. 1.5   **B.** 4   **C.** 6   **D.** 3   2. _____

3. Find the value of $3^n \cdot 3^{n+1} \cdot 3^{n+2}$.
   A. 12^{3n+3} **B.** $12^{(n)(n+1)(n+2)}$ **C.** 3^{3n+3} **D.** $3^{(n)(n+1)(n+2)}$ 3. _____

4. If x and y are odd integers, which of the following must be true?
   A. $2x + y$ is even.   **B.** $x \cdot y$ is even.
   C. x^3 is even.   **D.** $x + y$ is even.   4. _____

5. Which is the best estimate of $\sqrt{73}$?
   A. 9.4   **B.** 8.5   **C.** 8.2   **D.** 2.7   5. _____

6. If the volume of a cube is 0.064 units^3, what is its surface area?
   A. 0.96 units^2 **B.** 0.24 units^2 **C.** 0.8 units^2 **D.** 0.08 units^2 6. _____

7. There are fewer than 40 apples in a bushel basket. If they are packed 4 in a bag, there will be 3 left over. If they are packed 5 in a bag, there will be 2 left over. How many apples are in the bushel basket?
   A. 23   **B.** 27   **C.** 37   **D.** 39   7. _____

8. If $5^2 + 6(5) - 5 = (5 - 6)(5 - k)$, find the value of k.
   A. −45   **B.** 21   **C.** 50   **D.** 55   8. _____

9. A red light flashes every 4 seconds. A blue light flashes every 6 seconds. How many times in one minute will the lights flash together if they both flash at $t = 0$?
   A. 4   **B.** 5   **C.** 6   **D.** 7   9. _____

10. A tower casts a shadow 56 meters long. At the same time, a pole 2.5 meters tall casts a shadow 8 meters long. How high is the tower?
    A. 7 m   **B.** 8 m   **C.** 17.5 m   **D.** 20 m   10. _____

Chapter 6 Test, Form 1A

Write the letter for the correct answer in the blank at the right of each problem.

1. Find the values of θ for which the equation $\sin \theta = -1$ is true.
   A. $360k°$ **B.** $90° + 360k°$ **C.** $180° + 360k°$ **D.** $270° + 360k°$ 1. _____

2. State the domain and range for the function $y = \dfrac{1}{\cos x}$.
   A. $D =$ all $x \neq 90° + 180k°$, where k is any integer; $R = y \leq -1$ and $y \geq 1$
   B. $D =$ all $x \neq 180k°$, where k is any integer; $R = y \leq -1$ and $y \geq 1$
   C. $D =$ all $x \neq 360k°$, where k is any integer; $R = -1 \leq y \leq 1$
   D. $D =$ all real numbers; $R = -1 \leq y \leq 1$ 2. _____

3. State the amplitude, period, and phase shift of the function
   $y = \dfrac{1}{2} \cot \left(4x - \dfrac{\pi}{4} \right)$.
   A. none, $\dfrac{\pi}{2}$, $\dfrac{\pi}{16}$ **B.** none, $\dfrac{\pi}{4}$, $\dfrac{\pi}{16}$ **C.** $\dfrac{1}{2}$, $\dfrac{\pi}{4}$, $-\dfrac{\pi}{4}$ **D.** $\dfrac{1}{2}$, $\dfrac{\pi}{2}$, $-\dfrac{\pi}{4}$ 3. _____

4. State the amplitude, period, and phase shift of the function
   $y = -3 \cos 3\left(x + \dfrac{\pi}{2}\right)$.
   A. $3, 2\pi, -\dfrac{\pi}{2}$ **B.** $3, \dfrac{2\pi}{3}$, $-\dfrac{\pi}{2}$ **C.** $3, 2\pi, \dfrac{\pi}{2}$ **D.** $3, \dfrac{2\pi}{3}$, $\dfrac{3\pi}{2}$ 4. _____

5. Write an equation of the sine function with amplitude 3, period 270°, and phase shift 45°.
   A. $y = 3 \sin \left(\dfrac{3}{2}x - 45° \right)$ **B.** $y = -3 \sin \left(\dfrac{4}{3}x - 45° \right)$
   C. $y = -3 \sin \left(\dfrac{3}{2}x - 67.5° \right)$ **D.** $y = 3 \sin \left(\dfrac{4}{3}x - 60° \right)$ 5. _____

6. Find the values of x in the interval $-180° \leq x \leq 180°$ that satisfy the equation
   $x = \arcsin \dfrac{\sqrt{3}}{2}$.
   A. $-150°, -30°$ **B.** $60°, 120°$ **C.** $-30°, 30°$ **D.** $-150°, 150°$ 6. _____

7. Evaluate $\tan \left(\sin^{-1} \dfrac{1}{2} \right)$. Assume that the angle is in Quadrant I.
   A. $\dfrac{\sqrt{3}}{3}$ **B.** $\sqrt{3}$ **C.** 2 **D.** $\dfrac{1}{2}$ 7. _____

8. Evaluate $\cos (\arcsin 0) + \sin (\arctan \sqrt{3})$.
   A. $\dfrac{\sqrt{3}}{2}$ **B.** $\dfrac{\sqrt{3}}{3}$ **C.** $\dfrac{\sqrt{3} + 2}{2}$ **D.** $\dfrac{\sqrt{3} + 1}{2}$ 8. _____

9. Evaluate $\cos \left(\text{Sin}^{-1} \dfrac{\sqrt{2}}{2} \right)$.
   A. $\dfrac{\sqrt{2}}{2}$ **B.** $\sqrt{2}$ **C.** $\dfrac{1}{2}$ **D.** 2 9. _____

10. Evaluate $\tan \left(\text{Cos}^{-1} \dfrac{\sqrt{3}}{2} + \text{Tan}^{-1} \dfrac{\sqrt{3}}{3} \right)$.
    A. $\sqrt{3}$ **B.** $\dfrac{\sqrt{3}}{3}$ **C.** 0 **D.** undefined   10. _____

11. State the domain and range of the relation $y = \text{Arctan } x$.
    A. $D =$ all real numbers; $R = -90° < y < 90°$
    B. $D =$ all real numbers; $R = 0° \leq y \leq 180°$
    C. $D = -90° \leq x \leq 90°$; $R =$ all real numbers
    D. $D = 0° \leq x \leq 180°$; $R =$ all real numbers   11. _____

Glencoe Division, Macmillan/McGraw-Hill

12. Which of the following values would *not* produce a counterexample to the equation $\text{Tan}^{-1} x = \text{Tan}^{-1}(-x)$ for $-1 \le x \le 1$?

    A. $x = -1$ **B.** $x = 1$ **C.** $x = 0$ **D.** $x = 0.5$ 12. _____

13. Find the amplitude, period, frequency, and phase shift of the function

    $y = \dfrac{1}{2} \sin\left(\dfrac{\pi}{4}x - \dfrac{\pi}{2}\right)$.

    A. $\dfrac{1}{2}, 8, \dfrac{1}{8}, \dfrac{1}{2}$ **B.** $\dfrac{1}{2}, \dfrac{1}{8}, 8, \dfrac{1}{2}$ **C.** $\dfrac{1}{2}, \dfrac{1}{8}, 8, -2$ **D.** $\dfrac{1}{2}, 8, \dfrac{1}{8}, 2$ 13. _____

14. Write an equation with phase shift 0 to represent simple harmonic motion with initial position -7, amplitude 7, and period $\dfrac{1}{2}$.

    A. $y = 7 \sin \pi t$ **B.** $y = -7 \sin 4\pi t$ **C.** $y = 7 \cos \pi t$ **D.** $y = -7 \cos 4\pi t$ 14. _____

15. A tractor tire has a diameter of 6 feet and is revolving at a rate of 45 rpm. At $t = 0$, a certain point is at height 0. Write an equation with phase shift 0 to describe the height of the point above the ground after t seconds.

    A. $h = 3 \cos\left(\dfrac{3\pi}{2}t\right) + 3$ **B.** $h = -3 \cos\left(\dfrac{3\pi}{2}t\right) + 3$

    C. $h = 3 \sin\left(\dfrac{8\pi}{3}t\right) + 3$ **D.** $h = -3 \sin\left(\dfrac{8\pi}{3}t\right) + 3$ 15. _____

16. What is the equation for the graph shown at the right?

    A. $y = \tan 2\theta$
    B. $y = \tan (2\theta + 90°)$
    C. $y = \cot 2\theta$
    D. $y = \cot (2\theta + 90°)$ 16. _____

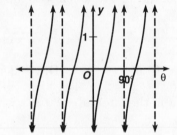

17. What is the equation for the graph shown at the right?

    A. $y = \cos x + \cos 2x$
    B. $y = \cos x + \sin x$
    C. $y = \cos 3x$
    D. $y = \sin (x + 2)$ 17. _____

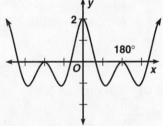

18. What is the equation of the inverse of the graph shown at the right?

    A. $y = \text{Arccos } x$
    B. $y = \text{Arcsin } x$
    C. $y = \text{Arccos } (x - 1)$
    D. $y = \text{Arcsin } (x - 1)$ 18. _____

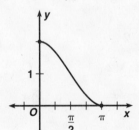

Bonus

Which function does not have an inverse that is a function?

   A. $\tan x, -90° \le x \le 90°$ **B.** $\cot x, -90° \le x \le 90°$

   C. $\sec x, -90° \le x \le 90°$ **D.** $\csc x, -90° \le x \le 90°$ **Bonus:** _____

Chapter 6 Test, Form 1B

Write the letter for the correct answer in the blank at the right of each problem.

1. Find the values of θ for which the equation $\cos \theta = -1$ is true.
   A. $360k°$ **B.** $90° + 360k°$ **C.** $180° + 360k°$ **D.** $270° + 360k°$ 1. _____

2. State the domain and range for the function $y = \dfrac{1}{\sin x}$.
   A. $D =$ all real numbers; $R = -1 \le y \le 1$
   B. $D =$ all $x \ne 360k°$, where k is any integer; $R = -1 \le y \le 1$
   C. $D =$ all $x \ne 90° + 180k°$, where k is any integer; $R = y \le -1$ and $y \ge 1$
   D. $D =$ all $x \ne 180k°$, where k is any integer; $R = y \le -1$ and $y \ge 1$ 2. _____

3. State the amplitude, period, and phase shift of the function
   $y = \dfrac{1}{3} \sin \left(2x - \dfrac{\pi}{3}\right)$.

   A. $\dfrac{1}{3}$, π, $\dfrac{\pi}{6}$ **B.** $\dfrac{1}{3}$, 4π, $-\dfrac{\pi}{6}$ **C.** $\dfrac{1}{3}$, π, $-\dfrac{\pi}{3}$ **D.** $\dfrac{1}{3}$, 4π, $\dfrac{\pi}{3}$ 3. _____

4. State the amplitude, period, and phase shift of the function
   $y = -4 \tan \dfrac{1}{2}\left(x + \dfrac{3\pi}{4}\right)$.

   A. none, 2π, $-\dfrac{3\pi}{4}$ **B.** none, π, $\dfrac{3\pi}{8}$ **C.** 4, 2π, $\dfrac{3\pi}{8}$ **D.** 4, π, $-\dfrac{3\pi}{8}$ 4. _____

5. Write an equation of the cosine function with amplitude 2, period 180°, and phase shift 90°.
   A. $y = -2 \cos \left(\dfrac{x}{2} - 45°\right)$ **B.** $y = 2 \cos \left(\dfrac{x}{2} + 180°\right)$

   C. $y = -2 \cos (2x - 90°)$ **D.** $y = 2 \cos (2x - 180°)$ 5. _____

6. Find the values of x in the interval $-180° \le x \le 180°$ that satisfy the equation
   $x = \arccos \left(\dfrac{\sqrt{2}}{2}\right)$.

   A. $-135°$, $135°$ **B.** $-45°$, $45°$ **C.** $45°$, $135°$ **D.** $-45°$, $-135°$ 6. _____

7. Evaluate $\cot \left(\cos^{-1} \dfrac{1}{2}\right)$. Assume that the angle is in Quadrant I.

   A. 2 **B.** $\dfrac{1}{2}$ **C.** $\dfrac{\sqrt{3}}{3}$ **D.** $\sqrt{3}$ 7. _____

8. Evaluate $\tan (\arccos 1) + \tan \left(\arcsin \dfrac{1}{2}\right)$. Assume that the angles are in Quadrant I.

   A. $\dfrac{\sqrt{3}}{3}$ **B.** $\sqrt{3}$ **C.** $\sqrt{3} + 1$ **D.** $\sqrt{3} + 3$ 8. _____

9. Evaluate $\sin (\text{Tan}^{-1} 1)$.

   A. 0 **B.** $\dfrac{\sqrt{2}}{2}$ **C.** $\dfrac{1}{2}$ **D.** 1 9. _____

10. Evaluate $\cos \left(\text{Tan}^{-1} \dfrac{\sqrt{3}}{3} + \text{Sin}^{-1} \dfrac{1}{2}\right)$.

    A. $\dfrac{\sqrt{3}}{2}$ **B.** $\sqrt{3}$ **C.** 0 **D.** $\dfrac{1}{2}$ 10. _____

11. State the domain and range of the relation $y = \arcsin x$.
    A. $D =$ all real numbers; $R = -90° \le y \le 90°$
    B. $D =$ all real numbers; $R = 0° \le y \le 180°$
    C. $D = -1 \le x \le 1$; $R =$ all real numbers
    D. $D = -1 \le x \le 1$; $R = -90° \le y \le 90°$ 11. _____

Glencoe Division, Macmillan/McGraw-Hill

12. Which of the following values would not produce a counterexample to the
equation Arccos x = Arccos $(-x)$ for $-1 \le x \le 1$.

    A. 0   **B.** 0.5   **C.** 1   **D.** -1 **12.** _____

13. Find the amplitude, period, frequency, and phase shift of the function
$y = -\dfrac{3}{4} \cos\left(\pi t + \dfrac{2\pi}{3}\right)$.

    A. $\dfrac{3}{4}, 2, \dfrac{1}{2}, \dfrac{2}{3}$ **B.** $\dfrac{3}{4}, 2, \dfrac{1}{2}, -\dfrac{3}{2}$ **C.** $\dfrac{3}{4}, 2, \dfrac{1}{2}, -\dfrac{2}{3}$ **D.** $-\dfrac{3}{4}, \dfrac{1}{2}, 2, -\dfrac{3}{2}$ **13.** _____

14. Write an equation with phase shift 0 to represent simple harmonic motion
with initial position -4, amplitude 4, and period $\dfrac{1}{3}$.

    A. $y = -4 \sin 6\pi t$ **B.** $y = -4 \cos 6\pi t$ **C.** $y = 4 \sin \dfrac{2\pi}{3} t$ **D.** $y = 4 \cos \dfrac{2\pi}{3} t$ **14.** _____

15. Kala is jumping rope and the rope touches the ground every time she jumps.
She jumps at the rate of 40 jumps per minute, and the distance from the
ground to the middle of the rope at its highest point is 5 feet. Write an
equation with phase shift 0 to describe the height of the midpoint (initial
position 0) of the rope above the ground after t seconds.

    A. $h = 2.5 \cos 3\pi t + 2.5$ **B.** $h = 2.5 \sin 3\pi t + 2.5$

    C. $h = -2.5 \sin \dfrac{4\pi}{3} t + 2.5$ **D.** $h = -2.5 \cos \dfrac{4\pi}{3} t + 2.5$ **15.** _____

16. What is the equation for the graph shown
at the right?

    A. $y = \sin 3x$
    B. $y = \cos (x - 2)$
    C. $y = \cos x + \sin x$
    D. $y = \sin x - \sin 2x$ **16.** _____

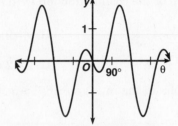

17. What is the equation for the graph shown
at the right?

    A. $y = \tan\left(\dfrac{\theta}{3} + 45°\right)$

    B. $y = \tan \dfrac{\theta}{3}$

    C. $y = \cot\left(\dfrac{\theta}{3} + 45°\right)$

    D. $y = \cot \dfrac{\theta}{3}$ **17.** _____

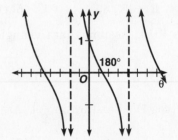

18. What is the equation of *the inverse* of the
graph shown at the right?

    A. $y = $ Arcsin x
    B. $y = $ Arccos x
    C. $y = $ Arcsin $2x$
    D. $y = $ Arccos $2x$ **18.** _____

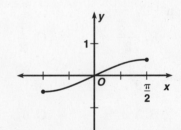

Bonus

Which function does not have an inverse that is a function?

    A. $\tan x, 0° \le x \le 180°$ **B.** $\cot x, 0° \le x \le 180°$
    C. $\csc x, 0° \le x \le 180°$ **D.** $\sec x, 0° \le x \le 180°$ **Bonus:** _____

Chapter 6 Test, Form 2A

1. Find the values of θ for which the equation $\sec \theta = -1$ is true.

1. _____

2. Find the values of θ for which the equation $\cot \theta = 0$ is true.

2. _____

3. Find the domain and range for the function $y = \dfrac{\sin x}{\cos x}$.

3. _____

State the amplitude, period, and phase shift for each function.

4. $y = 6 \cos \left(\dfrac{1}{2} x + \pi \right)$

4. _____

5. $y = -3 \cot \dfrac{1}{2}(x - 2\pi)$

5. _____

6. Write an equation of the cosine function with amplitude 5, period 45°, and phase shift −180°.

6. _____

7. Write an equation of the sine function with amplitude $\dfrac{2}{3}$, period 4π, and phase shift $\dfrac{\pi}{2}$.

7. _____

8. Find the values of x in the interval $0° \le x \le 360°$ that satisfy the equation $x = \arcsin 0$.

8. _____

9. Find the values of x in the interval $-180° \le x \le 180°$ that satisfy the equation $x = \sec^{-1} \sqrt{2}$.

9. _____

10. Graph the function $y = \sin x$ on the interval $180° \le x \le 540°$.

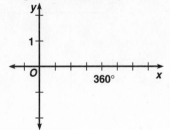

10. _____

Find each value.

11. $\sin \left(\text{Tan}^{-1} \sqrt{3} \right)$

11. _____

12. $\text{Sin}^{-1} \left(\cos \dfrac{\pi}{4} \right)$

12. _____

13. $\sin \left[\text{Cos}^{-1} \left(-\dfrac{\sqrt{2}}{2} \right) - \dfrac{\pi}{4} \right]$

13. _____

14. $\cos \left(2 \, \text{Arctan} \dfrac{3}{4} \right)$

14. _____

Find each value. Assume that all angles are in Quadrant I.

15. $\sin(\sec^{-1} 2)$

15. _____

16. $\tan\left(\arccos \dfrac{4}{5}\right)$

16. _____

17. $\cot(\arcsin 1) - \tan(\arccos 1)$

17. _____

18. State the domain and range of the function $y = \text{Cos } x$.

18. _____

19. Determine a value for x that would *not* produce a counterexample to the equation $\text{Sin}^{-1}(-x) = -\text{Cos}^{-1} x$ for $-1 \le x \le 1$.

19. _____

20. State the amplitude, period, frequency, and phase shift of the functon $y = 2\cos\left(2\pi t - \dfrac{3\pi}{2}\right)$.

20. _____

21. Write an equation with phase shift 0 to represent simple harmonic motion with initial position $\dfrac{1}{2}$, amplitude $\dfrac{1}{2}$, and period 4.

21. _____

22. The Coast Guard observes a raft floating on the water bobbing up and down a total of 8 feet. Beginning at the top of the wave, the raft completes a full cycle every 5 seconds. Write an equation with phase shift 0 to represent the height of the raft after t seconds.

22. _____

Graph each equation.

23. $y = 2\cos\left(\dfrac{\theta}{4} + 180°\right)$

24. $y = \cos x - \sec x$

23. _____

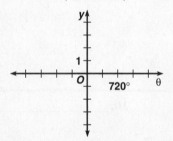

24. _____

25. Graph the inverse of the function $y = \text{Arccos } x + \dfrac{\pi}{4}$.

25. _____

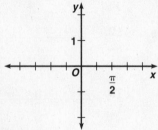

Bonus

State the period, amplitude, and phase shift for the function $y = a \sin b(x + c)$.

Bonus: _____

Chapter 6 Test, Form 2B

1. Find the values of θ for which the equation $\csc \theta = 1$ is true.

1. _____

2. Find the values of θ for which the equation $\tan \theta = -1$ is true.

2. _____

3. Find the domain and range for the function $y = \dfrac{\cos x}{\sin x}$.

3. _____

State the amplitude, period, and phase shift for each function.

4. $y = -\dfrac{1}{2} \cos \left(3x + \dfrac{4\pi}{3} \right)$

4. _____

5. $y = 4 \tan 2 \left(x - \dfrac{\pi}{2} \right)$

5. _____

6. Write an equation of the sine function with amplitude 4, period 135°, and phase shift −60°.

6. _____

7. Write an equation of the cosine function with amplitude $\dfrac{1}{4}$, period 3π, and phase shift $\dfrac{\pi}{2}$.

7. _____

8. Find the values of x in the interval $0° \le x \le 360°$ that satisfy the equation $x = \arccos 1$.

8. _____

9. Find the values of x in the interval $-180° \le x \le 180°$ that satisfy the equation $x = \csc^{-1} 2$.

9. _____

10. Graph the function $y = \cos x$ on the interval $-360° \le x \le 360°$.

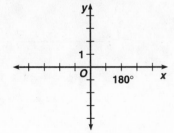

10. _____

Find each value.

11. $\cos \left[\operatorname{Sin}^{-1}(0.5) \right]$

11. _____

12. $\operatorname{Sin}^{-1}(\tan 0°)$

12. _____

13. $\tan \left[\operatorname{Cos}^{-1}\left(-\dfrac{\sqrt{3}}{2} \right) - \dfrac{2\pi}{3} \right]$

13. _____

14. $\sin \left(2 \operatorname{Tan}^{-1} \dfrac{3}{4} \right)$

14. _____

Chapter 6 Test, Form 2B (continued)

Find each value. Assume that all angles are in Quadrant I.

15. $\cos (\csc^{-1} 1)$

15. _____

16. $\cot \left(\arcsin \dfrac{3}{5} \right)$

16. _____

17. $\sin (\arctan \sqrt{3}) + \cos (\text{arccot } \sqrt{3})$

17. _____

18. State the domain and range of the function $y = \text{Arccos } x$.

18. _____

19. Determine a value for x that would *not* produce a counterexample to the equation $\text{Arcsin } x = -\text{Arccos } (-x)$ for $-1 \le x \le 1$.

19. _____

20. State the amplitude, period, frequency, and phase shift of the function $y = -4 \sin \left(\dfrac{\pi}{2} t + \dfrac{\pi}{6} \right)$.

20. _____

21. Write an equation with phase shift 0 to represent simple harmonic motion with initial position $\dfrac{1}{4}$, amplitude $\dfrac{1}{4}$, and period 6.

21. _____

22. An oar is floating on the water bobbing up and down a total of 12 feet. From the bottom of the wave, the oar completes a full cycle every 15 seconds. Write an equation with phase shift 0 to represent the height of the oar after t seconds.

22. _____

Graph each equation.

23. $y = 4 \sin \left(\dfrac{\theta}{2} - 90° \right)$

24. $y = 2 \cos x + \sin x$

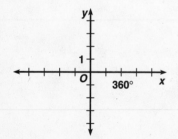

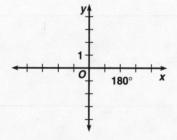

23. _____

24. _____

25. Graph the inverse of the function $y = \text{Arcsin } x - \dfrac{\pi}{2}$.

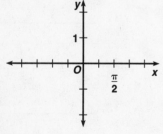

25. _____

Bonus

State the period, amplitude, and phase shift for the function $y = a \tan b(x - c)$.

Bonus: _____

Chapter 6, Quiz A (Lessons 6-1 through 6-2)

1. Find the values of θ for which the equation $\tan \theta = 1$ is true.

1. _____

2. State the domain and range for the function $y = -\csc x$.

3. Graph $y = \sec x$ on the interval $-90° \le x \le 360°$.

4. Graph $y = \frac{1}{2} \sin x$ on the interval $-180° \le x \le 180°$.

2. _____

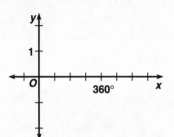

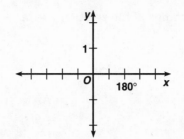

3. _____

4. _____

5. State the amplitude, period, and phase shift for the function $y = \frac{1}{3} \sin \left(x + \frac{\pi}{6} \right)$.

5. _____

6. Write an equation of the cosine function with amplitude 7, period π, and phase shift $\frac{3\pi}{2}$.

6. _____

Chapter 6, Quiz B (Lessons 6-3 through 6-4)

1. Graph the equation $\frac{1}{3}y = \sin \left(\frac{1}{2}x - 45° \right)$.

2. Graph the equation $y = \cos^2 x$.

1. _____

2. _____

3. Find the values of x in the interval $-180° \le x \le 180°$ that satisfy the equation $x = \cot^{-1} \sqrt{3}$.

3. _____

4. Evaluate $\sin (\csc^{-1} 2)$. Assume the angle is in Quadrant I.

4. _____

5. Evaluate $\cot \left(\arccos \frac{\sqrt{2}}{2} \right)$. Assume the angle is in Quadrant I.

5. _____

Glencoe Division, Macmillan/McGraw-Hill

Chapter 6, Quiz C (Lessons 6-5 through 6-6)

Find each value.

1. $\sin\left(\text{Sin}^{-1}\,\dfrac{1}{2}\right)$

2. $\tan\left[\text{Arccos}\,\dfrac{1}{2}\right]$

3. $\text{Cos}^{-1}\left(\tan\,\dfrac{\pi}{4}\right)$

4. $\tan\left(\dfrac{1}{2}\,\text{Sin}^{-1}\,\dfrac{12}{13}\right)$

5. $\cos\left[\text{Cos}^{-1}\left(-\dfrac{1}{2}\right)+\text{Sin}^{-1}\left(\dfrac{\sqrt{3}}{2}\right)\right]$

6. State the domain and range of the relation $y = \tan x$.

7. State the domain and range of the relation $y = \text{Arcsin}\,x$.

Graph the inverse of each function.

8. $y = \text{Sin}\,(x + 90°)$

9. $y = \text{Arctan}\,x + \dfrac{\pi}{4}$

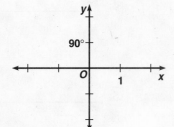

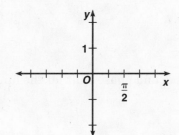

10. Determine a value for x that would *not* produce a counterexample to the equation $\text{Sin}^{-1}\,x = \text{Tan}^{-1}\,x - \dfrac{\pi}{4}$.

1. _____

2. _____

3. _____

4. _____

5. _____

6. _____

7. _____

8. _____

9. _____

10. _____

Chapter 6, Quiz D (Lesson 6-7)

1. State the amplitude, period, frequency, and phase shift for the function $y = -0.4 \cos\left(20\pi t + \dfrac{\pi}{2}\right)$.

1. _____

2. State the amplitude, period, frequency, and phase shift for the function $y = 100 \cos\left(\dfrac{\pi}{6}\,t\right) + 5$.

2. _____

3. Write an equation with phase shift 0 to represent simple harmonic motion with initial position 0, amplitude 5, and period 3.

3. _____

4. Write an equation with phase shift 0 to represent simple harmonic motion with initial position −12, amplitude 12, and period $\dfrac{1}{2}$.

4. _____

5. The paddle wheel of a boat measures 16 feet in diameter and is revolving at a rate of 20 rpm. If the lowest point of the wheel is 1 foot under water, write an equation in terms of cosine to describe the height of the initial point after t seconds.

5. _____

Chapter 6 Mid-Chapter Test (Lessons 6-1 through 6-4)

1. Find the values of θ for which the equation $\sin \theta = 0$ is true.

1. _____

2. Find the values of θ for which the equation $\cot \theta = 1$ is true.

2. _____

3. State the domain and range for the function $y = \cos(180° + x)$.

4. Graph the function $y = \csc x$ on the interval $-180° \le x \le 270°$.

3. _____

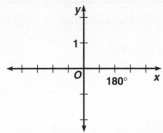

4. _____

State the amplitude, period, and phase shift for each function.

5. $y = 2 \sin 3\left(x - \dfrac{\pi}{4}\right)$

5. _____

6. $y = -\cos\left(2x + \dfrac{\pi}{4}\right)$

6. _____

7. Write an equation of the cosine function with amplitude 3, period 150°, and phase shift 180°.

7. _____

8. Write an equation of the sine function with amplitude $\dfrac{1}{6}$, period $\dfrac{\pi}{6}$, and phase shift $-\dfrac{\pi}{2}$.

8. _____

9. Find the values of x in the interval $0° \le x \le 360°$ that satisfy the equation $x = \csc^{-1}(-\sqrt{2})$.

9. _____

10. Find the values of x in the interval $-180° \le x \le 180°$ that satisfy the equation $x = \arcsin(-0.5)$.

10. _____

Find each value. Assume that all angles are in Quadrant I.

11. $\sec(\cos^{-1} 1)$

11. _____

12. $\tan\left(\arcsin \dfrac{\sqrt{2}}{2}\right)$

12. _____

13. $\cos\left(\text{arccot } \sqrt{3} - \arctan \dfrac{\sqrt{3}}{3}\right)$

13. _____

Graph each equation.

14. $y = \dfrac{1}{2} \cos(2\theta + 90°)$ 15. $y = \tan^2 x$

14. _____

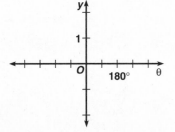   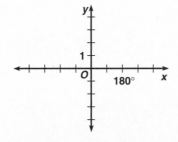

15. _____

Standardized Test Questions (Chapters 1-6)

1. In $\triangle DEF$, $m\angle D = 72°$ and $m\angle F = 44°$. Point T is the midpoint of side $\overline{FE}$. Of the following line segments, which is the shortest?

   A. $\overline{FE}$ **B.** $\overline{DE}$ **C.** $\overline{DT}$ **D.** $\overline{FT}$

   1. _____

2. If the sum of two consecutive multiples of 7 is 49, what is the greater of those two multiples?

   A. 28   **B.** 21   **C.** 14   **D.** 7

   2. _____

3. If the product of three *different* integers is 5, which of the following could be the least of these integers?

   A. 0   **B.** –5   **C.** –1   **D.** 1

   3. _____

4. There are between 160 and 175 marbles in a jar. If they are counted out 4 at a time, there is 1 left over. If they are counted out 5 at a time, there are 4 left over. How many marbles are in the jar?

   A. 173   **B.** 169   **C.** 164   **D.** 161

   4. _____

5. Triangle STU has a right angle at T. If the length of $\overline{TU}$ is x and the length of $\overline{SU}$ is y, which of the following statements *cannot* be true?

   A. $2x = y$ **B.** $x + 4 = y$ **C.** $x - 3 = y$ **D.** $x = y - 6$

   5. _____

6. Two times the greater of three consecutive even integers is 2 less than three times the least. Find the greatest of the three integers.

   A. 12   **B.** 16   **C.** 10   **D.** 14

   6. _____

7. Let $\dagger x$ be defined as $\dagger x = x^2 - 2x$. What is the value of $\dagger(-3) - \dagger 1$?

   A. 16   **B.** 2   **C.** 14   **D.** 12

   7. _____

8. Find an expression equivalent to $\left(\dfrac{3x^{-2}y^4}{x^4yz^{-1}} \right)^2$.

   A. $\dfrac{9y^6z^2}{x^{12}}$ **B.** $\dfrac{3y^5z^2}{x^4}$ **C.** $9x^4y^6z^2$ **D.** $\dfrac{6y^5z^3}{x^6}$

   8. _____

9. If $x = 4y$ and $x \neq 0$, then y is what percent of x?

   A. 4%   **B.** 40%   **C.** 400%   **D.** 25%

   9. _____

10. If two positive single-digit numbers, x and y, are added together, the result is a two-digit number. How many digits must the product of x and y have?

    A. 1

    B. 2

    C. 3

    D. cannot be determined from the information given

   10. _____

Glencoe Division, Macmillan/McGraw-Hill

Chapter 7 Test, Form 1A

Write the letter for the correct answer in the blank at the right of each problem.

1. Solve for the value of tan θ between $0°$ and $90°$ if $\cos \theta = 0.25$.

   A. 4 B. $\frac{1}{16}$ C. $\sqrt{15}$ D. $\frac{\sqrt{15}}{15}$

   1. _____

2. If $\cot \theta = \frac{5}{12}$, find $\csc \theta$ for θ between $0°$ and $90°$.

   A. $\frac{12}{13}$ B. $\frac{5}{12}$ C. $\frac{-5}{12}$ D. $\frac{13}{12}$

   2. _____

3. Express $\sin 750°$ as a function of an angle in Quadrant I.

   A. $\sin 30°$ B. $-\sin 30°$ C. $\sin 15°$ D. $-\sin 15°$

   3. _____

4. Simplify $\dfrac{1-\cot^2\theta \sec^2\theta}{\cot^2\theta}$.

   A. $\sec \theta$ B. 1 C. $\cot \theta$ D. -1

   4. _____

5. Which equation is a trigonometric identity?

   A. $\tan \theta = \sin \theta \sec \theta$ B. $\sec^2 \theta - \csc^2 \theta = 1$
   C. $\tan x \sin x = \cos x$ D. $\tan^2 \theta = \sec^2 \theta + 1$

   5. _____

6. Find a numerical value of one trigonometric function if $\cos x \csc x = 2$.

   A. $\sec x = \frac{1}{2}$ B. $\sin x = \frac{1}{2}$ C. $\tan x = 2$ D. $\cot x = 2$

   6. _____

7. Find the value of $\tan (x - y)$ for $0° < x < 90°$ and $0° < y < 90°$ when $\sin x = \frac{15}{17}$ and $\cos y = \frac{8}{17}$.

   A.$- \frac{289}{64}$ B. $- \frac{240}{161}$ C. $\frac{240}{161}$ D. 0

   7. _____

8. Use a sum or difference identity to find the exact value of $\cos 150°$.

   A. $\frac{\sqrt{3}}{2}$ B. $-\frac{\sqrt{3}}{2}$ C. $\frac{\sqrt{3}-\sqrt{2}}{2}$ D. $-\frac{\sqrt{2}}{2}$

   8. _____

9. Which expression is equivalent to $\cos (90° - \theta)$?

   A. $\sin \theta$ B. $-\sin \theta$ C. $\cos \theta$ D. $-\cos \theta$

   9. _____

10. Use a half-angle identity to find the exact value of $\cos 67.5°$.

    A. $\frac{1}{2}\sqrt{2 - \sqrt{2}}$ B. $-\frac{1}{2}\sqrt{2 - \sqrt{2}}$ C. $-\frac{1}{2}\sqrt{2 + \sqrt{2}}$ D. $\sqrt{3 + 2\sqrt{2}}$

    10. _____

11. Which expression is *not* equivalent to $\cos 2\theta$ for all values of θ?

    A. $\cos^2 \theta - \sin^2 \theta$ B. $2 \sin \theta \cos \theta$
    C. $1 - 2 \sin^2 \theta$ D. $2 \cos^2 \theta - 1$

    11. _____

12. If $\sin \theta = -\frac{4}{5}$ and θ terminates in Quadrant III, find the exact value of $\sin 2\theta$.

    A. $\frac{16}{25}$ B. $- \frac{24}{25}$ C. $\frac{24}{25}$ D. $-\frac{9}{25}$

    12. _____

Chapter 7 Test, Form 1A (continued)

13. Solve $2 \sin^2 x - 3 \sin x + 1 = 0$ for principal values of x.
    A. $0°, 30°$　　　　B. $30°$　　　　　　C. $30°, 90°$　　　　D. $0°, 60°$

    13. _____

14. Which value is *not* a solution of $2 \sin x + 1 = 0$?
    A. $\dfrac{\pi}{6}$　　　　B. $-\dfrac{\pi}{6}$　　　　C. $210°$　　　　D. $-30°$

    14. _____

15. Write the equation $x + y = 5$ in normal form to find $(\cos \theta, \sin \theta)$.
    A. $\left(\dfrac{\sqrt{2}}{2}, -\dfrac{\sqrt{2}}{2}\right)$　B. $\left(\dfrac{\sqrt{2}}{2}, \dfrac{\sqrt{2}}{2}\right)$　C. $\left(-\dfrac{\sqrt{2}}{2}, \dfrac{\sqrt{2}}{2}\right)$　D. $\left(-\dfrac{\sqrt{2}}{2}, -\dfrac{\sqrt{2}}{2}\right)$

    15. _____

16. Write the equation $3x + y - 1 = 0$ in normal form to find the length, in units, of the normal, p.
    A. $-\dfrac{\sqrt{10}}{10}$　　　B. $\dfrac{\sqrt{10}}{10}$　　　C. $\dfrac{\sqrt{2}}{4}$　　　D. $-\dfrac{\sqrt{2}}{4}$

    16. _____

17. Write the equation $\sqrt{3}x + y - 4 = 0$ in normal form to find the angle, ϕ, that the normal to the line makes with the positive x-axis.
    A. $45°$　　　　B. $90°$　　　　C. $60°$　　　　D. $30°$

    17. _____

18. Find the distance, in units, between $P(-2, 1)$ and the line with equation $3x - 4y + 1 = 0$.
    A. -1.8　　　　B. 1.8　　　　C. 1　　　　D. -2

    18. _____

19. Find the distance, in units, between the lines with equations $2x - 5y = 8$ and $y = \dfrac{2}{5}x - 3$.
    A. $-\dfrac{23\sqrt{29}}{29}$　　B. $\dfrac{7\sqrt{29}}{29}$　　C. $-\dfrac{7\sqrt{29}}{29}$　　D. $\dfrac{23\sqrt{29}}{29}$

    19. _____

20. Find the equation of the line that bisects the acute angle formed by the graphs of the equations $6x + 3y - 1 = 0$ and $2x + 2y - 3 = 0$.
    A. $\left(6\sqrt{5} + 12\sqrt{2}\right)x + \left(6\sqrt{5} + 6\sqrt{2}\right)y + 9\sqrt{5} + 2\sqrt{2} = 0$
    B. $\left(6\sqrt{5} + 12\sqrt{2}\right)x + \left(6\sqrt{5} + 6\sqrt{2}\right)y - 9\sqrt{5} - 2\sqrt{2} = 0$
    C. $\left(6\sqrt{5} - 12\sqrt{2}\right)x + \left(6\sqrt{5} - 6\sqrt{2}\right)y + 9\sqrt{5} + 2\sqrt{2} = 0$
    D. $\left(6\sqrt{5} - 12\sqrt{2}\right)x + \left(6\sqrt{5} - 6\sqrt{2}\right)y - 9\sqrt{5} - 2\sqrt{2} = 0$

    20. _____

Bonus

If $-90° < \theta < 0°$ and $\sin \theta = -\dfrac{12}{13}$, find $\cos 4\theta$.

    A. $\dfrac{239}{28,561}$　　　B. $-\dfrac{239}{28,561}$　　　C. $\dfrac{238}{169}$　　　D. $-\dfrac{239}{169}$

    Bonus: _____

Chapter 7 Test, Form 1B

Write the letter for the correct answer in the blank at the right of each problem.

1. Which is *not* a trigonometric identity?

   A. $\sin A = \dfrac{1}{\sec A}$ **B.** $\sec A = \dfrac{1}{\cos A}$

   C. $\tan A = \dfrac{1}{\cot A}$ **D.** $\cot A = \dfrac{1}{\tan A}$ 1. _____

2. If $\sin \theta = -\dfrac{15}{17}$, and the terminal side of θ lies in Quadrant III, find $\cos \theta$.

   A. $\dfrac{8}{17}$ **B.** $-\dfrac{2}{17}$ **C.** $\dfrac{2}{17}$ **D.** $-\dfrac{8}{17}$ 2. _____

3. Express $\csc(-400)°$ as a function of an angle in Quadrant I.

   A. $-\csc 60°$ **B.** $-\csc 20°$ **C.** $-\csc 80°$ **D.** $-\csc 40°$ 3. _____

4. Simplify $(\cot x)\left(\dfrac{1}{\csc x}\right)$.

   A. 1   **B.** $\sin x$ **C.** $\cos x$ **D.** -1 4. _____

5. Which equation is *not* a trigonometric identity?

   A. $\tan \theta = \dfrac{\cos \theta}{\sin \theta \cot^2 \theta}$

   B. $\sin^2 \theta = 1 - \cos^2 \theta$
   C. $\cos \theta \sec \theta - \cos^2 \theta = \sin^2 \theta$
   D. $\cos \theta \tan \theta = -\sin \theta$ 5. _____

6. Find a numerical value of one trigonometric function if $\sin \theta \cot \theta = 1$.

   A. $\cos \theta = 1$ **B.** $\sin \theta = 1$ **C.** $\tan \theta = 1$ **D.** $\csc \theta = 1$ 6. _____

7. Use a sum or difference identity to find the exact value of $\cos 285°$.

   A. $\dfrac{-\sqrt{6}-\sqrt{2}}{4}$ **B.** $\dfrac{\sqrt{6}-\sqrt{2}}{4}$ **C.** $\dfrac{\sqrt{2}-\sqrt{6}}{4}$ **D.** $\dfrac{\sqrt{2}+\sqrt{6}}{4}$ 7. _____

8. Find the value of $\sin (\alpha + \beta)$ if $\sin \alpha = \dfrac{3}{5}$, $\cos \beta = \dfrac{12}{13}$, $0° < \alpha < 90°$,

   and $0° < \beta < 90°$.

   A. $\dfrac{56}{65}$ **B.** $\dfrac{16}{65}$ **C.** $\dfrac{63}{65}$ **D.** $\dfrac{33}{65}$ 8. _____

9. Which equation is *not* an identity?

   A. $\sin (180° - \theta) = \sin \theta$ **B.** $\cos (180° - \theta) = -\cos \theta$
   C. $\tan (90° - \theta) = \cot \theta$ **D.** $\cot (90° - \theta) = -\tan \theta$ 9. _____

10. Use a half-angle identity to find the exact value of $\cos 105°$.

    A. $\dfrac{1}{2}\sqrt{2 - \sqrt{3}}$ **B.** $-\dfrac{1}{2}\sqrt{2 - \sqrt{3}}$ **C.** $-\dfrac{1}{2}\sqrt{2 + \sqrt{3}}$ **D.** $\sqrt{3 + 2\sqrt{2}}$ 10. _____

Glencoe Division, Macmillan/McGraw-Hill

~ Chapter 7 Test, Form 1B (continued)

11. If $\cos \theta = -0.6$, and $180° < \theta < 270°$, find the exact value of $\sin 2\theta$.

   A. 0.96   **B.** 0.64   **C.** -0.36 **D.** -0.96 11. _____

12. Which equation is *not* a trigonometric identity?

   A. $\cos 2\theta = \cos^2 \theta + \sin^2 \theta$ **B.** $\cos 2\theta = 1 - 2 \sin^2 \theta$
   C. $\sin 2\theta = 2 \sin \theta \cos \theta$ **D.** $\cos 2\theta = 2 \cos^2 \theta - 1$ 12. _____

13. Which expression is *not* a solution of $\sin x = \cos 2x$?

   A. $30°$ **B.** $30° + 360k°$ **C.** $120°$ **D.** $150° + 360k°$ 13. _____

14. Solve $2 \sin x \cos x = 3 \sin x$ for $0° \le x < 360°$.

   A. $0°$ **B.** $0°, 180°$ **C.** $180°$ **D.** $0°, 270°$ 14. _____

15. Write the equation $2x + 3y = 5$ in normal form.

   A. $\dfrac{2x}{\sqrt{13}} + \dfrac{3y}{\sqrt{13}} + \dfrac{5}{\sqrt{13}} = 0$ **B.** $-\dfrac{2x}{\sqrt{13}} - \dfrac{3y}{\sqrt{13}} + \dfrac{5}{\sqrt{13}} = 0$

   C. $-\dfrac{2x}{\sqrt{13}} - \dfrac{3y}{\sqrt{13}} - \dfrac{5}{\sqrt{13}} = 0$ **D.** $\dfrac{2x}{\sqrt{13}} + \dfrac{3y}{\sqrt{13}} - \dfrac{5}{\sqrt{13}} = 0$ 15. _____

16. Write the equation $-5x + 4y + 3 = 0$ in normal form to find the length, in units, of the normal, p.

   A. $\dfrac{3\sqrt{41}}{41}$ **B.** $-\dfrac{3\sqrt{41}}{41}$ **C.** $\sqrt{41}$ **D.** $-\sqrt{41}$ 16. _____

17. Write the standard form of the equation of a line for which the length of the normal is 2 and the normal makes a $30°$ angle with the positive x-axis.

   A. $x \pm \sqrt{3}y - 4 = 0$ **B.** $x \pm \sqrt{3}y + 4 = 0$
   C. $\sqrt{3}x + y - 4 = 0$ **D.** $\sqrt{3}x + y + 4 = 0$ 17. _____

18. Find the distance, in units, between $P(3, -2)$ and the line with equation $x + 2y - 3 = 0$.

   A. $\dfrac{\sqrt{5}}{5}$ **B.** $-\dfrac{\sqrt{5}}{5}$ **C.** $-\dfrac{4\sqrt{5}}{5}$ **D.** $\dfrac{4\sqrt{5}}{5}$ 18. _____

19. Find the distance between the lines with equations $3y - 5x = 3$ and $y = \dfrac{5}{3}x + 1$.

   A. $-\dfrac{3\sqrt{34}}{17}$ units   **B.** $\dfrac{3\sqrt{34}}{17}$ units   **C.** 0   **D.** $\dfrac{11\sqrt{34}}{34}$ units   19. _____

20. Find the coefficient of x for the equation of the line that bisects the acute angles formed by the lines graphed at the right.

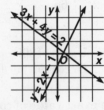

   A. $3\sqrt{5} + 10$ **B.** $-3\sqrt{5} + 10$ **C.** $4\sqrt{5} - 5$ **D.** $4\sqrt{5} + 5$ 20. _____

Bonus

   If $-90° < \theta < 0°$, express $\sin \theta$ in terms of $\cot \theta$.

   A. $\sqrt{1 + \cot^2 \theta}$ **B.** $-\sqrt{1 + \cot^2 \theta}$ **C.** $\dfrac{-1}{\sqrt{1 + \cot^2 \theta}}$ **D.** $\dfrac{1}{\sqrt{1 + \cot^2 \theta}}$ Bonus: _____

Glencoe Division, Macmillan/McGraw-Hill

Chapter 7 Test, Form 2A

1. If $\sin A = -0.6$, find $\csc A$.

1. _____

2. If $\cot A = \frac{3}{4}$, find $\sin A$ for A between π and $\frac{3\pi}{2}$.

2. _____

3. Express $\sin -750°$ as a function of $30°$.

3. _____

4. Simplify $\cos \theta \sec \theta \tan^2\theta$.

4. _____

5. In which quadrant(s) does $\cos \theta = -\sqrt{1 - \sin^2\theta}$?

5. _____

6. If $\cot x \sin x = \frac{1}{2}$, find the numerical value of $\sec x$.

6. _____

7. Verify that $\tan x \csc x = \sec x$ is an identity.

7. _____

8. Find the exact value of $\sin 165°$.

8. _____

9. If $\sin \alpha = \frac{15}{17}$ for $90° < \alpha < 180°$ and $\cos \beta = \frac{4}{5}$ for $270° < \beta < 360°$, find $\sin (\alpha + \beta)$.

9. _____

10. Use a half-angle identity to find the exact value of $\cos \frac{11\pi}{12}$.

10. _____

11. If $\cos y = -\frac{2}{\sqrt{5}}$ and y is in the second quadrant, find $\cos 2y$.

11. _____

12. For how many values of θ does $\cos \theta = -\frac{1}{2}$?

12. _____

13. Solve $\sin^2 x + 2 \sin x - 3 = 0$ for $0 \le x \le 180°$.

13. _____

14. Solve $(\tan x - 1)(2 \cos x + 1) = 0$ for all values of x.

14. _____

15. Simplify $x \cos 30° + y \sin 30° + 7 = 0$.

15. _____

16. Write the normal form of $y = 2x + 3$.

16. _____

17. Find the angle the normal for the equation $4x + 3y - 1 = 0$ makes with the x-axis.

17. _____

18. Find the distance between $P(0, 5)$ and the line with equation $-2x + y - 3 = 0$.

18. _____

19. Find the distance between two parallel lines with equations $2x - 2y = 5$ and $y = x - 1$.

19. _____

20. Find the equation of the line that bisects the acute angle formed by the graphs of the equations $3x + y = -6$ and $2x - y = 1$.

20. _____

Bonus

How are the lines that bisect the angles formed by the equations $3x + y = 6$ and $x - 3y = 1$ related to each other?

Bonus: _____

Chapter 7 Test, Form 2B

1. For what value(s) of θ does the equation $\sin \theta = \dfrac{1}{\csc \theta}$ hold?

1. _____

2. If $\sin \theta = \dfrac{3}{4}$ and $\cos \theta < 0$, find $\tan \theta$.

2. _____

3. Express $\tan 245°$ as a function of an angle in Quadrant I.

3. _____

4. Simplify $\dfrac{\cos x}{\csc x - \sin x}$.

4. _____

5. In which quadrant(s) does $\sin \theta = \sqrt{1 - \cos^2 \theta}$?

5. _____

6. Find a numerical value of one trigonometric function
   of x if $\tan x \csc^2 x \cos x = 1$.

6. _____

7. Verify that $\sec \theta \csc \theta - \tan \theta = \cot \theta$ is an identity.

7. _____

8. Find the exact value of $\cos 105°$.

8. _____

9. If $\cos \alpha = \dfrac{4}{5}$ and $\cos \beta = \dfrac{12}{13}$, find $\sin (\alpha + \beta)$ when α and β are
   the measures of two first-quadrant angles.

9. _____

10. Use a half-angle identity to find the exact value of $\tan 22.5°$.

10. _____

11. If $\cos y = \dfrac{-12}{13}$ and y is in Quadrant II, find $\sin 2y$.

11. _____

12. Verify that $\cos x \sin x = \dfrac{\sin 2x}{2}$ is an identity.

12. _____

13. Solve $4 \sin^2 x = 2$ for $0° \le x \le 180°$.

13. _____

Glencoe Division, Macmillan/McGraw-Hill

14. Solve $\cos 2x - 2\sin^2 x + 2 = 0$ for all values of x.

14. _____

15. Find $\sqrt{A^2 + B^2}$ for $3x - 5y + 12 = 0$.

15. _____

16. Write the normal form of the equation $5x = y - 3$.

16. _____

17. Find the length of the normal, p, for the equation $4x + 3y - 5 = 0$.

17. _____

18. Find the distance between $P(-1, 4)$ and the line with equation $4x - 2y + 3 = 0$.

18. _____

19. Find the distance between the two lines with equations $x - 2y = 3$ and $y = \frac{1}{2}x - 2$.

19. _____

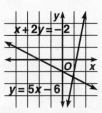

20. Find the equation of the line that bisects the acute angle formed by the lines that are graphed at the right.

20. _____

Bonus

Prove that $\cot(x + y) = \dfrac{\cot x \cot y - 1}{\cot x + \cot y}$ by using

the identity $\cot \theta = \dfrac{\cos \theta}{\sin \theta}$ and the sum identities

for sine and cosine.

Bonus: _____

Chapter 7, Quiz A (Lessons 7-1 through 7-2)

1. If $\cot \theta = -\dfrac{2}{7}$, and θ is in the second quadrant, find $\csc \theta$.

1. _____

2. Express $\cos 240°$ as a function of an angle in Quadrant I.

2. _____

3. Simplify $\cot x \sin^2 x \csc x$.

3. _____

4. Find a numerical value of one trigonometric function
   of x if $\sin \theta \sec \theta = \dfrac{\sqrt{3}}{3}$.

4. _____

5. Verify that $\dfrac{1 + \tan^2 \theta}{\tan^2 \theta} = \csc^2 \theta$ is an identity.

5. _____

Chapter 7, Quiz B (Lessons 7-3 through 7-4)

1. Find the exact value of $\cos 225°$.

1. _____

2. If $\cos \alpha = \dfrac{7}{25}$, and $\sin \beta = \dfrac{3}{5}$, and α and β are both
   measures of angles in the first quadrant, find $\sin (\alpha + \beta)$.

2. _____

3. If $\sin x = -\dfrac{4}{5}$, and $\pi < x < \dfrac{3\pi}{2}$, find $\sin 2x$.

3. _____

4. Use a half-angle identity to find the exact value of $\sin 22.5°$.

4. _____

5. Verify that $\cos (90° - \theta) = \sin \theta$ is an identity.

5. _____

NAME _____ DATE _____

~

Chapter 7, Quiz C (Lessons 7-5 through 7-6)

Solve each equation for principal values of x.

1. $\sin^2 x = \sin x$

2. $2\cos^2 x - \cos x = 3$

1. _____

2. _____

3. Solve $\tan^2 x = 1$ for all values of x.

3. _____

4. Write the standard form of the equation of a line for which
the length of the normal, p, is $\sqrt{2}$, and the normal makes
a 30° angle with the positive x-axis.

4. _____

5. Write the equation of the line $x - y = 5$ in normal form.

5. _____

NAME _____ DATE _____

Chapter 7, Quiz D (Lesson 7-7)

1. Find the distance from the graph of $4x - y + 3 = 0$
to the point $C(-3, 2)$.

1. _____

2. How far is it from the graph of $5x + y + 1 = 0$ to the point $C(-1, 4)$?

2. _____

3. The lines whose equations are $x + 3y = 6$ and $2x + 6y - 10 = 0$
are parallel. Find the distance between these lines.

3. _____

Refer to the graph below for Exercises 4 and 5.

4. For the equations graphed, how are
the values of d_1 and d_2 related when
finding the equation of the line that
bisects the acute angle formed ?

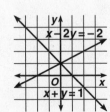

4. _____

5. Find the equation of the line that
bisects the acute angles formed
by the lines that are graphed at the right.

5. _____

Glencoe Division, Macmillan/McGraw-Hill

Chapter 7 Mid-Chapter Test (Lessons 7-1 through 7-4)

Solve for values of θ between 0° and 90° if cos θ = 0.

1. sin θ

2. tan θ

Express each value as a function of an angle in Quadrant I.

3. sin 120°

4. tan −135°

5. Simplify $\sec^2 A - \tan^2 A$.

Find a numerical value of one trigonometric function of x.

6. $\dfrac{\cot x}{\csc x} = \dfrac{1}{2}$

7. $\cos^2 x \sec x = -1$

Use the sum and difference identities to find the exact value of each function.

8. sin 345°

9. cos 75°

If α and β are the measures of two first-quadrant angles, find the exact value of each function.

10. For sin $\alpha = \dfrac{12}{13}$, cos $\beta = \dfrac{8}{17}$, find cos $(\alpha - \beta)$.

11. For tan $\alpha = \dfrac{3}{4}$, cot $\beta = \dfrac{12}{5}$, find tan $(\alpha + \beta)$.

12. Verify that cos $(180° - x) = -\cos x$ is an identity.

13. Find cos $2y$ if y is in Quadrant IV and cot $y = -\dfrac{7}{24}$.

14. Use a half-angle identity to find the exact value of tan $\dfrac{\pi}{12}$.

15. Verify that $\dfrac{4}{\sin 2\theta} = 2 \csc \theta \sec \theta$ is an identity.

1. _____

2. _____

3. _____

4. _____

5. _____

6. _____

7. _____

8. _____

9. _____

10. _____

11. _____

12. _____

13. _____

14. _____

15. _____

Glencoe Division, Macmillan/McGraw-Hill

~Standardized Test Questions (Chapters 1 – 7)

The questions below involve comparing two quantities, one in Column A and one in Column B. In certain questions, information related to one or both quantities is centered above them. All variables represent real numbers.

Directions:
Write A if the quantity in column A is greater.
Write B if the quantity in column B is greater.
Write C if the two quantities are equal.
Write D if there is not enough information to determine the relationship.

Column A	Column B	
1. the number of complex roots of $x^2 + 2 = 0$	the number of real roots of $x - 2 = 0$	**1.** _____
2. the discriminant of $x^2 - 14x + 49 = 0$	the discriminant of $x^2 = -36 - 12x$	**2.** _____
3. $\quad\quad f(x, y) = 2x + 3y - 1$ $f(3, 2)$	$f(1.5, 5.5)$	**3.** _____
4. $\cos \dfrac{5\pi}{6}$	$\csc \dfrac{5\pi}{3}$	**4.** _____
5. $\quad\quad \left| \begin{matrix} y-3 \\ y \end{matrix} \right| = \left| \begin{matrix} x \\ -2x \end{matrix} \right|$ x	y	**5.** _____
6. the remainder for $\dfrac{x^3 - 4x^2 + 2x - 6}{x - 4}$	the remainder for $\dfrac{x^2 + 1}{x + 1}$	**6.** _____
7. $\quad\quad \tan \theta = 0.5$ $\cot \theta$	$\sin \theta$	**7.** _____

Choose the best answer. Write A, B, C, or D.

8. Which graph is the general shape of the graph of a polynomial function of degree 4?

8. _____

A. 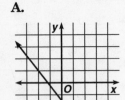   **B.** 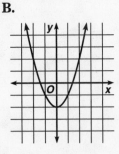   **C.** 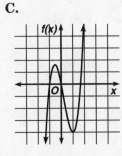   **D.**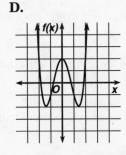

Glencoe Division, Macmillan/McGraw-Hill

Chapter 8 Test, Form 1A

Write the letter for the correct answer in the blank at the right of each problem.

1. $\vec{u}$ has a magnitude of 2.4 cm and an amplitude of 32°. Find the magnitude of its vertical component.

   A. 2.04 cm   **B.** 1.27 cm   **C.** 2.83 cm   **D.** 4.53 cm   1. _____

2. What is an expression for $\vec{x}$ involving $\vec{r}$ and $\vec{s}$?

   A. $-3\vec{r} + \vec{s}$
   B. $3\vec{r} + \vec{s}$
   C. $3\vec{r} - \vec{s}$
   D. $-3\vec{r} - \vec{s}$

   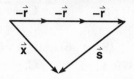

        2. _____

3. $\vec{a}$ has a magnitude of 8.1 cm, and $\vec{b}$ has a magnitude of 5.4 cm. Both vectors have the same direction. Which of the following is true?

   A. $\vec{a} = 2\vec{b}$ **B.** $3\vec{a} = 2\vec{b}$ **C.** $3\vec{a} = \vec{b}$ **D.** $2\vec{a} = 3\vec{b}$ 3. _____

4. If $\overrightarrow{AB}$ is a vector from $A(-2, 1)$ to $B(4, -4)$, find the magnitude of $\overrightarrow{AB}$.

   A. 1   **B.** 7.81   **C.** 6.71   **D.** 3.61   4. _____

5. If $\overrightarrow{AB}$ is a vector from $A(12, -5, 5)$ to $B(-8, 9\ 7)$, find the magnitude of $\overrightarrow{AB}$.

   A. 14.70   **B.** 13.27   **C.** 24.49   **D.** 23.66   5. _____

6. Write $\overrightarrow{MN}$ as the sum of unit vectors for $M(12, 3, -9)$ and $N(-4, 0, 18)$.

   A. $-16\vec{i} + 3\vec{j} + 9\vec{k}$ **B.** $8\vec{i} + 3\vec{j} - 27\vec{k}$
   C. $-16\vec{i} - 3\vec{j} + 27\vec{k}$ **D.** $8\vec{i} - 3\vec{j} - 9\vec{k}$ 6. _____

Find an ordered pair or an ordered triple to represent $\vec{u}$ in each equation if $\vec{v} = (-2, 4)$, $\vec{w} = (6, 3)$, $\vec{r} = (0, -5, 3)$, and $\vec{s} = (9, -4, -5)$.

7. $\vec{u} = 2\vec{v} + \vec{w}$

   A. (2, 11)   **B.** (4, 7)   **C.** (10, 10)   **D.** (10, -5)   7. _____

8. $\vec{u} = \vec{w} - 3\vec{v}$

   A. (12, -9)   **B.** (0, 15)   **C.** (-20, -5)   **D.** (7, 10)   8. _____

9. $\vec{u} = \vec{r} - \vec{s}$

   A. (-9, -1, 8)   **B.** (-9, -9, -2)   **C.** (9, 1, -8)   **D.** (9, -9, -2)   9. _____

10. $\vec{u} = 4\vec{s} + 2\vec{r}$

    A. (18, -28, 2)   **B.** (-18, 12, 2)   **C.** (36, -26, -14)   **D.** (36, -6, -26)   10. _____

Chapter 8 Test, Form 1A (continued)

For Exercises 11-12, find the inner product and state whether the vectors are perpendicular.

11. $(6, -7) \cdot (-4, -3)$

    A. 0; yes   **B.** -8; no   **C.** -3; no   **D.** -45; no   11. _____

12. $(8, 0, -5) \cdot (-3, 8, 5)$

    A. 0; yes   **B.** 1; no   **C.** -49; yes   **D.** -49; no   12. _____

13. Find the cross product of $(9, -6, 5)$ and $(3, -5, 1)$.

    A. $(-31, -24, -63)$ **B.** $(19, 6, -27)$ **C.** $(-27, -6, 19)$ **D.** $(27, 30, 5)$ 13. _____

14. Find the magnitude of the resultant vector of two 15-pound forces that act on an object with an angle of 40° between them.

    A. 28.2 lb   **B.** 10.3 lb   **C.** 12.7 lb   **D.** 24.9 lb   14. _____

15. A 17 N force acting at 67° and a 23 N force acting at 13° act concurrently on a point. What is the magnitude and direction of a third force that produces equilibrium at the point?

    A. 35.7 N; 31°25'   **B.** 35.7 N; 215°38'

    C. 26.1 N; 21°32'   **D.** 26.1 N; 45°28'   15. _____

16. Write the equation of the line $2x - 3y = 6$ in parametric form.

    A. $x = t$; $y = \dfrac{3}{2}t - 2$ **B.** $x = t$; $y = -\dfrac{3}{2}t + 2$

    C. $x = t$; $y = -\dfrac{2}{3}t - 2$ **D.** $x = t$; $y = \dfrac{2}{3}t - 2$ 16. _____

For Exercises 17-18, write an equation of the line with the given parametric equations in slope-intercept form.

17. $x = -2t + 1; y = 4t - 11$

    A. $y = -2x - 3$ **B.** $y = 2x - 19$ **C.** $y = -2x - 9$ **D.** $y = 2x - 13$ 17. _____

18. $x = 6t - 4; y = -5t - 3$

    A. $y = \dfrac{5}{6}x + 17$ **B.** $y = \dfrac{5}{6}x + 9$ **C.** $y = -\dfrac{5}{6}x - \dfrac{19}{3}$ **D.** $y = -\dfrac{5}{6}x + \dfrac{1}{3}$ 18. _____

Angie kicked a kickball with an initial velocity of 33 ft/s at an angle of 29° to the ground. Use this information for Exercises 19-20.

19. After 1.1 seconds, how far has the ball traveled horizontally?

    A. 17.6 ft   **B.** 0.0 ft   **C.** 31.7 ft   **D.** 14.1 ft   19. _____

20. After 0.5 seconds, how far has the ball traveled vertically?

    A. 8.0 ft   **B.** 14.4 ft   **C.** 10.4 ft   **D.** 4.0 ft   20. _____

Bonus

Find parametric equations for the line through $(-1, 5)$ and $(-3, 1)$.

    A. $x = t; y = 2t + 7$ **B.** $x = t; y = \dfrac{2}{3}t + 3$

    C. $x = t; y = \dfrac{1}{2}t + \dfrac{5}{2}$ **D.** $x = t; y = \dfrac{3}{2}t + \dfrac{11}{2}$ Bonus: _____

Chapter 8 Test, Form 1B

Write the letter for the correct answer in the blank at the right of each problem.

1. $\vec{u}$ has a magnitude of 6.1 in. and an amplitude of 55°. Find the magnitude of its vertical component.
   A. 5.00 in.   B. 10.64 in.   C. 7.45 in.   D. 3.50 in.

   1. _____

2. What is an expression for $\vec{x}$ involving $\vec{r}$ and $\vec{s}$?
   A. $\vec{r} + 2\vec{s}$
   B. $-\vec{r} + 2\vec{s}$
   C. $\vec{r} - 2\vec{s}$
   D. $-\vec{r} - 2\vec{s}$

   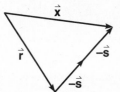

   2. _____

3. $\vec{a}$ has a magnitude of 2.4 cm, and $\vec{b}$ has a magnitude of 1.8 cm. Both vectors have the same direction. Which of the following is true?
   A. $4\vec{a} = 3\vec{b}$ B. $3\vec{a} = 4\vec{b}$ C. $\vec{a} = 2\vec{b}$ D. $2\vec{a} = \vec{b}$

   3. _____

4. If $\overrightarrow{AB}$ is a vector from $A(9, 2)$ to $B(-6, 3)$, find the magnitude of $\overrightarrow{AB}$.
   A. 15.03   B. 5.83   C. 3.74   D. 2.83

   4. _____

5. If $\overrightarrow{AB}$ is a vector from $A(-3, 5, 6)$ to $B(-6, 8, 6)$, find the magnitude of $\overrightarrow{AB}$.
   A. 19.85   B. 9.49   C. 4.24   D. 13.34

   5. _____

6. Write $\overrightarrow{MN}$ as the sum of unit vectors for $M(-14, 8, 6)$ and $N(7, 9, -2)$.
   A. $-7\vec{i} - \vec{j} - 8\vec{k}$ B. $-7\vec{i} - \vec{j} + 8\vec{k}$
   C. $-21\vec{i} - \vec{j} + 8\vec{k}$ D. $21\vec{i} + \vec{j} - 8\vec{k}$

   6. _____

For Exercises 7-10, find an ordered pair or an ordered triple to represent $\vec{u}$ in each equation if $\vec{v} = (-4, 0)$, $\vec{w} = (-3, 4)$, $\vec{r} = (2, 11, -5)$, and $\vec{s} = (-2, 8, 6)$.

7. $\vec{u} = \vec{v} + 3\vec{w}$
   A. $(-13, 12)$ B. $(5, 12)$ C. $(-7, 4)$ D. $(-15, 4)$

   7. _____

8. $\vec{u} = 4\vec{w} - 2\vec{v}$
   A. $(-20, 16)$ B. $(-4, 16)$ C. $(-10, -8)$ D. $(-22, 8)$

   8. _____

9. $\vec{u} = \vec{r} - 2\vec{s}$
   A. $(-2, 27, 7)$ B. $(6, -5, -17)$ C. $(2, 17, -1)$ D. $(-6, -14, 16)$

   9. _____

10. $\vec{u} = 3\vec{s} - 5\vec{r}$
    A. $(4, 79, -7)$ B. $(-16, -31, 43)$ C. $(-2, 17, -1)$ D. $(16, -7, -45)$

    10. _____

~ **Chapter 8 Test, Form 1B (continued)**

For Exercises 11-12, find the inner product and state whether the vectors are perpendicular.

11. $(1, -2) \cdot (12, -6)$

    A. 0; yes   **B.** 5; no   **C.** 21; no   **D.** 24; no   **11.** _____

12. $(4, -2, -2) \cdot (-7, -2, 4)$

    A. 0; yes   **B.** −32; yes   **C.** −40; no   **D.** −32; no   **12.** _____

13. Find the cross product of $(-9, 4, -8)$ and $(6, -2, 4)$.

    A. $(-54, -8, -32)$ **B.** $(0, -12, -6)$ **C.** $(32, 84, 42)$ **D.** $(-6, -12, 0)$ **13.** _____

14. Find the magnitude of the resultant vector of two 5-pound forces that act on an object with an angle of 70° between them.

    A. 5.7 lb   **B.** 8.2 lb   **C.** 1.7 lb   **D.** 7.7 lb   **14.** _____

15. A 22 N force acting at 36° and a 43 N force acting at 51° act concurrently on a point. What is the magnitude and direction of a third force that produces equilibrium at the point?

    A. 64.5 N; 225°56'   **B.** 64.5 N; 5°4'

    C. 47.3 N; 6°55'   **D.** 47.3 N; 44°5'   **15.** _____

16. Write the equation of the line $x + 4y = 5$ in parametric form.

    A. $x = t \; ; y = -4t + \dfrac{5}{4}$ **B.** $x = t \; ; y = 4t + \dfrac{5}{4}$

    C. $x = t \; ; y = -\dfrac{1}{4}t + \dfrac{5}{4}$ **D.** $x = t \; ; y = \dfrac{1}{4}t - \dfrac{5}{4}$ **16.** _____

For exercises 17-18, write an equation of the line with the given parametric equations in slope-intercept form.

17. $x = -3t - 8; y = -2t + 9$

    A. $y = -\dfrac{2}{3}x + \dfrac{11}{3}$ **B.** $y = -\dfrac{2}{3}x + \dfrac{43}{3}$ **C.** $y = \dfrac{2}{3}x + \dfrac{43}{3}$ **D.** $y = \dfrac{2}{3}x + \dfrac{11}{3}$ **17.** _____

18. $x = 4t + 5; y = -4t - 5$

    A. $y = x - 10$ **B.** $y = -x - 10$ **C.** $y = x$ **D.** $y = -x$ **18.** _____

Aaron kicked a soccer ball with an initial velocity of 39 ft/s at an angle of 44° to the ground. Use this information for Exercises 19-20.

19. After 0.9 seconds, how far has the ball traveled horizontally?

    A. 24.4 ft   **B.** 12.3 ft   **C.** 11.4 ft   **D.** 25.2 ft   **19.** _____

20. After 1.5 seconds, how far has the ball traveled vertically?

    A. 6.1 ft   **B.** 40.6 ft   **C.** 4.6 ft   **D.** 42.1 ft   **20.** _____

Bonus

Find parametric equations for the line through $(3, 2)$ and $(5, -3)$.

    A. $x = t \; ; y = 8t - 22$ **B.** $x = t \; ; y = \dfrac{1}{8}t + \dfrac{13}{8}$

    C. $x = t \; ; y = -\dfrac{2}{5}t + \dfrac{16}{5}$ **D.** $x = t \; ; y = -\dfrac{5}{2}t + \dfrac{19}{2}$ **Bonus:** _____

Chapter 8 Test, Form 2A

1. $\vec{\mathbf{u}}$ has a magnitude of 11.4 m and an amplitude of 19°.
   Find the magnitude of its horizontal component.

   1. _____

2. What is an expression for $\vec{\mathbf{x}}$ involving $\vec{\mathbf{r}}$ and $\vec{\mathbf{s}}$ in the figure below?

   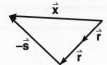

   2. _____

3. $\vec{\mathbf{c}}$ has a magnitude of 12.3 in. and $\vec{\mathbf{d}}$ has a magnitude of 4.1 in.
   The two vectors have opposite direction. What is the value of k in
   the equation $\vec{\mathbf{c}} = k\,\vec{\mathbf{d}}$?

   3. _____

For Exercises 4-5, find the magnitude of $\overrightarrow{AB}$ with the given coordinates.

4. $A(6, 12)$ and $B(-3, -4)$

   4. _____

5. $A(4, 3, 0)$ and $B(1, 5, -2)$

   5. _____

6. Write $\overrightarrow{CD}$ as the sum of unit vectors for $C(-2, 8, -1)$ and $D(9, 4, 3)$.

   6. _____

7. Find an ordered triple that represents the vector from
   $A(4, 5, -3)$ to $B(6, -10, -1)$.

   7. _____

For exercises 8-12, find an ordered pair or an ordered triple to represent $\vec{\mathbf{u}}$ in each equation if $\vec{\mathbf{v}} = (3, 6)$, $\vec{\mathbf{w}} = (-9, 1)$, $\vec{\mathbf{r}} = (1, -7, 0)$, and $\vec{\mathbf{s}} = (4, 11, -10)$.

8. $\vec{\mathbf{u}} = \vec{\mathbf{v}} + 4\vec{\mathbf{w}}$

   8. _____

9. $\vec{\mathbf{u}} = -2\vec{\mathbf{v}} - \vec{\mathbf{w}}$

   9. _____

10. $\vec{\mathbf{u}} = -\vec{\mathbf{r}}$

    10. _____

11. $\vec{\mathbf{u}} = 2\vec{\mathbf{r}} - 2\vec{\mathbf{s}}$

    11. _____

12. $\vec{\mathbf{u}} = 3\vec{\mathbf{s}} - 5\vec{\mathbf{r}}$

    12. _____

For exercises 13-14, find each inner product and state whether the vectors are perpendicular. Write yes or no.

13. $(10, -1) \cdot (-2, 7)$

    13. _____

14. $(0, -3, 9) \cdot (7, 3, 1)$

    14. _____

~ Chapter 8 Test, Form 2A (continued)

For Exercises 15-16, find each cross product.

15. $(-7, 5, 1) \times (-5, 1, -8)$

15. _____

16. $(4, 9, 4) \times (-7, 4, 6)$

16. _____

17. Find a vector perpendicular to the plane containing the points $(0, 4, 2)$, $(-4, 5, 5)$, and $(-2, 5, 4)$.

17. _____

18. A force F_1 of 14 N pulls on an object at an angle of 66° above due east. A force F_2 of 27 N also pulls at an angle of 19° below due west. Find the magnitude and direction of the resultant force.

18. _____

19. Jason is riding his sled down a hill. If the hill is inclined at an angle of 53° from level ground, find the force that propels Jason down the hill if he weighs 96 pounds.

19. _____

For exercises 20-21, write each equation in parametric form.

20. $y = -3x + 4$

20. _____

21. $5x - 3y = 1$

21. _____

For exercises 22-23, write an equation in slope-intercept form of the line with the given parametric equations.

22. $x = 4t - 3; y = 4t + 3$

22. _____

23. $x = 4t + 4; y = 2t - 3$

23. _____

Jana hit a golf ball with an initial velocity of 102 ft/s at an angle of 67° to the ground. Use this information for Exercises 24-25.

24. After 2 seconds, how far has the ball traveled horizontally?

24. _____

25. After 0.8 seconds, how far has the ball traveled vertically?

25. _____

Bonus

Find parametric equations for the line through $(4, 8)$ with slope 3.

Bonus: _____

Chapter 8 Test, Form 2B

1. $\vec{\mathbf{u}}$ has a magnitude of 10.6 yd and an amplitude of 77°.
   Find the magnitude of its horizontal component.

   1. _____

2. What is an expression for $\vec{\mathbf{x}}$ involving $\vec{\mathbf{r}}$ and $\vec{\mathbf{s}}$ in the figure below?

   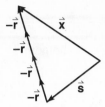

   2. _____

3. $\vec{\mathbf{c}}$ has a magnitude of 21.6 in. and $\vec{\mathbf{d}}$ has a magnitude of 5.4 in.
   The two vectors have opposite direction. What is the value of k in
   the equation $\vec{\mathbf{c}} = k\vec{\mathbf{d}}$?

   3. _____

For Exercises 4-5, find the magnitude of $\overrightarrow{AB}$ given the coordinates.

4. $A(8, -6)$ and $B(2, 3)$

   4. _____

5. $A(1, 0, -8)$ and $B(7, -3, -5)$

   5. _____

6. Write $\overrightarrow{CD}$ as the sum of unit vectors for $C(1, -2, 7)$ and
   $D(-8, -7, 5)$.

   6. _____

7. Find an ordered triple that represents the vector from
   $A(5, -8, 9)$ to $B(-2, 2, 2)$.

   7. _____

For Exercises 8-12, find an ordered pair or an ordered triple to represent $\vec{\mathbf{u}}$ in each equation if $\vec{\mathbf{v}} = (1, -6)$, $\vec{\mathbf{w}} = (2, -5)$, $\vec{\mathbf{r}} = (1, -1, 1)$, and $\vec{\mathbf{s}} = (10, -6, 5)$.

8. $\vec{\mathbf{u}} = \vec{\mathbf{v}} + 3\vec{\mathbf{w}}$

   8. _____

9. $\vec{\mathbf{u}} = -3\vec{\mathbf{v}} - \vec{\mathbf{w}}$

   9. _____

10. $\vec{\mathbf{u}} = -3\vec{\mathbf{r}}$

    10. _____

11. $\vec{\mathbf{u}} = \vec{\mathbf{r}} + 4\vec{\mathbf{s}}$

    11. _____

12. $\vec{\mathbf{u}} = 6\vec{\mathbf{s}} - 3\vec{\mathbf{r}}$

    12. _____

For Exercises 13-14, find each inner product and state whether the vectors are perpendicular. Write yes or no.

13. $(8, 2) \cdot (0, -6)$

    13. _____

14. $(3, -7, 4) \cdot (-4, -2, 1)$

    14. _____

Chapter 8 Test, Form 2B (continued)

For Exercises 15-16, find each cross product.

15. $(6, -4, 3) \times (4, 2, -6)$

15. _____

16. $(-2, 7, -4) \times (-5, -6, 2)$

16. _____

17. Find a vector perpendicular to the plane containing the points $(-4, 3, -2)$, $(1, 6, 5)$, and $(-2, 5, 2)$.

17. _____

18. A force F_1 of 27 N pulls at an angle of 23° above due east. A force F_2 of 33 N pulls at an angle of 55° below due west. Find the magnitude and direction of the resultant force.

18. _____

19. Anita is riding a toboggan down a hill. If the hill is inclined at an angle of 72° from level ground, find the force that propels Anita down the hill if she weighs 87 pounds.

19. _____

For exercises 20-21, write each equation in parametric form.

20. $y = -x + 3$

20. _____

21. $2x + 4y = 5$

21. _____

For exercises 22-23, write an equation in slope-intercept form of the line with the given parametric equations.

22. $x = -t + 6; y = 2t - 4$

22. _____

23. $x = -2t - 5; y = 4t + 2$

23. _____

Joe kicked a football with an initial velocity of 30 ft/s at an angle of 58° to the ground. Use this information for Exercises 24-25.

24. After 1.5 seconds, how far has the ball traveled horizontally?

24. _____

25. After 0.3 seconds, how far has the ball traveled vertically?

25. _____

Bonus

Find parametric equations for the line through $(2, -2)$ with slope -4.

Bonus: _____

NAME _____ DATE _____

Chapter 8, Quiz A (Lessons 8-1 through 8-2)

1. $\vec{v}$ has a magnitude of 13 mm and an amplitude of 84°.
   Find the magnitude of its vertical and horizontal components.   1. _____

2. $\vec{a}$ has a magnitude of 6.3 m. If $\vec{b} = -2\vec{a}$, what is the
   magnitude of $\vec{b}$?   2. _____

3. Justin rides his bike from home to school. He rides 0.5 miles
   north and 2 miles east. How far is his school from his home?   3. _____

4. Use a metric ruler and a protractor to find the magnitude of
   $2\vec{a} - \vec{b}$.   4. _____

5. Find the ordered pair that represents the vector from
   $A(1, -3)$ to $B(-6, -8)$.   5. _____

6. If $\overrightarrow{AB}$ is a vector from $A(4, 5)$ to $B(10, 1)$, find the magnitude of $\overrightarrow{AB}$.   6. _____

7. Write $\overrightarrow{CD}$ as the sum of unit vectors for points $C(7, -4)$ and $D(-8, 1)$.   7. _____

Find an ordered pair to represent $\vec{u}$ in each equation if $\vec{v} = (6, -6)$ and $\vec{w} = (3, -4)$.

8. $\vec{u} = -5\vec{w}$ 8. _____

9. $\vec{u} = 2\vec{v} + 3\vec{w}$ 9. _____

10. $\vec{u} = 4\vec{w} - \vec{v}$ 10. _____

NAME _____ DATE _____

Chapter 8, Quiz B (Lessons 8-3 through 8-4)

1. If $\overrightarrow{CD}$ is a vector from $C(7, 11, -3)$ to $D(8, -1, -3)$, find an ordered
   triple that represents $\overrightarrow{CD}$.   1. _____

2. If $\overrightarrow{AB}$ is a vector from $A(2, -2, 4)$ to $B(6, 11, -8)$, find the
   magnitude of $\overrightarrow{AB}$.   2. _____

3. Write $\vec{v} = (10, 3, -9)$ as the sum of unit vectors.   3. _____

Find an ordered triple to represent $\vec{u}$ in each equation if $\vec{v} = (9, -2, 1)$ and $\vec{w} = (8, 0, -3)$.

4. $\vec{u} = 6\vec{v} + \vec{w}$ 5. $\vec{u} = 8\vec{w} - 3\vec{v}$ 4. _____

                                                                           5. _____

Find each inner product and state whether the vectors are perpendicular. Write yes or no.

                                                                           6. _____

6. $(-8, 5) \cdot (3, 13)$ 7. $(7, -3, 8) \cdot (5, -2, -4)$ 7. _____

For Exercises 8-9, find each cross product.

                                                                           8. _____

8. $(-6, 3, 2) \times (3, 4, -1)$ 9. $(5, -5, 4) \times (2, 3, -6)$ 9. _____

10. Find a vector perpendicular to the plane containing the points
    $(4, -1, -5)$, $(-1, 3, 1)$, and $(1, 5, 1)$.   10. _____

Glencoe Division, Macmillan/McGraw-Hill

Chapter 8, Quiz C (Lessons 8-5 through 8-6)

1. Find the magnitude and direction of the resultant vector for the diagram below.

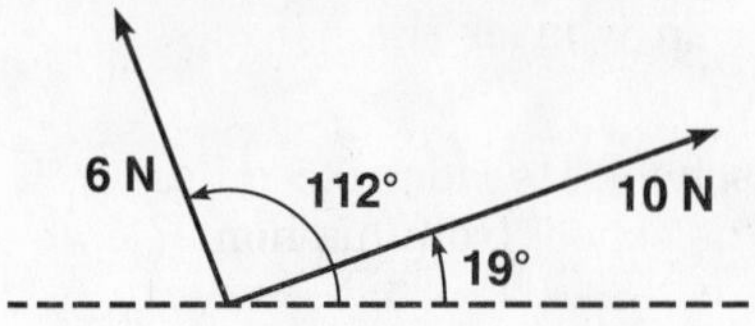

6 N   112°   10 N
19°

1. _____

2. Maggie is pulling a tarp along level ground with a force of 25 N on the tarp. If the tarp makes an angle of 50° with the ground, find the vertical and horizontal components of the force.

2. _____

3. Write parametric equations for the line $6x - y = 2$.

3. _____

Write an equation in slope-intercept form of the line with the given parametric equations.

4. $x = 6t + 8$
   $y = -t + 4$

5. $x = 3t - 10$
   $y = -4t + 2$

4. _____

5. _____

Chapter 8, Quiz D (Lesson 8-7)

Kelly launched a rocket off level ground with an initial velocity of 63 ft/s at an angle of 84° with the ground. Use this information for Exercises 1-2.

1. After 3 seconds, how far has the rocket traveled vertically?

1. _____

2. After 3 seconds, how far has the rocket traveled horizontally?

2. _____

Manuel kicked a football off level ground with an initial velocity of 66 ft/s at an angle of 40° with the ground. Use this information for Exercises 3-5.

3. Find the time the ball is in the air.

3. _____

4. Where does the ball land if it is kicked from the 25-yard line and aimed straight down the field?

4. _____

5. Find the maximum height of the ball.

5. _____

NAME _____ DATE _____

Chapter 8 Mid-Chapter Test (Lessons 8-1 through 8-4)

1. **ā** has a magnitude of 12 in. and an amplitude of 36°. Find the magnitude of its horizontal and vertical components.

1. _____

2. **ū** has a magnitude of 9.9 cm. If **v̄** = −4**ū**, what is the magnitude of **v̄**?

2. _____

3. Alice drove from her house to the grocery store. She drove 6 miles west and 3 miles south. How far is the grocery store from her house?

3. _____

4. Use a metric ruler and a protractor to find the magnitude of $2\vec{a} - 2\vec{b}$.

4. _____

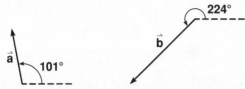

5. Find an ordered triple that represents the vector from $C(2, -2, 5)$ to $D(-3, -1, -8)$.

5. _____

If $\overrightarrow{AB}$ is a vector from A to B, find the magnitude of $\overrightarrow{AB}$ in Exercises 6-8.

6. $A(7, 6), B(-3, 6)$

6. _____

7. $A(3, -9), B(2, 2)$

7. _____

8. $A(10, 1, -5), B(0, -7, 7)$

8. _____

9. Write $\overrightarrow{RS}$ as the sum of unit vectors from $R(1, -3, 3)$ to $S(6, 0, -1)$.

9. _____

Find an ordered pair or an ordered triple to represent $\vec{u}$ in each equation if $\vec{v} = (7, 4)$, $\vec{w} = (-1, 0)$, $\vec{r} = (2, 5, 12)$, and $\vec{s} = (5, -3, 6)$.

10. $\vec{u} = -6\vec{r}$

10. _____

11. $\vec{u} = \vec{v} - \vec{w}$

11. _____

12. $\vec{u} = 2\vec{v} + 3\vec{w}$

12. _____

13. $\vec{u} = \vec{r} + 2\vec{s}$

13. _____

14. $\vec{u} = 3\vec{s} - 4\vec{r}$

14. _____

15. $\vec{u} = 6\vec{v} - \vec{w} - 2\vec{v}$

15. _____

Find each inner product and state whether the vectors are perpendicular. Write yes or no.

16. $(6, -4) \cdot (2, 4)$

16. _____

17. $(4, -3, 1) \cdot (8, 12, 4)$

17. _____

For Exercises 18-19, find each cross product.

18. $(9, 1, 0) \times (-3, 2, 5)$

18. _____

19. $(6, -4, -2) \times (1, 1, -3)$

19. _____

20. Find a vector perpendicular to the plane containing the points $(-4, 4, 1)$, $(2, 5, 3)$, and $(-1, 1, 2)$.

20. _____

Glencoe Division, Macmillan/McGraw-Hill

~ # Standardized Test Questions (Chapters 1-8)

The questions on this page involve comparing two quantities, one in Column A and one in Column B. In certain questions, information related to one or both quantities is centered above them. All variables used stand for real numbers.

Directions:
Write A if the quantity in Column A is greater.
Write B if the quantity in Column B is greater.
Write C if the quantities are equal.
Write D if there is not enough information to determine the relationship.

Column A	Column B	
1. $y = \dfrac{a^5 b^3 c^4}{a^2 b^2 c^4}$		
the value of y when $a = 1$, $b = 2$, and $c = 3$	2	1._____
2. $a > 0,$ $b < 0$		
$a \cdot b$	$\dfrac{a}{b}$	2._____
3. $xy = 3$		
$\dfrac{x}{y}$	0	3._____
4. $(a + e)(f + j)$	$(j + f)(e + a)$	4._____
5. $3k + 5^2 = 8^2$		
2	k	5._____
6. Angles P, Q, and R are the angles of a right triangle.		
$180° -$ measure of angle P	$90°$	6._____
7. $x < -1$		
$(5 - x)(1 + x)$	0	7._____
8. 1, 6, 16, x, y, 76, 106,...		
$x + y$	$2x$	8._____
9. A bag of marbles contains 6 red, 11 blue, and 5 green marbles.		
probability of selecting a blue marble	probability of *not* selecting a blue marble	9._____
10. $r \le 2$		
area of the circle	circumference of the circle	10._____

Glencoe Division, Macmillan/McGraw-Hill

Unit Test, Chapters 5-8

1. *True* or *false*: $\sin(-85°) = -\sin 85°$.

1. _____

2. Find the area of $\triangle ABC$ if $a = 12$ cm, $b = 15$ cm, and $c = 23$ cm. Round your answer to the nearest square centimeter

2. _____

3. Write the equation $5x + y - 2 = 0$ in normal form.

3. _____

4. Graph the function $y = 2\cos(\theta + 60°)$.

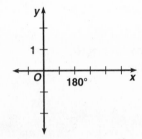

4. _____

5. Find the length of an arc that subtends a central angle of $60°$ in a circle of radius 15 inches. Write your answer in terms of π.

5. _____

6. A vector has a magnitude of 18.3 cm and an amplitude of $38°$. Find the magnitude of its vertical and horizontal components to the nearest tenth.

6. _____

7. Write the equation of the line $y = 5x - 2$ in parametric form.

7. _____

8. Find the value of $\text{Sin}^{-1}\left(\sin\dfrac{5\pi}{6}\right)$.

8. _____

9. Use the law of sines to solve triangle ABC when $a = 1.43$, $b = 4.21$, and $A = 30.4°$. If there is no solution, write *no solution*.

9. _____

10. Use a sum or difference identity to find the exact value of $\sin 105°$.

10. _____

11. Find the distance from the point at $(7, -4)$ to the line $x - 3y + 5 = 0$. Round your answer to the nearest tenth.

11. _____

12. Find the inner product of vectors $(2, 5)$ and $(4, -2)$. Then state whether the vectors are perpendicular. Write *yes* or *no*.

12. _____

13. Find the value of $\sin\theta$ if θ is in standard position and the point $(-3, 2)$ lies on its terminal side.

13. _____

Glencoe Division, Macmillan/McGraw-Hill

~ Unit Test, Chapters 5-8 (continued)

14. Solve $\sin \theta = -1$ for all values of θ.

14. _____

15. A car's flywheel has a timing mark on its outer edge. The height of the timing mark on the rotating flywheel is given by $y = 3.55 \sin \left(x - \frac{\pi}{4}\right)$. Graph one full cycle of this function.

15. _____

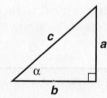

16. Find the ordered pair that represents $-3\vec{w}$ if $\vec{w} = (6, -4)$.

16. _____

17. Write $\overline{XY}$ as the sum of unit vectors for $X(8, 2, -9)$ and $Y(-12, -1, 10)$.

17. _____

18. In the triangle at the right, $b = 6.2$ and $c = 8.2$. Find α to the nearest tenth.

18. _____

19. If $0° < \theta < 90°$ and $\tan \theta = \dfrac{\sqrt{3}}{2}$, find $\cos \theta$.

19. _____

20. Solve $\sin^2 x - \sin x - 2 = 0$ for $0° \leq x \leq 360°$.

20. _____

21. Write the equation $\tan \beta = \dfrac{\sqrt{3}}{3}$ in the form of an inverse relation.

21. _____

22. Verify that $\dfrac{\tan x \csc x}{\sec x} = 1$ is an identity. Write your answer on a separate piece of paper.

Unit Test, Chapters 5-8 (continued)

23. Find the cross product of vectors (2, −1, 4) and (6, −2, 1). Is the resulting vector perpendicular to the given vectors? Write *yes* or *no*.

23. _____

24. A triangular shelf is to be placed in a curio cabinet whose sides meet at an angle of 105°. If the edges of the shelf along the sides measure 56 cm and 65 cm, how long is the outside edge of the shelf? Round your answer to the nearest tenth.

24. _____

25. If $\sin \theta = \dfrac{3}{5}$ and θ is a second quadrant angle, find $\tan 2\theta$.

25. _____

26. Graph the function $y = \sin x$ on the interval $-90° \le x \le 90°$.

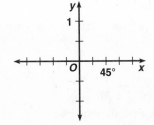

26. _____

27. Change $\dfrac{7\pi}{9}$ radians to degree measure.

27. _____

28. Nathaniel pulls a sled along level ground with a force of 30 N in the rope attached to the sled. If the rope makes an angle of 20° with the horizontal when it is pulled taut, find the horizontal and vertical components of the force to the nearest tenth.

28. _____

29. State the amplitude, period, and phase shift of the function $y = -2 \sin \theta$.

29. _____

30. If α and β are both second quadrant angles, $\tan \alpha = -\dfrac{1}{2}$, and $\tan \beta = -\dfrac{2}{3}$, find $\cos (\alpha + \beta)$.

30. _____

31. A surveyor sets a stake, and then walks 150 feet north where she sets a second stake. She then walks 300 feet east and sets a third stake. How far from the first stake is the third stake? Round your answer to the nearest tenth.

31. _____

Glencoe Division, Macmillan/McGraw-Hill

~ Unit Test, Chapters 5-8 (continued)

32. Find the value of $\operatorname{Tan}^{-1}\!\left(\dfrac{1}{\sqrt{3}}\right)$.

32. _____

33. Use the law of cosines to solve $\triangle ABC$ with $b = 45$, $c = 62.5$, and $A = 126°18'$. Round angle measures to the nearest degree and side measures to the nearest tenth.

33. _____

34. Write an equation in slope-intercept form of the line with parametric equations $x = 2 + 3t$ and $y = 4 + t$.

34. _____

35. Verify that $\cos\left(x + \dfrac{\pi}{2}\right) = -\sin x$ is an identity. Write your answer on a separate piece of paper.

36. Write the equation for the inverse of the function $y = \operatorname{Cos} x$. Then graph the function and its inverse.

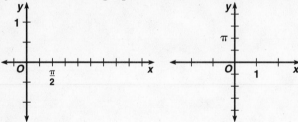

36. _____

37. Find $\sin\left(\operatorname{Sin}^{-1} \dfrac{1}{4}\right)$.

37. _____

38. A sector has a central angle measuring $\dfrac{5\pi}{6}$ radians in a circle with a radius of 8 cm. Find the area of the sector to the nearest tenth.

38. _____

39. Find the reference angle for $400°$.

39. _____

40. A golf ball is hit with an initial velocity of 135 ft/s at an angle of 22° above the horizontal. Will the ball clear a 25-foot wide sand trap whose nearest edge is 300 feet from the golfer?

40. _____

Chapter 9 Test, Form 1A

*Write the letter for the correct answer in the blank at the right of
each problem.*

1. Which is the graph of the point $\left(2, \frac{5\pi}{6}\right)$?

   A. 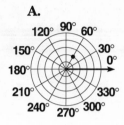 **B.** 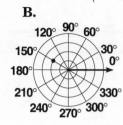 **C.** 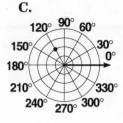 **D.**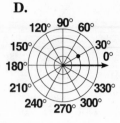

   1. _____

2. Which pair of polar coordinates does not represent the point $(1, 210°)$?

   A. $(-1, 390°)$ **B.** $(-1, 30°)$ **C.** $(1, 570°)$ **D.** $(1, 150°)$

   2. _____

3. Choose the graph of the polar equation $\theta = -100°$.

   A. 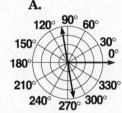 **B.** 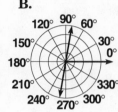 **C.** 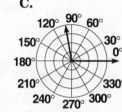 **D.**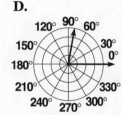

   3. _____

4. Choose the polar equation whose graph is a rose.

   A. $r = 4 \sin 4\theta$ **B.** $r = 4 + 4 \sin \theta$
   C. $r^2 = 4 \cos 2\theta$ **D.** $r = 8 + 4 \cos \theta$

   4. _____

5. Find the polar coordinates of the point with rectangular coordinates $(3, 3)$.

   A. $\left(3\sqrt{2}, \frac{\pi}{4}\right)$ **B.** $\left(\frac{1}{2}, \frac{\pi}{2}\right)$ **C.** $\left(-3\sqrt{2}, \frac{\pi}{4}\right)$ **D.** $\left(-\frac{1}{2}, \frac{\pi}{4}\right)$

   5. _____

6. Find the rectangular coordinates of the point with polar coordinates $\left(1, \frac{\pi}{6}\right)$.

   A. $\left(\frac{1}{2}, \frac{\sqrt{3}}{2}\right)$ **B.** $\left(-\frac{1}{2}, -\frac{\sqrt{3}}{2}\right)$ **C.** $\left(\frac{\sqrt{3}}{2}, \frac{1}{2}\right)$ **D.** $\left(-\frac{\sqrt{3}}{2}, \frac{1}{2}\right)$

   6. _____

7. Write the rectangular equation $y = 2$ in polar form.

   A. $r \sin \theta = \sqrt{2}$ **B.** $r \sin \theta = 2$
   C. $r = 4 \sin \theta$ **D.** $r \sin \theta = 4$

   7. _____

8. Write the rectangular form of the polar equation $r = 6$.

   A. $r = 6 \csc \theta$ **B.** $x^2 + y^2 = 36$
   C. $x^2 + y^2 = 12$ **D.** $6r = \csc \theta$

   8. _____

9. Which is the graph of $r = \dfrac{1.2}{\cos\left(\theta + \frac{\pi}{2}\right)}$?

   A. 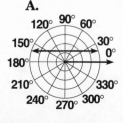 **B.** 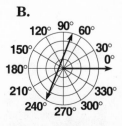 **C.** 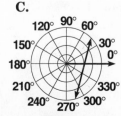 **D.**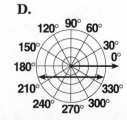

   9. _____

Glencoe Division, Macmillan/McGraw-Hill

10. Write the polar form of the rectangular equation $2x + y = 5$.
   A. $-\sqrt{5} = r \cos(\theta - 27°)$ **B.** $\sqrt{5} = r \cos(\theta - 27°)$
   C. $-\sqrt{5} = r \cos(\theta + 27°)$ **D.** $\sqrt{5} = r \cos(\theta + 27°)$

   10. _____

11. Simplify i^{33}.
   A. 1   **B.** i **C.** -1 **D.** $-i$

   11. _____

12. Simplify $(5 - 3i) + (-10 - 8i)$.
   A. $-5 - 11i$ **B.** $-5 - 3i$ **C.** -8 **D.** -16

   12. _____

13. Simplify $(3 - i)(4 + 2i)$.
   A. $10 + 2i$ **B.** $14 - 2i$ **C.** $14 + 2i$ **D.** $12 + 4i^2$

   13. _____

14. Simplify $\dfrac{1 + 3i}{2 + 5i}$.

   A. $\dfrac{i - 13}{29}$ **B.** $\dfrac{-13 + i}{29}$ **C.** $\dfrac{17 + i}{-21}$ **D.** $\dfrac{17 + i}{29}$

   14. _____

15. Express $10 + 10i\sqrt{3}$ in polar form.

   A. $20(\cos \pi + i \sin \pi)$ **B.** $10\left(\cos \dfrac{\pi}{3} + i \sin \dfrac{\pi}{3}\right)$

   C. $20\left(\cos \dfrac{\pi}{3} + i \sin \dfrac{\pi}{3}\right)$ **D.** $10\left(\cos \dfrac{\pi}{6} + i \sin \dfrac{\pi}{6}\right)$

   15. _____

16. Express $3\left(\cos \dfrac{\pi}{2} + i \sin \dfrac{\pi}{2}\right)$ in rectangular form.
   A. $3i$ **B.** $-3i$ **C.** 3   **D.** -3

   16. _____

For Exercises 17 and 18, let $c_1 = 4(\cos 30° + i \sin 30°)$ and $c_2 = 0.5(\cos 60° + i \sin 60°)$.

17. Express $c_1 c_2$ in rectangular form.
   A. $-2i$ **B.** $2i$ **C.** $1 + 2i$ **D.** 2

   17. _____

18. Express $\dfrac{c_1}{c_2}$ in rectangular form.

   A. $2\sqrt{3} - 2i$ **B.** $2\sqrt{3} + 2i$ **C.** $4\sqrt{3} + 4i$ **D.** $4\sqrt{3} - 4i$

   18. _____

19. Simplify $(2 + 3i)^3$.
   A. $-27 + 9i$ **B.** $27 - 9i$ **C.** $-46 + 9i$ **D.** $37 - 9i$

   19. _____

20. Find $\sqrt[3]{i}$.
   A. 1   **B.** $\dfrac{1}{2} + \dfrac{\sqrt{3}}{2}i$ **C.** $\dfrac{\sqrt{3}}{2} + \dfrac{1}{2}i$ **D.** $\dfrac{\sqrt{3}}{2} - \dfrac{1}{2}i$

   20. _____

Bonus

Express $5\left(\cos \dfrac{\pi}{6} + i \sin \dfrac{\pi}{6}\right)$ in rectangular form.

   A. $\dfrac{5\sqrt{3}}{2} + \dfrac{5}{2}i$ **B.** $-\dfrac{5\sqrt{3}}{2} + \dfrac{5}{2}i$ **C.** $\dfrac{5\sqrt{3}}{2} - \dfrac{5}{2}i$ **D.** $-\dfrac{5\sqrt{3}}{2} - \dfrac{5}{2}i$

   Bonus: _____

Chapter 9 Test, Form 1B

Write the letter for the correct answer in the blank at the right of each problem.

1. Choose the graph of the point $(-2, 135°)$.

   A.   **B.**   **C.**   **D.**

   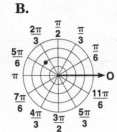 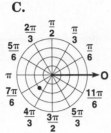 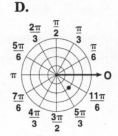

   1. _____

2. Which pair of polar coordinates represents the point $\left(-3, \dfrac{\pi}{4}\right)$?

   A. $\left(3, -\dfrac{3\pi}{4}\right)$ **B.** $\left(-3, -\dfrac{3\pi}{4}\right)$ **C.** $\left(3, \dfrac{4\pi}{5}\right)$ **D.** $\left(-3, -\dfrac{5\pi}{4}\right)$

   2. _____

3. Choose the graph of the polar equation $r = \sqrt{2}$.

   A.   **B.**   **C.**   **D.**

   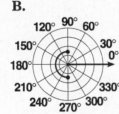 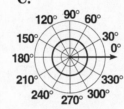 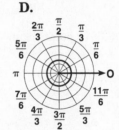

   3. _____

4. Identify the classical curve represented by the polar equation $r^2 = 3 \sin 2\theta$.

   A. rose   **B.** lemniscate   **C.** limaçon   **D.** cardioid

   4. _____

5. Find the polar coordinates of the point whose rectangular coordinates are $\left(2, 2\sqrt{3}\right)$.

   A. $\left(-4, \dfrac{\pi}{3}\right)$ **B.** $\left(4, \dfrac{\pi}{3}\right)$ **C.** $\left(4, \dfrac{\pi}{6}\right)$ **D.** $\left(-4, \dfrac{\pi}{6}\right)$

   5. _____

6. A point P has polar coordinates $(-3, 15°)$. Find the rectangular coordinates of P.

   A. $(-2.90, 0.78)$ **B.** $(-2.90, -0.78)$
   C. $(2.90, -0.78)$ **D.** $(2.90, 0.78)$

   6. _____

7. Write the rectangular equation $x^2 + y^2 = 8$ in polar form.

   A. $r = \pm 2\sqrt{2} \sin \theta$ **B.** $r = \pm 4$
   C. $r = \pm 2\sqrt{2}$ **D.** $r = \pm 8$

   7. _____

8. Write the polar equation $r = 3 \csc \theta$ in rectangular form.

   A. $y = 3$ **B.** $y = 9$ **C.** $x = 3$ **D.** $x = 9$

   8. _____

9. Identify the graph of the polar equation $3 = 2r \cos (\theta + 90°)$.

   A.   **B.**   **C.**   **D.**

   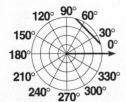 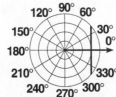 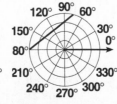 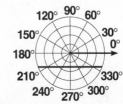

   9. _____

~ Chapter 9 Test, Form 1B (continued)

10. Write $x + y - 3 = 0$ in polar form.

   A. $-\dfrac{3\sqrt{2}}{2} = r \cos(\theta - 45°)$ **B.** $\dfrac{3\sqrt{2}}{2} = r \cos(\theta - 45°)$

   C. $\dfrac{3\sqrt{2}}{2} = r \cos(\theta + 45°)$ **D.** $-\dfrac{3\sqrt{2}}{2} = r \cos(\theta + 45°)$ **10.** _____

11. Simplify $i^{50} - i^{38}$.

   A. 0   **B.** $1 - i$ **C.** $i - 1$ **D.** -2 **11.** _____

12. Simplify $(4 + \sqrt{-3}) + (4 + \sqrt{-3})$.

   A. $8 + 2i\sqrt{3}$ **B.** $8 - 9i$ **C.** 8   **D.** 0   **12.** _____

13. Simplify $(5 + i)^2$.

   A. $24 + 25i$ **B.** $25 - 25i$ **C.** $24 + 10i$ **D.** $25 + 10i$ **13.** _____

14. Simplify $\dfrac{3 - 2i}{4i}$.

   A. $\dfrac{2 + 3i}{8}$ **B.** $\dfrac{-2 - 3i}{8}$ **C.** $\dfrac{-2 - 3i}{4}$ **D.** $\dfrac{2 + 3i}{4}$ **14.** _____

15. Express $-4 + 0i$ in polar form.

   A. $4(\cos 2\pi + i \sin 2\pi)$ **B.** $4(\cos \pi + i \sin \pi)$

   C. $4\left(\cos \dfrac{\pi}{2} + i \sin \dfrac{\pi}{2}\right)$ **D.** $4\left(\cos -\dfrac{\pi}{2} + i \sin -\dfrac{\pi}{2}\right)$ **15.** _____

16. Express $4\left(\cos \dfrac{7\pi}{6} + i \sin \dfrac{7\pi}{6}\right)$ in rectangular form.

   A. $-2\sqrt{3} - 2i$ **B.** $2\sqrt{3} - 2i$ **C.** $2\sqrt{3} + 2i$ **D.** $-2\sqrt{3} + 2i$ **16.** _____

For exercises 17 and 18, let $c_1 = 2\left(\cos \dfrac{\pi}{4} + i \sin \dfrac{\pi}{4}\right)$ *and*

$c_2 = 3\left(\cos \dfrac{\pi}{4} + i \sin \dfrac{\pi}{4}\right).$

17. Write the rectangular form of $c_1 c_2$.

   A. -6 **B.** 6   **C.** $6i$ **D.** $-6i$ **17.** _____

18. Write the rectangular form of $\dfrac{c_1}{c_2}$.

   A. $\dfrac{2}{3}$ **B.** $\dfrac{2}{3} + \dfrac{2i}{3}$ **C.** $\dfrac{2i}{3}$ **D.** 0   **18.** _____

19. Simplify $(1 - i)^{10}$.

   A. -32 **B.** $-32 - 32i$ **C.** $32i$ **D.** $-32i$ **19.** _____

20. Find $\sqrt[3]{-i}$.

   A. 1   **B.** $\dfrac{\sqrt{3}}{2} + \dfrac{1}{2}i$ **C.** i **D.** $\dfrac{1}{2} - \dfrac{\sqrt{3}}{2}i$ **20.** _____

Bonus

Find $(\cos \theta + i \sin \theta)^2$.

   A. $\cos 2\theta + i \sin 2\theta$ **B.** $\cos^2 \theta + i \sin^2 \theta$

   C. $\cos^2 \theta - i \sin^2 \theta$ **D.** $\cos 2\theta - i \sin 2\theta$ **Bonus:** _____

Glencoe Division, Macmillan/McGraw-Hill

Chapter 9 Test, Form 2A

1. Graph the point $\left(-3, \dfrac{-3\pi}{2}\right)$.

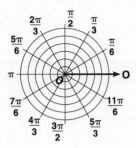

1. _____

2. Name another pair of polar coordinates that represent the point $\left(6, \dfrac{-\pi}{6}\right)$.

2. _____

3. Graph the polar equation $r = 2.3$.

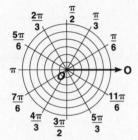

3. _____

4. Graph the polar equation $r = 1 + \cos\theta$. Identify the classical curve it represents.

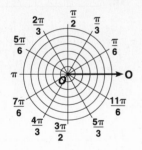

4. _____

5. What are the polar coordinates of the point whose rectangular coordinates are $\left(-\sqrt{2}, \sqrt{2}\right)$?

5. _____

6. If a point P has polar coordinates $(4, -95°)$, find its rectangular coordinates.

6. _____

7. Write the rectangular equation $x = 3$ in polar form.

7. _____

8. The polar form of an equation is $r = \sqrt{5}$. Write the equation in rectangular form.

8. _____

Chapter 9 Test, Form 2A (continued)

9. Graph the polar equation $1 = r \cos(\theta - 15°)$.

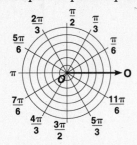

9. _____

10. Find the polar form of the rectangular equation $4x + 3y = 5$.

10. _____

Simplify.

11. $i^{14}(8 - i^{12})$

11. _____

12. $(7 - 3i) - (-10 + 4i)$

12. _____

13. $(2 + 3i\sqrt{5})(2 - 3i\sqrt{5})$

13. _____

14. $(2 - 3i) \div (-i)$

14. _____

15. Express $-8 + 0i$ in polar form.

15. _____

16. Express $5(\cos 4 + i \sin 4)$ in rectangular form.

16. _____

For exercises 17 and 18, let $c_1 = \dfrac{4}{3}\left(\cos \dfrac{5\pi}{4} + i \sin \dfrac{5\pi}{4}\right)$ *and*

$c_2 = 3\left(\cos \dfrac{\pi}{4} + i \sin \dfrac{\pi}{4}\right).$

17. Express $c_1 c_2$ in rectangular form.

17. _____

18. Express $\dfrac{c_1}{c_2}$ in rectangular form.

18. _____

19. Simplify $\left(-\dfrac{1}{2} - \dfrac{\sqrt{3}}{2}i\right)^3$.

19. _____

20. Find $(0 - 8i)^{\frac{1}{3}}$.

20. _____

Bonus

If $3 + i\sqrt{3} = 2\sqrt{3}(\cos 30° + i \sin 30°)$, find $3 - i\sqrt{3}$.

Bonus: _____

Chapter 9 Test, Form 2B

1. Graph the point (2.5, −45°).

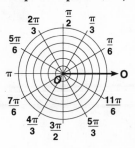

1. _____

2. Name another pair of polar coordinates that represent
the point (−1.5, 30°) if −360° ≤ θ ≤ 360°.

2. _____

3. Graph the polar equation $\theta = -30°$.

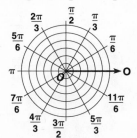

3. _____

4. State the general form of a polar equation whose graph forms
the spiral of Archimedes. Then graph $r = -2\theta$.

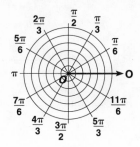

4. _____

5. Find the polar coordinates of the
point whose rectangular coordinates are $\left(-\dfrac{\sqrt{3}}{2}, \dfrac{1}{2}\right)$.

5. _____

6. Find the rectangular coordinates
of a point with polar coordinates $\left(4, \dfrac{2\pi}{3}\right)$.

6. _____

7. Write the polar form of the rectangular equation $y = 3$.

7. _____

8. Write the rectangular form of the polar equation $\theta = -90°$.

8. _____

~ Chapter 9 Test, Form 2B (continued)

9. Graph the polar equation $1.7 = r \cos\left(\theta - \dfrac{\pi}{4}\right)$.

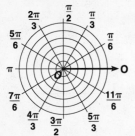

9. _____

10. Write the rectangular equation $x + 2y - 4 = 0$ in polar form.

10. _____

Simplify.

11. $2i^{19}$

11. _____

12. $\left(\sqrt{6} + 3i\right) + \left(\sqrt{6} - 5i\right)$

12. _____

13. $(3 - 7i)(2 + i)$

13. _____

14. $\dfrac{4 - i}{5 + 2i}$

14. _____

15. Express $1 + i$ in polar form.

15. _____

16. Express $2\left(\cos \dfrac{7\pi}{4} + i \sin \dfrac{7\pi}{4}\right)$ in rectangular form.

16. _____

For Exercises 17 and 18, let $c_1 = 12(\cos 270° + i \sin 270°)$ and $c_2 = 2(\cos 60° + i \sin 60°)$.

17. Express $c_1 c_2$ in rectangular form.

17. _____

18. Express $\dfrac{c_1}{c_2}$ in rectangular form.

18. _____

19. Express $\left(1 + i\sqrt{3}\right)^4$ in rectangular form.

19. _____

20. Find $(-16)^{\frac{1}{4}}$.

20. _____

Bonus

If $2 + 2i = 2\sqrt{2}(\cos 45° + i \sin 45°)$, find $2 - 2i$.

Bonus: _____

Chapter 9, Quiz A (Lessons 9-1 through 9-2)

1. Graph the point $(-2.5, -45°)$.

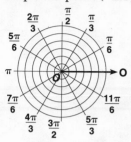

1. _____

2. Find three more pairs of polar coordinates that represent the point $R(4, -75°)$.

2. _____

Graph each polar equation.

3. $\theta = -\dfrac{\pi}{4}$

4. $r = 1 + \sin\theta$

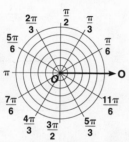

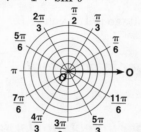

3. _____

4. _____

5. Identify the classical curve that the graph of $r = 2\sin\theta$ represents.

5. _____

Chapter 9, Quiz B (Lessons 9-3 through 9-4)

1. Find the polar coordinates of the point $\left(\dfrac{3\sqrt{2}}{2}, -\dfrac{3\sqrt{2}}{2}\right)$.

1. _____

2. Find the rectangular coordinates of the point whose polar coordinates are $(-3, -90°)$.

2. _____

3. Write the polar equation $r = 2$ in rectangular form.

3. _____

4. Graph the polar equation $1 = r\cos\left(\theta + \dfrac{\pi}{6}\right)$.

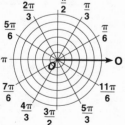

4. _____

5. Write $x + y - 4 = 0$ in polar form.

5. _____

Chapter 9, Quiz C (Lessons 9-5 through 9-6)

Simplify

1. $i^{17}(4 - 5i)$

2. $-3i^{30}$

3. $(\sqrt{3} + 4i)^2$

4. $\dfrac{1 - 7i}{4i}$

Two AC circuits are connected in series, one with an impedance of 2 + 3j ohms and the other with an impedance of 3 − 5j ohms.

5. Find the total impedance of the two circuits.

6. Find the current if the total voltage is 120 volts. $(E = I \cdot Z)$

Express each complex number in polar form.

7. $-4\sqrt{3} + 4i$

8. $2 - i$

Express each complex number in rectangular form.

9. $2(\cos 3 + i \sin 3)$

10. $10\left(\cos \dfrac{3\pi}{4} + i \sin \dfrac{3\pi}{4} \right)$

1. _____

2. _____

3. _____

4. _____

5. _____

6. _____

7. _____

8. _____

9. _____

10. _____

Chapter 9, Quiz D (Lessons 9-7 Through 9-8)

1. Simplify $(1 - i)^5$.

2. Simplify $\dfrac{2 - 3i}{-2i}$.

3. Find $3\sqrt{2}\left(\cos \dfrac{\pi}{4} + i \sin \dfrac{\pi}{4} \right) \cdot 2\left(\cos \dfrac{3\pi}{2} + i \sin \dfrac{3\pi}{2} \right)$.
    Write the product in rectangular form.

4. Find $(\cos 120° + i \sin 120°) \div 0.5(\cos 30° + i \sin 30°)$.
    Write the quotient in rectangular form.

5. Consider the equation $z^4 + 4 = 0$.

    a. How many complex roots does the equation have?

    b. If two roots of the equation are $-1 + i$ and $-1 - i$, find the other root(s).

1. _____

2. _____

3. _____

4. _____

5a. _____

5b. _____

~Chapter 9 Mid-Chapter Test (Lessons 9-1 through 9-4)

Name four different pairs of polar coordinates that represent point A.

1.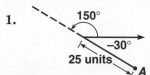

2. $A\left(2, \dfrac{\pi}{3}\right)$

1. _____

Graph each point or equation.

2. _____

3. $\left(1.5, \dfrac{5\pi}{4}\right)$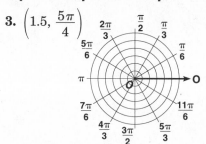

4. $r = \sqrt{10}$

3. _____

4. _____

5. $\theta = -270°$

6. $r = 2 \sin 2\theta$

5. _____

6. _____

Identify the classical curve represented by the graph of each equation.

7. $r = 1 + 2 \cos \theta$

8. $r = 4\theta$

7. _____

8. _____

Find the polar coordinates of each point with the given rectangular coordinates

9. $(-2, -2\sqrt{3})$

10. $(-1, -\sqrt{3})$

9. _____

10. _____

Find the rectangular coordinates of each point with the given polar coordinates

11. $(3, 150°)$

12. $\left(-2, \dfrac{\pi}{3}\right)$

11. _____

12. _____

13. Write $y = -3$ in polar form.

14. Write $r = -4 \csc \theta$ in rectangular form.

13. _____

14. _____

Graph each polar equation.

15. $3 = r \cos (\theta + 20°)$

16. $r = \dfrac{1.4}{\cos (\theta - 10°)}$

15. _____

16. _____

Glencoe Division, Macmillan/McGraw-Hill

Standardized Test Questions (Chapters 1-9)

The questions below involve comparing two quantities, one in Column A and one in Column B. In certain questions, information related to one or both quantities is centered above them. All variables represent real numbers.

Directions:
Write A if the quantity in column A is greater.
Write B if the quantity in column B is greater.
Write C if the two quantities are equal.
Write D if there is not enough information to determine the relationship.

Column A	Column B	
1. $\sin \alpha = \dfrac{4}{5}; \sin \beta = \dfrac{5}{13}$		
$\sin(\alpha + \beta)$	$\sin(\alpha - \beta)$	1. _____
2. i^{54}	i^{12}	2. _____
3. $y \geq 0, x - y \geq -2, 0 \leq x \leq 5$		
the minimum value of $f(x, y) = x + 3y$	the minimum value of $f(x, y) = 2x - 2y$	3. _____
4. the measure of the reference angle for $-140°$	the measure of the reference angle for $220°$	4. _____
5. $(3, -2) \cdot (3, 5)$	$(5, 1) \cdot (-2, 4)$	5. _____

Choose the best answer. Write A, B, C, or D.

6. State the amplitude of the function $y = -2 \sin \theta$.

    A. -2 **B.** 2   **C.** $\dfrac{1}{2}$ **D.** $-\dfrac{1}{2}$ 6. _____

7. A graph contains the point $(-b, -a)$ whenever it contains the point (a, b). In which line does the graph have symmetry?

    A. $y = 0$ **B.** $x = 0$ **C.** $y = x$ **D.** $y = -x$ 7. _____

8. Find the slope of the line tangent to the graph of $y = -3x^2$ at the point $(2, -12)$.

    A. 72   **B.** -24 **C.** -12 **D.** -10 8. _____

9. Find the ordered pair that represents the vector from $A(7, 2)$ to $B(4, -8)$.

    A. $(3, 10)$ **B.** $(3, -6)$ **C.** $(-3, -10)$ **D.** $(-3, -6)$ 9. _____

Chapter 10 Test, Form 1A

Write the letter for the correct answer in the blank at the right of each problem.

Exercises 1-3 refer to the parabola $y^2 - 12 - 16x - 4y = 0.$

1. Find the coordinates of the focus.
   A. $(-1, 2)$　　**B.** $(2, -1)$　　**C.** $(3, 2)$　　**D.** $(-5, 2)$

   1. _____

2. Find the equation of the directrix.
   A. $x = -1$　　**B.** $x = -5$　　**C.** $y = -5$　　**D.** $y = 2$

   2. _____

3. Find the coordinates of the vertex and the equation of the axis of symmetry.
   A. $(-1, 2)$ and $y = 2$　　　　**B.** $(-1, 2)$ and $x = 2$
   C. $(-5, 2)$ and $x = -5$　　　**D.** $(3, 2)$ and $y = 2$

   3. _____

4. Determine the eccentricity of the conic represented by
   $4x^2 + 9y^2 + 16x - 36y = -16.$
   A. $\dfrac{3}{2}$　　**B.** $\dfrac{2}{3}$　　**C.** $\dfrac{\sqrt{5}}{3}$　　**D.** $\sqrt{5}$

   4. _____

5. For $4x^2 - 4xy + y^2 = 4$, find θ, the angle of rotation about the origin, to the nearest degree.
   A. $26.6°$　　**B.** $63.4°$　　**C.** $333.4°$　　**D.** $306.8°$

   5. _____

6. Find the coordinates of one focus of the hyperbola represented by
   $y^2 - 6x^2 + 36x = 60.$
   A. $(3 + \sqrt{7}, 0)$　　**B.** $(3, \sqrt{7})$　　**C.** $(0, 3 + \sqrt{7})$　　**D.** $(0, \sqrt{7})$

   6. _____

Exercises 7 and 8 refer to P(5, 7) and the conic represented by
$(x - 2)^2 + (y - 3)^2 = 25.$

7. Write the equation of the tangent to the curve through point P in standard form.
   A. $4x + 3y - 43 = 0$　　　**B.** $3x + 4y - 43 = 0$
   C. $7x - 5y = 0$　　　　　**D.** $7x + 5y - 5 = 0$

   7. _____

8. Write the equation of the normal to the curve through point P in standard form.
   A. $4x - 3y - 13 = 0$　　　**B.** $3x + 4y - 78 = 0$
   C. $3x - 4y - 102 = 0$　　**D.** $4x - 3y + 1 = 0$

   8. _____

9. Solve the system of equations: $x^2 + y^2 = 36$ and $y = -3x + 1$. Round the coordinates of the solution to the nearest tenth.
   A. $(2.2, -5.6); (-1.6, 5.8)$　　**B.** $(-2.2, 5.6); (1.6, 5.8)$
   C. no solution　　　　　　　　**D.** $(\pm 2.2, \pm 5.8)$

   9. _____

10. Identify the conic represented by $9y^2 + 4x^2 - 108y + 24x = -144.$
    A. parabola　　**B.** hyperbola　　**C.** ellipse　　**D.** circle

    10. _____

11. Write the equation of the graph of $y^2 - x^2 = 5$ rotated through $45°$.
    A. $xy = -2.5$　　**B.** $xy = -5$　　**C.** $y^2 - x^2 = 2.5$　　**D.** $x^2 = 2.5y$

    11. _____

Chapter 10 Test, Form 1A (continued)

12. Choose the graph of $2x^2 + 8x + 2y^2 - 12y + 4 = 0$.

A. 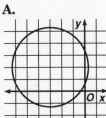 **B.** 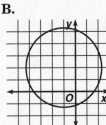 **C.** **D.**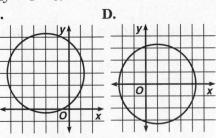

12. _____

Exercises 13-15 refer to the hyperbola represented by
$12x^2 + 24x - 12y^2 + 48y = 48$.

13. Find the coordinates of the vertices.
  A. $(-1, -1); (0, -1)$
  C. $(-1 + \sqrt{2}, 0); (-1 - \sqrt{2}, 0)$
  B. $(-1, 3); (-1, 1)$
  D. $(0, 2); (-2, 2)$

13. _____

14. Write the equations of the asymptotes.
  A. $y - 1 = \pm(x - 2)$
  C. $y + 2 = \pm(x - 1)$
  B. $y = \pm x$
  D. $y - 2 = \pm(x + 1)$

14. _____

15. Find the coordinates of the foci.
  A. $(-1 + \sqrt{2}, 2); (-1 - \sqrt{2}, 2)$
  C. $(0, 1); (0, -1)$
  B. $(1, 1); (-1, -1)$
  D. $(1, 0); (-1, 0)$

15. _____

16. Write the standard form of the equation of the hyperbola for which $a = 1$ if the transverse axis is horizontal and the equations of the asymptotes are $y = \pm 2x$.
  A. $\dfrac{x^2}{4} - \dfrac{y^2}{1} = 1$ **B.** $\dfrac{x^2}{4} + \dfrac{y^2}{1} = 1$ **C.** $\dfrac{x^2}{1} - \dfrac{y^2}{4} = 1$ **D.** $\dfrac{y^2}{4} - \dfrac{x^2}{1} = 1$

16. _____

17. Find the length of the tangent segment from $P(-10, 0)$ to the graph of $x^2 + 6x + y^2 - 12y = 4$.
  A. $\sqrt{42}$ **B.** 6 **C.** $2\sqrt{39}$ **D.** 10

17. _____

18. Write the standard form of the equation of the parabola whose directrix is $x = -4$ and whose focus is at $(2, 3)$.
  A. $(y - 3)^2 = 12(x + 1)$
  C. $(x + 1)^2 = 12(y - 3)^2$
  B. $(y + 3)^2 = 12(x + 1)$
  D. $(x - 1)^2 = 12(y + 3)$

18. _____

19. Write the standard form of the equation of the ellipse with foci at $(0, \pm 4)$ and whose semi-major axis is 5 units long.
  A. $\dfrac{x^2}{25} + \dfrac{y^2}{9} = 1$ **B.** $\dfrac{x^2}{9} + \dfrac{y^2}{25} = 1$ **C.** $\dfrac{x^2}{9} - \dfrac{y^2}{25} = 1$ **D.** $\dfrac{x^2}{25} - \dfrac{y^2}{9} = 1$

19. _____

20. Write the equation for the translation of the graph of $y^2 + 2y + 1 = 4x - 12$ for $T_{(-1, -1)}$.
  A. $(y - 2)^2 = 4(x - 3)$
  C. $(y + 2)^2 = 4(x + 3)$
  B. $(y + 2)^2 = 4(x - 2)$
  D. $y^2 = 4(x - 4)$

20. _____

Bonus

Find the coordinates of the points of intersection of the graphs of $x^2 - y^2 = 3$, $xy = 2$, and $y = -2x + 5$.
  A. $(\pm 2, \pm 1)$ **B.** $(1, -2)$ **C.** $(2, 1)$ **D.** no solutions

Bonus: _____

Chapter 10 Test, Form 1B

Write the letter for the correct answer in the blank at the right of each problem.

Exercises 1-3 refer to the parabola represented by
$x^2 + 2x + 12y + 37 = 0$.

1. Find the coordinates of the focus.
   A. $(-1, -12)$ **B.** $(-1, -6)$ **C.** $(-1, -9)$ **D.** $(-5, 2)$ 1. _____

2. Find the equation of the directrix.
   A. $y = -9$ **B.** $y = -12$ **C.** $y = 0$ **D.** $x = -1$ 2. _____

3. Find the coordinates of the vertex and the equation of the axis of symmetry.
   A. $(-1, -3)$ and $x = -1$ **B.** $(-1, -6)$ and $x = -1$
   C. $(-1, -12)$ and $x = -5$ **D.** $(3, 2)$ and $y = -9$ 3. _____

4. Determine the eccentricity of the conic represented by
   $y^2 + 4y - x^2 + 6x - 21 = 0$.
   A. $\dfrac{3}{2}$ **B.** -1 **C.** $\dfrac{\sqrt{2}}{4}$ **D.** $\sqrt{2}$ 4. _____

5. For $2x^2 + 3xy + y^2 = 1$, find θ, the angle of rotation about the origin, to the nearest tenth of a degree.
   A. $-9.3°$ **B.** $35.8°$ **C.** $-35.8°$ **D.** $324.2°$ 5. _____

6. Find the coordinates of one focus of the hyperbola represented by
   $x^2 - 6y^2 + 36y = 60$.
   A. $(0, 3 + \sqrt{7})$ **B.** $(\sqrt{7}, 3)$ **C.** $(3 + \sqrt{7}, 0)$ **D.** $(\sqrt{7}, 0)$ 6. _____

Exercises 7 and 8 refer to P(7, –5) and the conic represented by
$(x - 3)^2 + (y + 2)^2 = 25$.

7. Write the equation of the tangent to the curve through point P in standard form.
   A. $5x - 7y - 25 = 0$ **B.** $4x - 3y - 43 = 0$
   C. $7x - 5y - 25 = 0$ **D.** $4x - 3y + 41 = 0$ 7. _____

8. Write the equation of the normal to the curve through point P in standard form.
   A. $7x - 5y - 25 = 0$ **B.** $3x + 4y - 1 = 0$
   C. $3x + 4y - 13 = 0$ **D.** $5x + 7y = 0$ 8. _____

9. Solve the system of equations: $x^2 + y^2 = 4$ and $y = 2x - 1$. Round the coordinates of the solution to the nearest tenth.
   A. $(1.3, 1.5)$ **B.** $(1.3, 1.5); (-0.5, -1.9)$
   C. no solution   **D.** $(\pm 1.3, \pm 1.5); (\pm 0.5, \pm 1.9)$ 9. _____

10. Identify the conic section represented by $3y^2 - 3x^2 + 12y + 18x = 42$.
    A. parabola   **B.** hyperbola   **C.** ellipse   **D.** circle   10. _____

11. Write the equation of the graph of $y^2 - x^2 = 2$ rotated through $45°$.
    A. $xy = -1$ **B.** $xy = -2$ **C.** $y^2 - x^2 = 2$ **D.** $x^2 = y$ 11. _____

Glencoe Division, Macmillan/McGraw-Hill

~ Chapter 10 Test, Form 1B (continued)

12. Choose the graph of $y^2 + 4y + 16x - 44 = 0$.

A. 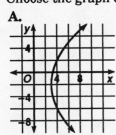 B. 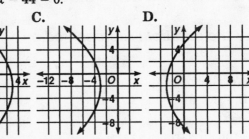 C. D.

12. _____

Exercises 13-15 refer to the hyperbola represented by
$y^2 + 4y - 36x^2 = 32$.

13. Find the coordinates of the vertices.
   A. $(-3, -2)$; $(5, -2)$ **B.** $(1, -1)$; $(1, -3)$
   C. $(0, 4)$; $(0, -8)$ **D.** $(-1, -4)$; $(-1, -8)$

13. _____

14. Write the equations of the asymptotes.
   A. $y - 1 = \pm 6(x - 2)$ **B.** $y = \pm 6x$
   C. $y + 2 = \pm 6(x - 1)$ **D.** $y + 2 = \pm 6x$

14. _____

15. Find the coordinates of the foci.
   A. $(0, 4 + \sqrt{37})$; $(0, -8 + \sqrt{37})$ **B.** $(0, 4)$; $(0, -8)$
   C. $(0, 4 + \sqrt{35})$; $(0, -8 + \sqrt{35})$ **D.** $(0, -2 \pm \sqrt{37})$

15. _____

16. Write the standard form of the equation of the hyperbola for which $a = 2$ if
   the transverse axis is vertical and the equations of the asymptotes are
   $y = \pm 2x$.
   A. $\dfrac{x^2}{4} - \dfrac{y^2}{1} = 1$ **B.** $\dfrac{x^2}{4} + \dfrac{y^2}{1} = 1$ **C.** $\dfrac{x^2}{1} - \dfrac{y^2}{4} = 1$ **D.** $\dfrac{y^2}{4} - \dfrac{x^2}{1} = 1$

16. _____

17. Find the length of the tangent segment from $P(-10, 0)$ to the graph of
   $3x^2 - 18x + 3y^2 + 12y + 15 = 0$.
   A. $\sqrt{165}$ **B.** 6   **C.** $\sqrt{53}$ **D.** $\sqrt{237}$

17. _____

18. Write the standard form of the equation of the parabola whose directrix is
   $y = -4$ and whose focus is $(2, 2)$.
   A. $(y - 2)^2 = 12(x + 2)$ **B.** $y + 1 = 12(x - 2)^2$
   C. $(x + 2)^2 = 12(y - 2)$ **D.** $(x - 2)^2 = 12(y + 1)$

18. _____

19. Write the standard form of the equation of the ellipse with foci at $(\pm 4, 0)$ and
   whose semi-minor axis is 5 units long.
   A. $\dfrac{x^2}{16} + \dfrac{y^2}{25} = 1$ **B.** $\dfrac{x^2}{25} + \dfrac{y^2}{41} = 1$ **C.** $\dfrac{x^2}{41} + \dfrac{y^2}{25} = 1$ **D.** $\dfrac{x^2}{25} - \dfrac{y^2}{41} = 1$

19. _____

20. Write the equation for the translation of the graph of $x^2 + 4x + 1 = 4y - 11$
   for $T_{(1, -2)}$.
   A. $(x + 2)^2 = 4(y - 2)$ **B.** $(x + 1)^2 = 4y$
   C. $(y + 2)^2 = 4(x + 3)$ **D.** $(x + 3)^2 = 4(y - 3)$

20. _____

Bonus

Find the coordinates of the points of intersection of the graphs of
$x^2 + y^2 = 5$, $xy = -2$, and $y = -3x + 1$.
   A. $(\pm 2, \pm 1)$ **B.** $(1, -2)$ **C.** $(2, 1)$ **D.** $(\pm 1, \pm 2)$

Bonus: _____

Chapter 10 Test, Form 2A

1. Identify the conic section represented by the equation
   $x^2 - 6x + 8y - 7 = 9$.

   1. _____

Solve each system of equations. Round the coordinates of the solution to the nearest tenth.

2. $x^2 + y^2 = 16$
   $y = 2x + 1$

3. $x^2 + y^2 = 81$
   $9x^2 + 4y^2 = 36$

   2. _____

   3. _____

4. Write the standard form of the equation of the circle represented
   by $x^2 + y^2 + 2x - 2y = 2$.

   4. _____

5. Graph the equation in Exercise 4
   on the grid at the right.

   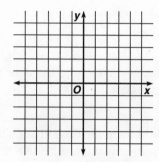

   5. _____

6. Find the coordinates of the center, foci, and vertices and the
   equations of the asymptotes of the graph of $y^2 - x^2 + 2x - 4y = 6$.

   6. _____

7. Graph the equation in Exercise 6
   on the grid at the right.

   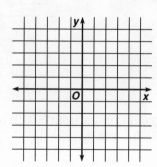

   7. _____

8. Determine the eccentricity of the conic section represented
   by $9x^2 + 16y^2 - 54x + 64y = -1$.

   8. _____

9. Find the equations in standard form of the tangent and the
   normal to the graph of $(x + 1)^2 + (y - 2)^2 = 36$ at $(-1, 8)$.

   9. _____

10. Identify the graph of $4x^2 + 7xy - 5y^2 + 3 = 0$. Then find θ, the
    angle of rotation about the origin, to the nearest degree.

    10. _____

~ **Chapter 10 Test, Form 2A (continued)**

11. Write the equation of the parabola whose focus is at $(-1, 2)$ and whose directrix has equation $x = 2$.

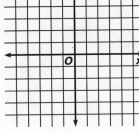

11. _____

12. Graph the equation in Exercise 11 on the grid at the right.

12. _____

13. Suppose that the graph of $y^2 - x^2 = 16$ is rotated about the origin through an angle of 30°. Find an equation of the rotated graph.

13. _____

14. Write $y^2 - 4y + 6 - 16x = -14$ in standard form. Find the coordinates of the focus and the vertex, and the equations of the directrix and the axis of symmetry.

14. _____

15. Write an equation in standard form for the ellipse whose foci are at $(0, -3)$ and $(0, 3)$ and whose semi-major axis is 8 units long.

15. _____

16. Find the coordinates of the center, foci, and vertices of the ellipse whose equation is $4x^2 + 9y^2 - 8x - 32 = 0$.

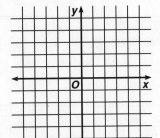

16. _____

17. Graph the equation in Exercise 16 on the grid at the right.

17. _____

18. Find the length of the tangent segment from $(-2, 2)$ to the circle with equation $(x - 3)^2 + (y + 5)^2 = 4$.

18. _____

19. Write the standard form of the equation that results from translating the graph of $9x^2 - 9y^2 = 324$ by $T_{(2, -2)}$.

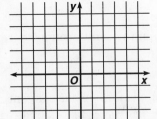

19. _____

20. Graph the equation found in Exercise 19 on the grid at the right.

20. _____

Bonus

Find the coordinates of any points of intersection of the graphs of $2x - y + 1 = 0$, $x^2 + y^2 = 10$, and $y = 4x^2 - 1$.

Bonus: _____

Chapter 10 Test, Form 2B

1. Identify the conic section represented by the equation
   $x^2 - 6x + 4y^2 + 8y - 3 = 0$.

   1. _____

Solve each system of equations. Round the coordinates of the solution to the nearest tenth.

2. $4x^2 + 16y^2 = 64$
   $y = -2x + 3$

3. $x^2 - y^2 = 81$
   $25x^2 + 4y^2 = 100$

   2. _____

   3. _____

4. Write the standard form of the equation of the circle represented by $2x^2 + 2y^2 + 4x - 8y = -2$.

   4. _____

5. Graph the equation in Exercise 4 on the grid at the right.

   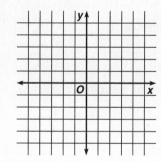

   5. _____

6. Find the coordinates of the center, foci, and vertices and the equations of the asymptotes of the graph of $x^2 - y^2 + 2x = 0$.

   6. _____

7. Graph the equation in Exercise 6 on the grid at the right.

   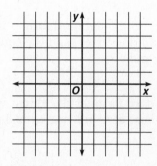

   7. _____

8. Determine the eccentricity of the conic section represented by $9x^2 - 16y^2 + 36x + 64y = 172$.

   8. _____

9. Find the equations in standard form of the tangent and the normal to the graph of $(x - 3)^2 + (y - 1)^2 = 50$ at $(8, 6)$.

   9. _____

10. Identify the graph of $3x^2 - 8xy - 3y^2 = 3$. Then find θ, the angle of rotation about the origin, to the nearest degree.

   10. _____

Glencoe Division, Macmillan/McGraw-Hill

~~~ **Chapter 10 Test, Form 2B (continued)**

11. Write the equation of the parabola whose focus is at (1, 1) and whose vertex is at (1, −2).

11. _____

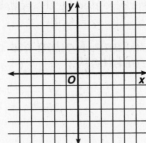

12. Graph the equation in Exercise 11 on the grid at the right.

12. _____

13. Suppose that the graph of $4y^2 + 9x^2 = 36$ is rotated about the origin through an angle of 60°. Find an equation of the rotated graph.

13. _____

14. Write $x^2 - 4x + 6 - 16y = -14$ in standard form. Find the coordinates of the focus and the vertex, and the equations of the directrix and the axis of symmetry.

14. _____

15. Write an equation in standard form for the ellipse whose foci are at (2, −3) and (2, 3) and whose semi-major axis is 8 units long.

15. _____

16. Find the coordinates of the center, foci, and vertices of the ellipse whose equation is $9x^2 + 4y^2 - 18x = 27$.

16. _____

17. Graph the equation in Exercise 16 on the grid at the right.

17. _____

18. Find the length of the tangent segment from (7, 2) to the circle with equation $(x - 1)^2 + (y - 4)^2 = 24$.

18. _____

19. Write the standard form of the equation that results from translating the graph of $8x^2 - 8y^2 = 128$ by $T_{(1, -2)}$.

19. _____

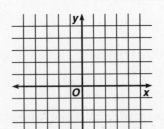

20. Graph the equation found in Exercise 19 on the grid at the right.

20. _____

Bonus

Find the coordinates of any points of intersection of the graphs of $x + y + 1 = 0$, $x^2 + y^2 = 5$, and $y = -3x^2 + 1$.

Bonus: _____

Glencoe Division, Macmillan/McGraw-Hill

Chapter 10, Quiz A (Lessons 10-1 through 10-2)

1. Write the standard form of the equation of the circle represented by $2x^2 + 8x + 2y^2 - 8y = 32$.

   1. _____

2. Write the standard form of the equation of the circle that passes through $(6, -2)$ and has its center at $(-3, 4)$.

   2. _____

3. Write the standard form of the equation of the parabola represented by $x^2 - 4x + 8y + 12 = 0$. Find the coordinates of the focus and the vertex, and the equations of the directrix and the axis of symmetry.

   3. _____

4. Write the equation of the parabola with focus at $(-2, 3)$ and whose directrix is $x = 4$. Graph the equation on the grid at the right.

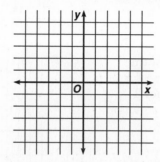

   4. _____

5. Write the standard form of the equation of the circle that passes through $(1, 7)$, $(-7, 3)$, and $(-2, 8)$.

   5. _____

Chapter 10, Quiz B (Lessons 10-3 through 10-4))

1. Find the coordinates of the center, foci, and vertices of the ellipse whose equation is $9y^2 + 4x^2 - 18y + 16x = 11$. Then graph the equation on the grid at the right.

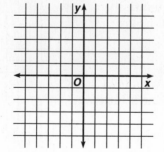

   1. _____

2. Write the equation of the ellipse whose horizontal semi-major axis has length 6 units, whose center is at $(2, -2)$, and $\frac{2}{3} = \frac{c}{a}$.

   2. _____

3. Graph $\dfrac{(x-1)^2}{4} - \dfrac{(y+2)^2}{9} = 1$ on the grid at the right.

   3. _____

4. Write the equation of the hyperbola whose center is at $(-2, 3)$, whose transverse axis has length 4 units, and has a focus at $(-5, 3)$.

   4. _____

5. State whether the graph of $3x^2 + 4y^2 - 18x = 7$ is a circle, an ellipse, a parabola, or a hyperbola.

   5. _____

Glencoe Division, Macmillan/McGraw-Hill

Chapter 10, Quiz C (Lessons 10-5 through 10-6)

1. Determine the eccentricity of the conic section represented by
   $16x^2 - 4y^2 + 64x + 16y - 32 = 0$.

   1. _____

2. Identify the conic represented by
   $(x - 1)^2 + 9(y + 2)^2 = 9$. Write the
   equation in standard form and graph
   the equation on the grid at the right.

   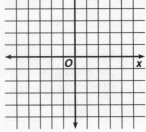

   2. _____

3. Write the equation of the hyperbola
   with eccentricity $\frac{5}{3}$ and foci at $(0, 9)$
   and $(0, -1)$.

   3. _____

4. Write the standard form of the
   equation of the translation of
   $-6x^2 + 24x + 4y - 8 = 0$ for $T_{(-1,\, 2)}$.
   Then graph the resulting equation
   on the grid at the right.

   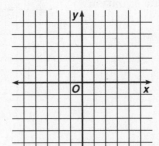

   4. _____

5. Find an equation for the rotation
   of $y^2 - x^2 = 16$ if the graph is rotated
   about the origin through $45°$.

   5. _____

Chapter 10, Quiz D (Lessons 10-7 through 10-8)

1. Graph the system of inequalities
   $x^2 + y^2 \leq 9$ and $xy \geq 1$ on the grid
   at the right.

   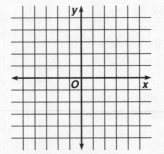

   1. _____

2. Solve the system $x^2 + y^2 = 9$ and $xy = 1$.
   Round the coordinates of the solution to
   the nearest tenth.

   2. _____

3. Find the equations of the tangent and the normal to the graph
   of $3x^2 + 3y^2 = 39$ at $(2, 3)$.

   3. _____

4. Find the length of the tangent segment from $(2, -4)$ to the graph
   of $2x^2 + 2y^2 = 18$.

   4. _____

5. Find the equations of the horizontal lines tangent to the graph
   of $4x^2 + 36y^2 = 144$.

   5. _____

Chapter 10 Mid-Chapter Test (Lessons 10-1 through 10-4)

1. Write the standard form of $x^2 + 4y^2 + 2x + 16y = -1$. Then graph the equation on the grid at the right.

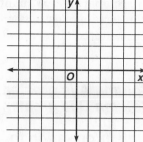

1. _____

2. Write the equation of the circle that passes through $(2, -3)$ and has its center at $(1, 3)$.

2. _____

3. Write the equation of the ellipse that has its center at the origin, has foci at $(0, -3)$ and $(0, 3)$, and $b = 2$.

3. _____

4. For the equation $y^2 + 6y + 12x = 27$, write the standard form, find the coordinates of the focus and vertex, and the equations of the directrix and axis of symmetry. Then graph the equation on the grid at the right.

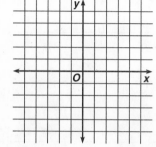

4. _____

5. State whether the graph of $3x^2 + 6x + 4y^2 - 16y = -7$ is a circle, an ellipse, a parabola, or a hyperbola.

5. _____

6. Find the coordinates of the center, the foci, and the vertices and the equations of the asymptotes of the hyperbola $4x^2 - y^2 + 2y - 5 = 0$. Graph the equation on the grid at the right.

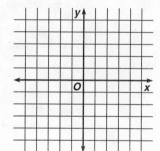

6. _____

7. Write the equation of the hyperbola that has center at $(-1, 3)$, $a = 4$, $b = 3$, and has a horizontal transverse axis.

7. _____

8. Write the equation of the parabola that has $x = -2$ as its axis, the focus is at $(-2, 3)$, and $p = -3$.

8. _____

9. For $4x^2 + 8x + 9y^2 + 18y - 23 = 0$, find the coordinates of the center, foci, and vertices. Graph the equation on the grid at the right.

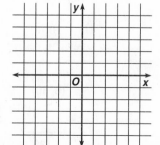

9. _____

10. Write the standard form of the equation of the circle that passes through $(5, 2)$, $(1, 6)$, and $(-3, 2)$.

10. _____

Glencoe Division, Macmillan/McGraw-Hill

~ Standardized Test Questions (Chapters 1-10)

The questions on this page involve comparing two quantities, one in Column A and one in Column B. In certain questions, information related to one or both quantities is centered above them. All variables stand for real numbers.

Directions:
Write A if the quantity in Column A is greater.
Write B if the quantity in Column B is greater.
Write C if the quantities are equal.
Write D if there is not enough information to determine the relationship.

Column A	Column B	
1. $\quad f(x) = x^4 + 5x^2 - 4$		1. _____
$f(x)$	$f(-x)$	
2. $\qquad x > 9$		2. _____
$2x + 4$	$3x - 5$	
3. $\qquad x > 4$		3. _____
$\dfrac{x+4}{x} + \dfrac{3}{x-4}$	$-\dfrac{16}{x^2 - 4x}$	
4. $\quad \theta$ is a third-quadrant angle.		4. _____
$\sin \theta \cos \theta$	0	
5. $\sqrt{5x + 4}$	8	5. _____
6. $\qquad a > b$		6. _____
the area inside the graph of $\dfrac{x^2}{a^2} + \dfrac{y^2}{b^2} = 1$	the area inside the graph of $\dfrac{x^2}{a^2} + \dfrac{y^2}{a^2} = 1$	
7. $\qquad n$ is an integer.		7. _____
$i^{4n + 44}$	$i^{4n + 46}$	
8. $\cos(\alpha - \beta)$	$\cos(\beta - \alpha)$	8. _____
9. $\qquad x > 0$		9. _____
$\dfrac{x^2 - 2x + 1}{x}$	$x - 2$	
10. $\quad \vec{u}$ and $\vec{v}$ are nonzero vectors.		10. _____
$\vec{u} \cdot \vec{v}$	$-\vec{u} \cdot \vec{v}$	
11. the period of $y = \cos(2x - \pi)$	the period of $y = \tan(3x - \pi)$	11. _____
12. the maximum value of $2x + 5y$ over the region shown	the maximum value of $3x + 4y$ over the region shown	12. _____

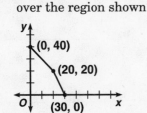

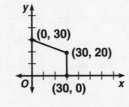

Chapter 11 Test, Form 1A

Write the letter for the correct answer in the blank at the right of each problem.

1. Evaluate $\left(4^{\frac{1}{2}} + 4^{\frac{1}{2}}\right)^{-\frac{1}{2}}$.

   A. $\dfrac{1}{2}$ **B.** $-\dfrac{1}{2}$ **C.** 2   **D.** -2

   1. _____

2. Express $\sqrt{225a^6b^7}$ using rational exponents.

   A. $45a^3b^{\frac{7}{2}}$ **B.** $15a^3b^{\frac{7}{2}}$ **C.** $15a^3b^{\frac{2}{7}}$ **D.** $15a^{\frac{1}{3}}b^{\frac{2}{7}}$

   2. _____

3. Express $\dfrac{x^{\frac{4}{5}}}{x^{\frac{3}{5}}}$ using radicals.

   A. $\sqrt[5]{x}$ **B.** $\sqrt{x^5}$ **C.** $-\left(\sqrt[5]{x}\right)$ **D.** $\dfrac{1}{\sqrt[5]{x}}$

   3. _____

4. Use a calculator to evaluate $4^{\frac{\pi}{2}}$ to the nearest ten-thousandth.

   A. 6.2340   **B.** 5.1517   **C.** 6.9356   **D.** 8.8250

   4. _____

5. Choose the graph of $y = -(2^x)$.

   A.   **B.**   **C.**   **D.**

   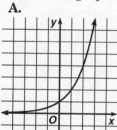 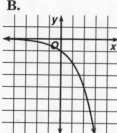 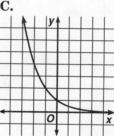 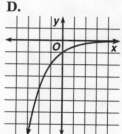

   5. _____

6. Choose the graph of $y \le 3^x$.

   A.   **B.**   **C.**   **D.**

   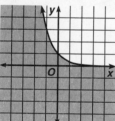 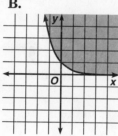 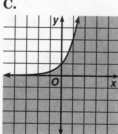 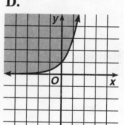

   6. _____

7. Use a calculator to evaluate $\dfrac{1}{5}e^{2.3}$ to the nearest ten-thousandth.

   A. 0.1667   **B.** 1.5841   **C.** 1.9948   **D.** 0.2000

   7. _____

Given the original principal, the annual interest rate, the amount of time for each investment, and the type of compounded interest, find the amount, to the nearest dollar, at the end of the investment period.

8. $P = \$8000$, $r = 6\%$, $t = 3$ years, compounded quarterly

   A. \$9565   **B.** \$8365   **C.** \$9147   **D.** \$10,146

   8. _____

9. $P = \$600$, $r = 5.5\%$, $t = 6$ months, compounded continuously

   A. \$835   **B.** \$617   **C.** \$620   **D.** \$602

   9. _____

~~ Chapter 11 Test, Form 1A (continued)

10. Write $2^{-3} = \dfrac{1}{8}$ in logarithmic form.

   A. $\log_2(-3) = \dfrac{1}{8}$ **B.** $\log_{\frac{1}{8}} 2 = -3$ **C.** $\log_2 \dfrac{1}{8} = -3$ **D.** $\log_{-3} \dfrac{1}{8} = 2$ **10.** _____

11. Evaluate $\log_a a^{-3}$.

   A. 3   **B.** -3 **C.** $\dfrac{1}{3}$ **D.** $-\dfrac{1}{3}$ **11.** _____

12. Solve $\log_5 \left(\sqrt{5}\right)^3 = x$.

   A. 5   **B.** 125   **C.** $\dfrac{2}{3}$ **D.** $\dfrac{3}{2}$ **12.** _____

13. Which is the graph of $y \le \log_4 x$?

   A.   **B.**   **C.**   **D.**

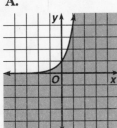 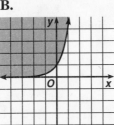 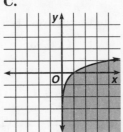 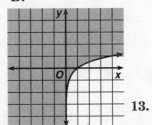

   13. _____

14. Use a calculator to find the common logarithm of 3194 to the nearest ten-thousandth.

   A. 0   **B.** 8.0690   **C.** 3.5043   **D.** 0.6947   **14.** _____

15. Use a calculator to find the antilogarithm of 5.4675 to the nearest whole number.

   A. 293,427   **B.** 474   **C.** 293,359   **D.** 7378   **15.** _____

16. Use logarithms to evaluate 243×5.1^4 to the nearest whole number.

   A. 16   **B.** 128,086   **C.** 235,888   **D.** 164,394   **16.** _____

17. Solve $4^{2x} = 21$ by using logarithms. Round your answer to the nearest ten-thousandth.

   A. 0.6667   **B.** 1.0981   **C.** 0.3333   **D.** 4.3923   **17.** _____

18. Solve $x > \log_2 32.5$. Round your answer to the nearest ten-thousandth.

   A. $x > 1.5119$ **B.** $x > 0.3100$ **C.** $x > 5.0224$ **D.** $x > -1.2121$ **18.** _____

19. Use a calculator to find the value of ln 452 to the nearest ten-thousandth.

   A. 0   **B.** 6.1137   **C.** 2.6551   **D.** 6.2953   **19.** _____

20. Solve $12 = 7e^{2k}$. Round your answer to the nearest ten-thousandth.

   A. 0.2695   **B.** 1.0780   **C.** 0.1170   **D.** 0.4681   **20.** _____

Bonus

Express $\sqrt[5]{\sqrt{x^6}}$ in exponential form. Assume $x > 0$.

   A. $x^{\frac{3}{5}}$ **B.** $x^{\frac{5}{3}}$ **C.** $x^{\frac{1}{60}}$ **D.** $x^{\frac{4}{5}}$ **Bonus:** _____

Chapter 11 Test, Form 1B

Write the letter for the correct answer in the blank at the right of each problem.

1. Evaluate $\left(\sqrt{81}\right)^{-\frac{1}{2}}$.

    A. -3 **B.** 3 **C.** $-\frac{1}{3}$ **D.** $\frac{1}{3}$ **1.** _____

2. Express $\sqrt[4]{256a^8b^{12}}$ using rational exponents.

    A. $16a^4b^3$ **B.** $4a^2b^3$ **C.** $4a^{\frac{1}{2}}b^{\frac{1}{3}}$ **D.** $16a^{\frac{1}{2}}b^{\frac{1}{3}}$ **2.** _____

3. Express $10x^{\frac{2}{3}}y^{\frac{1}{2}}$ using radicals.

    A. $10\sqrt[6]{x^4y^3}$ **B.** $10\sqrt{x^{\frac{1}{3}}y}$ **C.** $\frac{10}{3}\sqrt{x^3y}$ **D.** $\frac{10}{3}\sqrt[6]{x^4y^3}$ **3.** _____

4. Use a calculator to evaluate $5^{\sqrt{2}}$ to the nearest ten-thousandth.

    A. 25.0000 **B.** 9.7385 **C.** 3.1214 **D.** 2.2361 **4.** _____

5. Choose the graph of $y = 3^{x+1}$.

    A.   **B.**   **C.**   **D.**

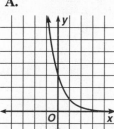 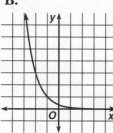 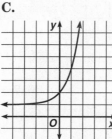 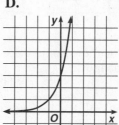

    5. _____

6. Choose the graph of $y < \left(\frac{1}{3}\right)^x$.

    A.   **B.**   **C.**   **D.**

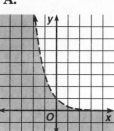 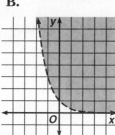 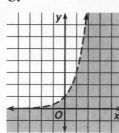 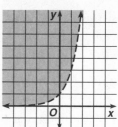

    6. _____

7. Use a calculator to evaluate $2\sqrt[3]{e}$ to the nearest ten-thousandth.

    A. 40.1711 **B.** -2.1972 **C.** 2.7912 **D.** 2.0000 **7.** _____

Given the original principal, the annual interest rate, the amount of time for each investment, and the type of compounded interest, find the amount, to the nearest dollar, at the end of the investment period.

8. $P = \$5000$, $r = 8\%$, $t = 2$ years, compounded monthly

    A. $\$5204$ **B.** $\$5067$ **C.** $\$5415$ **D.** $\$5864$ **8.** _____

9. $P = \$4800$, $r = 6.5\%$, $t = 5$ years, compounded continuously

    A. $\$6024$ **B.** $\$25,612$ **C.** $\$5122$ **D.** $\$6643$ **9.** _____

～ Chapter 11 Test, Form 1B (continued)

10. Write $\log_{\sqrt{5}} 25 = 4$ in exponential form.

   A. $\left(\sqrt{5}\right)^4 = 25$ **B.** $\left(\sqrt{25}\right)^4 = 5$ **C.** $\sqrt[4]{5} = 25$ **D.** $5^{\frac{2}{4}} = 25$ 10. _____

11. Evaluate $\log_8 8^{\frac{2}{3}}$.

   A. $-\dfrac{2}{3}$ **B.** $\dfrac{2}{3}$ **C.** -2 **D.** 3   11. _____

12. Solve $\log_3 5 + \log_3 4 = \log_3 x$.

   A. 9   **B.** $2\sqrt{5}$ **C.** 20   **D.** 1   12. _____

13. Which is the graph of $y = \log_2 (2x)$?

   A.   **B.**   **C.**   **D.**

   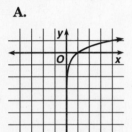 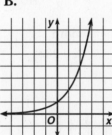 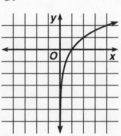 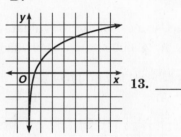

   13. _____

14. Use a calculator to find the common logarithm of 2.3×10^5 to the nearest ten-thousandth.

   A. 0   **B.** 5.3617   **C.** 4.3617   **D.** 6.3617   14. _____

15. Use a calculator to find antilog 0.0034 to the nearest ten-thousandth.

   A. 0.9999   **B.** -2.4685 **C.** 1.0079   **D.** 0   15. _____

16. Use logarithms to evaluate $853 \times 0.15 \times 17$.

   A. 2175.15   **B.** 870.15   **C.** 2860   **D.** 3348   16. _____

17. Use logarithms to solve $12^{x+2} = 10.25$. Round your answer to the nearest ten-thousandth.

   A. 2.9377   **B.** -0.0634 **C.** -1.0634 **D.** 0.9315   17. _____

18. Solve $\log_8 50 \geq x$ using logarithms. Round your answer to the nearest ten-thousandth.

   A. $x \leq 0.5316$ **B.** $x \geq 0.7959$ **C.** $x \geq -0.7959$ **D.** $x \leq 1.8813$ 18. _____

19. Use a calculator to find the value of antiln -0.124 to the nearest ten-thousandth.

   A. -0.9066 **B.** 0   **C.** 1.1320   **D.** 0.8834   19. _____

20. Solve $\ln 9.3 = \ln e^{0.015t}$. Round your answer to the nearest ten-thousandth.

   A. 64.5655   **B.** 148.6676   **C.** 62.0159   **D.** 1.0340   20. _____

Bonus

Express $\log_b 4x^2$ as the sum of logarithms.

    A. $\log_b 5 + 5\log_b x^2$ **B.** $\log_b 4 + 2\log_b x$

    C. $4\log_b x + 2\log_b x$ **D.** $4\log_b x + \log_b x^2$ **Bonus:** _____

Chapter 11 Test, Form 2A

1. Evaluate $\left(4^{\frac{1}{2}} + 2^{-2}\right)^{\frac{1}{2}}$.

1. _____

2. Express $\sqrt[3]{7x^6y^{15}}$ using rational exponents.

2. _____

3. Express $a^{\frac{2}{7}}b^{\frac{3}{7}}c^{\frac{1}{7}}$ using radicals.

3. _____

Use a calculator to evaluate each expression to the nearest ten-thousandth.

4. $3^{\sqrt{5}}$

4. _____

5. $\left(\dfrac{2}{3}\right)^{\pi}$

5. _____

Graph each equation or inequality.

6. $y = 1.5^x$ 7. $y > 2^x + 1$

6. _____

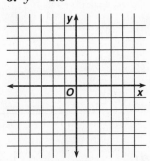   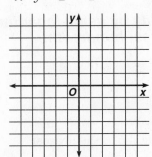

7. _____

8. Use a calculator to evaluate $\sqrt{e^3}$ to the nearest ten-thousandth.

8. _____

9. The yield, y, in millions of cubic feet of trees per acre for a forest stand that is t years old is given by $y = 6.7e^{-\frac{48.1}{t}}$. Find the approximate yield in millions of cubic feet after 20 years.

9. _____

10. Find the future value to the nearest dollar of $4500 invested at 7.5% for 10 years if the interest is compounded semiannually.

10. _____

11. Write $27^{\frac{1}{3}} = 3$ in logarithmic form.

11. _____

12. Write $\log_2 (x^2 - 1) = 3$ in exponential form.

12. _____

13. Evaluate $\log_4 32$.

13. _____

14. Solve $\log_4 (2x) = \log_4 8$.

14. _____

Glencoe Division, Macmillan/McGraw-Hill

~~ Chapter 11 Test, Form 2A (continued)

15. Graph $\log_5 y = x$.

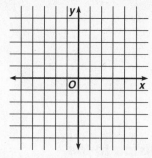

15. _____

16. Use a calculator to find the common logarithm of 0.0428 to the nearest ten-thousandth.

16. _____

17. Use a calculator to find the antilogarithm of 0.3571 to the nearest ten-thousandth.

17. _____

18. Use logarithms to evaluate $\sqrt{(45)(0.24)}$ to the nearest ten-thousandth.

18. _____

Solve each equation or inequality by using logarithms. Round your answer to the nearest hundredth.

19. $3.2^x \le 52.4$

19. _____

20. $x^{0.6} = 15.8$

20. _____

21. Use common logarithms to find $\log_6 35$ to the nearest ten-thousandth.

21. _____

Use a calculator to find each value to the nearest ten-thousandth.

22. $\ln 0.1374$

22. _____

23. antiln -1

23. _____

Solve each equation. Round your answer to the nearest ten-thousandth.

24. $2352 = 3e^{0.047t}$

24. _____

25. $\ln 10.4 = \ln\left(e^{0.5t}\right)$

25. _____

Bonus

Graph $y = 2^x$ and $y = x^2$ on the same set of axes. In how many points do the graphs intersect?

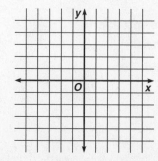

Bonus: _____

Chapter 11 Test, Form 2B

1. Evaluate $\dfrac{\sqrt[5]{32}}{32^{\frac{2}{5}}}$.

   1. _____

2. Express $\sqrt[6]{64b^4}$ using rational exponents.

   2. _____

3. Express $2^{\frac{1}{4}}x^{\frac{5}{4}}$ using radicals.

   3. _____

Use a calculator to evaluate each expression to the nearest ten-thousandth.

4. $2^{\sqrt{6}}$

   4. _____

5. 1.52^{π}

   5. _____

Graph each equation or inequality.

6. $y = 0.5^x + 2$

7. $y \leq 4^x$

   6. _____

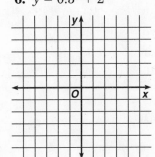

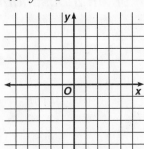

   7. _____

8. Use a calculator to evaluate $\dfrac{\sqrt[4]{e}}{2}$ to the nearest ten-thousandth.

   8. _____

9. Use Newton's Law of Cooling, $y = ae^{-kt} + c$, to find the temperature, y, to the nearest degree, of a liquid heated to 210°F in a 68°F room after 5 minutes if $a = 140$ and $k = 0.01$.

   9. _____

10. Find the future value, to the nearest dollar, of $2500 invested at 5.5% for 4 years if the interest is compounded quarterly.

   10. _____

11. Write $0.2^3 = 0.008$ in logarithmic form.

   11. _____

12. Write $\log_7 \left(\sqrt{7}\right)^6 = 3$ in exponential form.

   12. _____

13. Evaluate $\log_{27} 81$.

   13. _____

14. Solve $\log_2 0.125 = x$.

   14. _____

~ Chapter 11 Test, Form 2B (continued)

15. Graph $y < \log_4 x$.

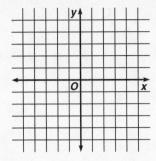

15. _____

16. Use a calculator to find the common logarithm of 0.0018 to the nearest ten-thousandth.

16. _____

17. Use a calculator to find the antilogarithm of 5.164 to the nearest whole number.

17. _____

18. Use logarithms to evaluate $\sqrt[3]{24.78}$ to the nearest ten-thousandth.

18. _____

Solve each equation or inequality by using logarithms. Round your answers to the nearest ten-thousandth.

19. $8^{-x} = 24$

19. _____

20. $x > \log_9 15$

20. _____

21. $x^{\frac{2}{3}} = 25.2$

21. _____

Use a calculator to find each value to the nearest ten-thousandth.

22. antiln 3.378

22. _____

23. $\ln\left(\dfrac{1}{4.5}\right)$

23. _____

24. Solve $\ln 6.7 = \ln e^{0.12t}$. Round your answer to the nearest hundredth.

24. _____

25. Solve $e^{2k} = 3$. Round your answer to the nearest ten-thousandth.

25. _____

Bonus

Graph $y = 2^x$ and $y = \left(\dfrac{1}{2}\right)^x$ on the same set of axes. What is the axis of symmetry for the two graphs?

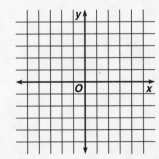

Bonus: _____

Chapter 11, Quiz A (Lessons 11-1 through 11-2)

1. Evaluate $\dfrac{8^{\frac{1}{3}}}{8^{\frac{2}{3}}}$.

1. _____

2. Express $\sqrt[4]{35ab^{20}}$ using rational exponents.

2. _____

3. Express $a^{\frac{2}{3}}b^{\frac{1}{3}}$ using radicals.

3. _____

4. Use a calculator to evaluate 7^{π} to the nearest ten-thousandth.

4. _____

5. Graph $y \le 2^{-x}$.

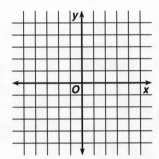

5. _____

Chapter 11, Quiz B (Lessons 11-3 through 11-4)

1. Use a calculator to evaluate $\dfrac{1}{3}\sqrt[5]{e^2}$ to the nearest ten-thousandth.

1. _____

2. To the nearest dollar, find the future value of $500 invested at 9% for 4 years in an account that is compounded continuously.

2. _____

3. Write $4^{-2} = \dfrac{1}{16}$ in logarithmic form.

3. _____

4. Solve $\log_x \dfrac{1}{216} = -3$.

4. _____

5. Graph $y < \log_2 x$.

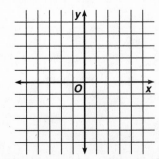

5. _____

Chapter 11, Quiz C (Lessons 11-5 through 11-6)

Use a calculator to find the common logarithm of each number to the nearest ten-thousandth.

1. 754.3

2. 21.7×10^{-3}

1. _____

2. _____

Use a calculator to find the antilogarithm of each number to the nearest hundredth.

3. −0.3215

4. 0.005

3. _____

4. _____

5. Evaluate $\dfrac{1.23 \times 5}{2.14}$ by using logarithms. Round your answer

   to the nearest hundredth.

5. _____

Solve each equation or inequality using logarithms. Round your answer to the nearest ten-thousandth.

6. $5^x = 45$

7. $2.1^{2x} > 30.4$

6. _____

7. _____

8. $6^{x+2} = 10.3$

9. $x < \log_4 28.9$

8. _____

9. _____

10. Use the change of base formula to find the value of $\log_5 32$ to the nearest ten-thousandth.

10. _____

Chapter 11, Quiz D (Lesson 11-7)

Use a calculator to find each value to the nearest ten-thousandth.

1. ln 43.19

1. _____

2. antiln −0.014

2. _____

Solve each equation. Round your answer to the nearest hundredth.

3. $54 = 4e^{3k}$

3. _____

4. $\ln 25 = \ln e^{0.035y}$

4. _____

5. If the number of years, $n(r)$, since two languages split from their common ancestral language is 3500, find the percent of words, r, that are common to both languages today.
   Use the formula $n(r) = -5000 \ln r$.

5. _____

Chapter 11 Mid-Chapter Test (Lessons 11-1 through 11-4)

Evaluate each expression.

1. 27^0

1. _____

2. $7^5 \cdot 7^{-3}$

2. _____

3. Express $-\left(\sqrt[5]{243x^{10}y^3}\right)$ using rational exponents.

3. _____

Express using radicals.

4. $v^{\frac{3}{4}}$

4. _____

5. $\left(a^6 b\right)^{\frac{2}{3}} \left(c^2\right)^{\frac{1}{3}}$

5. _____

6. Use a calculator to evaluate $4^{\sqrt{8}}$ to the nearest ten-thousandth.

6. _____

7. Graph $y > 2^x - 1$.

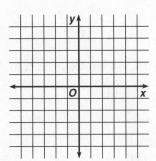

7. _____

Use a calculator to evaluate each expression to the nearest ten-thousandth.

8. $e^{2.175}$

8. _____

9. $5\sqrt[4]{e^3}$

9. _____

Given the original principal, the annual interest rate, the amount of time for each investment, and the type of compounded interest, find the amount, to the nearest dollar, at the end of the investment period.

10. $P = \$2000$, $r = 4\%$, $t = 2$ years, 6 months, compounded monthly

10. _____

11. $P = \$800$, $r = 6\%$, $t = 5$ years, compounded continuously

11. _____

12. Write $10^5 = 100{,}000$ in logarithmic form.

12. _____

13. Write $\log_{3x} 24 = 2$ in exponential form.

13. _____

14. Evaluate $4^{\log_4 12}$.

14. _____

15. Solve $\log_{10} 0.0001 = x$.

15. _____

Glencoe Division, Macmillan/McGraw-Hill

Standardized Test Questions (Chapters 1-11)

Choose the best answer. Write A, B, C, or D.

1. Which of the following functions resembles the graph of the parent function, $f(x) = x^2$, but is wider?

   A. $y = x^2 - 0.5$ **B.** $y = (2x)^2$ **C.** $y = 2x^2$ **D.** $y = 0.5x^2$

   1. _____

2. Use the sum and difference identities to find the exact value of sin 255°.

   A. $\dfrac{-\sqrt{6} - \sqrt{2}}{4}$ **B.** $\dfrac{\sqrt{2} - \sqrt{6}}{4}$ **C.** $\dfrac{\sqrt{6} + \sqrt{2}}{4}$ **D.** $\dfrac{\sqrt{6} - \sqrt{2}}{4}$

   2. _____

3. Write $\log_5 \dfrac{1}{125} = -3$ in exponential form.

   A. $\left(\dfrac{1}{\sqrt{5}}\right)^3 = 125$ **B.** $\left(\dfrac{1}{5}\right)^{-3} = \dfrac{1}{125}$ **C.** $\sqrt[3]{5} = \dfrac{1}{125}$ **D.** $5^{-3} = \dfrac{1}{125}$

   3. _____

4. Find the radius of the circle with equation $x^2 - 14x + y^2 - 6y + 54 = 0$.

   A. 4   **B.** 2   **C.** $\sqrt{2}$ **D.** $-\sqrt{2}$

   4. _____

The questions below involve comparing two quantities, one in Column A and one in Column B. In certain questions, information related to one or both quantities is centered above them. All variables used stand for real numbers.

Directions:
Write A if the quantity in column A is greater.
Write B if the quantity in column B is greater.
Write C if the two quantities are equal.
Write D if there is not enough information to determine the relationship.

Column A	Column B	
5. the distance from the point $(-3, 5)$ to		
$x + 2y = 4$	$-3x + 4y = 6$	5. _____
6. the number of complex roots of		
$8x^2 - 6x + 2 = 0$	$x^2 + 9 = 0$	6. _____
7. $|\overrightarrow{AB}|$ for		
$A(-6, -2), B(4, 5)$	$A(2, 2), B(6, 4)$	7. _____
8. $\sec \dfrac{2\pi}{3}$	$\cos -\dfrac{\pi}{6}$	8. _____
9. the slope of $\overleftrightarrow{PQ}$ for		
$P(4, 2), Q(6, -4)$	$P(-1, 1), Q(-2, 4)$	9. _____
10. $(0.25)^{\frac{3}{2}}$	$(-27)^{\frac{4}{3}}$	10. _____

Unit Test, Chapters 9-11

1. Evaluate $\log_6 \sqrt{6}$.

1. _____

2. Identify the graph of $3x^2 - 4xy + 2y^2 - 3y = 0$.

2. _____

3. Find the vertex and the axis of symmetry for the parabola with equation $2x^2 + 2x - y = -3$.

3. _____

4. Write the rectangular equation $x^2 + y^2 = 6$ in polar form.

4. _____

5. Simplify $\dfrac{1 - i}{3 + 2i}$.

5. _____

6. Graph the point with polar coordinates $\left(-2, \dfrac{3\pi}{2}\right)$.

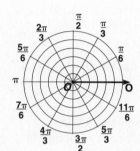

6. _____

7. Solve $6 = e^{0.2t}$. Round your answer to the nearest ten thousandth.

7. _____

8. Evaluate $(\sqrt{289})^{-3}$.

8. _____

9. Determine the eccentricity of the conic section represented by the equation $49x^2 + 36y^2 = 1764$.

9. _____

10. Use a calculator to find antilog 0.3537 to the nearest hundredth.

10. _____

11. Find the product $2(\cos 10° + i \sin 10°) \cdot 4(\cos 20° + i \sin 20°)$. Then write the result in rectangular form.

11. _____

12. Identify the classical curve that the graph of $r = 1 + \sin \theta$ represents.

12. _____

13. Write the standard form of the equation of the circle that passes through the point $(0, 4)$ and has its center at $(-3, -1)$.

13. _____

Glencoe Division, Macmillan/McGraw-Hill

~Unit Test, Chapters 9-11 (continued)

14. Graph the polar equation
$2 = r \cos(\theta + 180°)$.

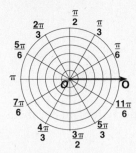

14. _____

15. Solve $6 = 15^{1-x}$ by using logarithms. Round your answer to the nearest thousandth.

15. _____

16. Find $(-64)^{\frac{1}{6}}$. Express the result in the form $a + bi$.

16. _____

17. Find the length of the tangent segment from $(7, 2)$ to the circle with equation $(x - 4)^2 + (y + 3)^2 = 25$.

17. _____

18. Write the equation of the ellipse with foci at $(0, -\sqrt{3})$ and $(0, \sqrt{3})$ and for which $2a = 4$.

18. _____

19. Find the future value to the nearest dollar of $2700 invested at 8% for 5 years in an account that compounds interest quarterly.

19. _____

20. Use a calculator to find $\ln 35.9$ to the nearest ten thousandth.

20. _____

21. Graph $y = \left(\frac{1}{4}\right)^x$.

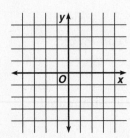

21. _____

22. Identify the conic section represented by the equation $5x^2 + 64y^2 + 30x + 128y - 211 = 0$. Write the equation in standard form and graph the equation.

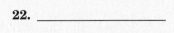

22. _____

23. Find the rectangular coordinates of the point whose polar coordinates are $(20, 140°)$. Round to the nearest hundredth.

23. _____

Unit Test, Chapters 9-11 (continued)

24. Find the equations of the horizontal lines tangent
   to the circle $x^2 + y^2 = 3$.

   24. _____

25. Evaluate $(1 + i)^{12}$ by using De Moivre's theorem.
   Express the result in rectangular form.

   25. _____

26. Express $\sqrt[3]{8a^3y^5}$ using rational exponents.

   26. _____

27. Simplify $(-1 - 2i) + (1 - 6i)$.

   27. _____

28. Graph the system of equations. Then solve.
   $x^2 + y^2 = 10$
   $xy = 3$

   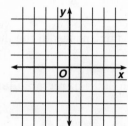

   28. _____

29. Express $8i$ in polar form.

   29. _____

30. Solve $50.8 = e^{0.21t}$. Round your answer to the nearest
   ten thousandth.

   30. _____

31. Identify the graph of the equation $4x^2 - 25y^2 = 100$. Write
   the equation of the graph for $T_{(5, -2)}$ in general form.

   31. _____

32. Write the polar equation $3 = r \cos(\theta - 315°)$ in rectangular form.

   32. _____

33. *True* or *false*: The graph of the polar equation
   $r^2 = 3 \sin 2\theta$ is a limaçon.

   33. _____

34. Use a calculator to find the common logarithm of 171.2 to
   the nearest ten thousandth.

   34. _____

35. Express $x^{\frac{2}{3}}(y^5z)^{\frac{1}{3}}$ using radicals.

   35. _____

36. Write the equation $\log_{343} 7 = \frac{1}{3}$ in exponential form.

   36. _____

37. Write the standard form of the equation of a circle that
   passes through the points (0, 8), (8, 0), and (16, 8). Then
   identify the center and the radius of the circle.

   37. _____

Glencoe Division, Macmillan/McGraw-Hill

~ Unit Test, Chapters 9-11 (continued)

38. Use a calculator to find antiln -0.049 to the nearest ten thousandth.

38. _____

39. Use a calculator to evaluate $9^{\sqrt{5}}$ to the nearest ten thousandth.

39. _____

40. Find the quotient $\dfrac{3\left(\cos \dfrac{5\pi}{12} + i \sin \dfrac{5\pi}{12}\right)}{6\left(\cos \dfrac{\pi}{12} + i \sin \dfrac{\pi}{12}\right)}$. Then write the result in rectangular form.

40. _____

41. Find the coordinates of the focus and the equation of the directrix of the parabola with equation $y^2 - 8y - 8x + 24 = 0$.

41. _____

42. Solve $9^{2x - 3} > 4$. Round your answer to the nearest hundredth.

42. _____

43. Express $2(\cos 300° + i \sin 300°)$ in rectangular form.

43. _____

44. State whether the graph of the equation $(x + 5)^2 + 0.5(y - 2)^2 = 4$ is a circle, an ellipse, a parabola, or a hyperbola.

44. _____

45. Graph the system of inequalities.
$\dfrac{(x - 3)^2}{9} + \dfrac{(y + 2)^2}{4} \le 1$

$(x - 3)^2 + (y + 2)^2 \ge 4$

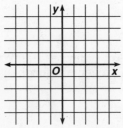

45. _____

46. Write the polar equation $\theta = 45°$ in rectangular form.

46. _____

47. Use a calculator to evaluate $e^{2.4}$ to the nearest ten thousandth.

47. _____

48. Write the equation $2^6 = 64$ in logarithmic form.

48. _____

49. Simplify $(3 + 2i)(2 - 5i)$.

49. _____

50. Find the coordinates of the center, the foci, and the vertices of the graph of the equation $\dfrac{(x + 1)^2}{2} - \dfrac{y^2}{8} = 1$.

50. _____

Chapter 12 Test, Form 1A

Write the letter for the correct answer in the blank at the right of each problem.

1. Find the eighth term of the geometric sequence $-\sqrt{7}, 7, -7\sqrt{7}, \cdots$.
   A. 2401   **B.** -2401 **C.** 16,807   **D.** $240\sqrt{7}$

   1. _____

Evaluate each limit, or state that the limit does not exist.

2. $\lim\limits_{n \to \infty} \dfrac{5n^3 + 2n^2}{11n^3 - 7n^2 + 3}$

   A. does not exist   **B.** 0   **C.** $\dfrac{11}{5}$ **D.** $\dfrac{5}{11}$

   2. _____

3. $\lim\limits_{n \to \infty} \dfrac{12n^4 - 5n}{9n^3 + n^2}$

   A. $\dfrac{4}{3}$ **B.** does not exist   **C.** 0   **D.** $\dfrac{7}{10}$

   3. _____

4. Write $0.476476476 \cdots$ as a fraction.
   A. $\dfrac{476}{999}$ **B.** $\dfrac{476}{99}$ **C.** $\dfrac{476}{9999}$ **D.** $\dfrac{999}{476}$

   4. _____

5. Express $0.9 + 0.009 + 0.00009 + \cdots$ using sigma notation.

   A. $\sum\limits_{k=1}^{\infty} (0.9)10^{k-1}$ **B.** $\sum\limits_{k=1}^{\infty} (9)10^{1-k}$

   C. $\sum\limits_{k=1}^{\infty} (9)10^{1-2k}$ **D.** $\sum\limits_{k=1}^{\infty} (0.9)10^{-k}$

   5. _____

Find the sum of each infinite series, or state that the sum does not exist.

6. $\dfrac{1}{7} + \dfrac{5}{14} + \dfrac{25}{28} + \cdots$

   A. does not exist   **B.** $\dfrac{5}{21}$ **C.** $\dfrac{5}{12}$ **D.** $\dfrac{1}{6}$

   6. _____

7. $\dfrac{11}{5} - \dfrac{33}{35} + \dfrac{99}{245} - \cdots$

   A. does not exist   **B.** $\dfrac{77}{50}$ **C.** $\dfrac{22}{7}$ **D.** $-\dfrac{77}{50}$

   7. _____

8. Find the seventh term in the sequence $-6 - \sqrt{6}, 0, 6 + \sqrt{6}, \cdots$.
   A. $42 + 7\sqrt{6}$ **B.** $24 + 4\sqrt{6}$ **C.** $36 + 6\sqrt{6}$ **D.** $30 + 5\sqrt{6}$

   8. _____

9. Find the sum of the first five terms of the series $2 + \dfrac{4}{3} + \dfrac{8}{9} + \cdots$.

   A. $\dfrac{422}{81}$ **B.** $\dfrac{81}{422}$ **C.** $\dfrac{260}{81}$ **D.** $\dfrac{130}{27}$

   9. _____

10. Find the sum of the first 20 terms of the series $11 + 3 - 5 - \cdots$.
    A. -149 **B.** 1300   **C.** -141 **D.** -1300

    10. _____

11. Find the eighth term of $(3x - y)^{11}$.
    A. $-26{,}730x^4y^7$ **B.** $26{,}730x^4y^7$ **C.** $26{,}730x^7y^4$ **D.** $-26{,}730x^7y^4$

    11. _____

12. Use the first five terms of the exponential series

$e^x = 1 + x + \dfrac{x^2}{2!} + \dfrac{x^3}{3!} + \dfrac{x^4}{4!} + \cdots$ to approximate $e^{0.7}$.

A. 1.0123   **B.** 2.0037   **C.** 2.0123   **D.** 2.1194   12. _____

13. Write $\displaystyle\sum_{k=1}^{3} 4\left(\dfrac{2}{3}\right)^k$ in expanded form and find the sum.

A. $4\left(\dfrac{2}{3}\right)^2 + \left(\dfrac{2}{3}\right)^2 + \left(\dfrac{2}{3}\right)^2; \dfrac{8}{3}$ **B.** $\left(\dfrac{4 \cdot 2}{3}\right)^2 + \left(\dfrac{4 \cdot 2}{3}\right)^3 + \left(\dfrac{4 \cdot 2}{3}\right)^4; \dfrac{4672}{9}$

C. $4\left(\dfrac{2}{3}\right) + 4\left(\dfrac{2}{3}\right)^2 + 4\left(\dfrac{2}{3}\right)^3; \dfrac{76}{9}$ **D.** $4\left(\dfrac{2}{3}\right) + 4\left(\dfrac{2}{3}\right)^2 + 4\left(\dfrac{2}{3}\right)^3; \dfrac{152}{27}$ 13. _____

14. Use the binomial theorem to expand $(x - 3\sqrt{2})^4$.
  A. $x^4 - 216\sqrt{2}x^3 + 108x^2 - 216\sqrt{2}x + 324$
  B. $-x^4 + 12\sqrt{2}x^3 - 108x^2 + 216\sqrt{2}x - 324$
  C. $x^4 + 12\sqrt{2}x^3 + 108x^2 + 216\sqrt{2}x + 324$
  D. $x^4 - 12\sqrt{2}x^3 + 108x^2 - 216\sqrt{2}x + 324$ 14. _____

15. Which of the following series is convergent?
  A. $1.5 + 3 + 4.5 + \cdots$ **B.** $1.5 - 3 + 4.5 - \cdots$
  C. $7.5 + 1.5 + 0.3 + \cdots$ **D.** $-7.5 + 7.5 - 7.5 + \cdots$ 15. _____

16. Evaluate $\dfrac{7!}{2!3!}$.

A. 840   **B.** 5040   **C.** 7   **D.** 420   16. _____

17. Express $1 + 1 \cdot 2 + 1 \cdot 2 \cdot 3 + \cdots + 1 \cdot 2 \cdot 3 \cdots 10$ using sigma notation.

A. $\displaystyle\sum_{k=1}^{10} k!$ **B.** $\displaystyle\sum_{k=0}^{10} k!$ **C.** $\displaystyle\sum_{k=1}^{10} (k-1)!$ **D.** $\displaystyle\sum_{k=0}^{10} (k-1!)$ 17. _____

18. Find $\ln(-25)$.
  A. 3.2189   **B.** $i\pi + 3.2189$ **C.** $i\pi - 3.2189$ **D.** -3.2189 18. _____

19. Write $6\sqrt{3} - 6i$ in exponential form.

A. $12e^{\frac{5\pi i}{6}}$ **B.** $12e^{\frac{11\pi i}{6}}$ **C.** $12e^{\frac{7\pi i}{6}}$ **D.** $6e^{\frac{11\pi i}{6}}$ 19. _____

20. Which step do you take first in proving a statement is true by mathematical induction?
  A. Show that the statement is true for the kth term.
  B. Show that the statement is true for the $(k + 1)$st term.
  C. Show that the statement is true for the first term.
  D. Assume that the statement is true for the kth term.   20. _____

Bonus

Evaluate $\displaystyle\sum_{k=1}^{10} (2k + 1) - \sum_{k=1}^{10} 2k$.

A. -10 **B.** -1 **C.** 10   **D.** 11   Bonus: _____

Chapter 12 Test, Form 1B

Write the letter for the correct answer in the blank at the right of each problem.

1. Find the sixth term of the geometric sequence 11, −44, 176, ⋯.
   - **A.** 11,264
   - **B.** −11,264
   - **C.** 45,056
   - **D.** −45,056

   1. _____

Evaluate each limit, or state that the limit does not exist.

2. $\lim\limits_{n \to \infty} \dfrac{4n^3 + 7n^2}{5n^3 - 7n^2 + 3}$

   - **A.** does not exist
   - **B.** 0
   - **C.** $\dfrac{4}{5}$
   - **D.** $\dfrac{5}{4}$

   2. _____

3. $\lim\limits_{n \to \infty} \dfrac{n^4 - 5n}{n^3 - 3n^2}$

   - **A.** $-\dfrac{4}{3}$
   - **B.** does not exist
   - **C.** 0
   - **D.** $\dfrac{4}{3}$

   3. _____

4. Write 0.123123 ⋯ as a fraction.
   - **A.** $\dfrac{123}{9999}$
   - **B.** $\dfrac{123}{99}$
   - **C.** $\dfrac{123}{999}$
   - **D.** $\dfrac{999}{123}$

   4. _____

5. Express 0.7 + 0.007 + 0.00007 + ⋯ using sigma notation.

   - **A.** $\sum\limits_{k=1}^{\infty} (0.7)10^{k-1}$
   - **B.** $\sum\limits_{k=1}^{\infty} (7)10^{1-2k}$
   - **C.** $\sum\limits_{k=1}^{\infty} (7)10^{1-k}$
   - **D.** $\sum\limits_{k=1}^{\infty} (0.7)10^{-k}$

   5. _____

Find the sum of each infinite series, or state that the sum does not exist.

6. $\dfrac{1}{7} - \dfrac{5}{14} + \dfrac{25}{28} - \cdots$

   - **A.** does not exist
   - **B.** $\dfrac{1}{21}$
   - **C.** $\dfrac{1}{12}$
   - **D.** $\dfrac{1}{6}$

   6. _____

7. $\dfrac{11}{5} - \dfrac{33}{55} + \dfrac{99}{605} - \cdots$

   - **A.** does not exist
   - **B.** $-\dfrac{121}{70}$
   - **C.** $\dfrac{22}{7}$
   - **D.** $\dfrac{121}{70}$

   7. _____

8. Find the eighth term in the sequence $-1 - 2\sqrt{2}$, 0, $1 + 2\sqrt{2}$, ⋯.
   - **A.** $8 + 16\sqrt{2}$
   - **B.** $5 + 10\sqrt{2}$
   - **C.** $6 - 12\sqrt{2}$
   - **D.** $6 + 12\sqrt{2}$

   8. _____

9. Find the sum of the first five terms of the series $2 - \dfrac{4}{3} + \dfrac{8}{9} - \cdots$.

   - **A.** $\dfrac{81}{55}$
   - **B.** $\dfrac{13}{27}$
   - **C.** $\dfrac{110}{81}$
   - **D.** $\dfrac{275}{81}$

   9. _____

10. Find the sum of the first 20 terms of the series $14 + 3 - 8 - \cdots$.
    - **A.** −195
    - **B.** −1810
    - **C.** 195
    - **D.** 1810

    10. _____

11. Find the third term of $(3x - y)^6$.
    - **A.** $1215x^4y^2$
    - **B.** $1215x^2y^4$
    - **C.** $-1215x^2y^4$
    - **D.** $-1215x^4y^2$

    11. _____

Glencoe Division, Macmillan/McGraw-Hill

~ Chapter 12 Test, Form 1B (continued)

12. Use the first five terms of the exponential series

$e^x = 1 + x + \dfrac{x^2}{2!} + \dfrac{x^3}{3!} + \dfrac{x^4}{4!} + \cdots$ to approximate $e^{3.9}$.

A. 39.40_4 **B.** 24.01 **C.** 32.03 **D.** 90.11 12. _____

13. Write $\displaystyle\sum_{k=2} 5\left(\dfrac{2}{3}\right)^k$ in expanded form and find the sum.

A. $5\left(\dfrac{2}{3}\right)^2 + \left(\dfrac{2}{3}\right)^2 + \left(\dfrac{2}{3}\right)^2 ; \dfrac{28}{9}$ **B.** $\left(\dfrac{5\cdot 2}{3}\right)^2 + \left(\dfrac{5\cdot 2}{3}\right)^3 + \left(\dfrac{5\cdot 2}{3}\right)^4 ; \dfrac{15{,}700}{81}$

C. $5\left(\dfrac{2}{3}\right)^1 + 5\left(\dfrac{2}{3}\right)^2 + 5\left(\dfrac{2}{3}\right)^3 ; \dfrac{190}{27}$ **D.** $5\left(\dfrac{2}{3}\right)^2 + 5\left(\dfrac{2}{3}\right)^3 + 5\left(\dfrac{2}{3}\right)^4 ; \dfrac{380}{81}$ 13. _____

14. Use the binomial theorem to expand $(x - 5\sqrt{2})^4$.
A. $x^4 + 20\sqrt{2}x^3 + 300x^2 + 1000\sqrt{2}x + 2500$
B. $x^4 - 20\sqrt{2}x^3 - 300x^2 - 1000\sqrt{2}x + 2500$
C. $x^4 - 20\sqrt{2}x^3 + 300x^2 - 1000\sqrt{2}x + 2500$
D. $x^4 - 40x^3 + 300x^2 - 2000x + 2500$ 14. _____

15. Which of the following series is convergent?
A. $7.5 + 1.5 + 0.3 + \cdots$ **B.** $1.2 - 3.6 + 10.8 - \cdots$
C. $1.2 + 3.6 + 10.8 + \cdots$ **D.** $-2.5 + 2.5 - 2.5 + \cdots$ 15. _____

16. Evaluate $\dfrac{7!}{4!3!}$.

A. 720 **B.** 35 **C.** 7 **D.** 5040 16. _____

17. Express $1 \cdot 2^2 + 2 \cdot 3^2 + 3 \cdot 4^2 + \cdots + 10 \cdot 11^2$ using sigma notation.

A. $\displaystyle\sum_{n=1}^{10} n \cdot (n+1)^2$ **B.** $\displaystyle\sum_{n=1}^{10} (n(n+1))^2$

C. $\displaystyle\sum_{n=1}^{10} (n(n+1))^n$ **D.** $\displaystyle\sum_{n=1}^{10} n \cdot (n^2+1)$ 17. _____

18. Find $\ln(-102)$.
A. 4.6250 **B.** $i\pi - 4.6250$ **C.** $i\pi + 4.6250$ **D.** -4.6250 18. _____

19. Write $15\sqrt{3} - 15i$ in exponential form.

A. $30e^{\frac{11\pi i}{6}}$ **B.** $30e^{\frac{5\pi i}{6}}$ **C.** $30e^{\frac{7\pi i}{6}}$ **D.** $15e^{\frac{11\pi i}{6}}$ 19. _____

20. What is the first step in proving $1 + 7 + 49 + \cdots + 7^{n-1} = \dfrac{1}{6}(7^n - 1)$
for whole numbers n by using mathematical induction?
A. $1 = \dfrac{1}{6}(7^1 - 1)$

B. $1 + 7 + 49 + \cdots + 7^{k-1} = \dfrac{1}{6}(7^k - 1)$
C. $1 + 7 + 49 + \cdots + 7^{k-1} + 7^k = \dfrac{1}{6}(7^k - 1)$

D. $0 = \dfrac{1}{6}(7^0 - 1)$ 20. _____

Bonus

Evaluate $\displaystyle\sum_{k=1}^{20} (3k + 1) - \sum_{k=1}^{20} 3k$.

A. -10 **B.** 20 **C.** -1 **D.** 11 Bonus: _____

Chapter 12 Test, Form 2A

Sequences and Series

1. Find the eighth term of the geometric sequence $\sqrt{3}, -3, 3\sqrt{3} \cdots$.

1. _____

Evaluate each limit, or state that the limit does not exist.

2. $\lim\limits_{n\to\infty} \dfrac{3n^3 - 2n^2}{9n^3 - 5n^2 + 4}$

3. $\lim\limits_{n\to\infty} \dfrac{13n^4 + 5n^2}{9n^3 - 5n^2 + 4}$

2. _____

3. _____

4. Write $0.373737 \cdots$ as a fraction.

4. _____

5. Express $0.2 + 0.002 + 0.00002 + \cdots$ using sigma notation.

5. _____

Find the sum of each infinite series, or state that the sum does not exist.

6. $\dfrac{2}{7} + \dfrac{6}{14} + \dfrac{18}{28} + \cdots$

6. _____

7. $\dfrac{11}{5} - \dfrac{22}{15} + \dfrac{44}{45} - \cdots$

7. _____

8. Find the sixth term in the sequence
$-3 - \sqrt{3}, -3, -3 + \sqrt{3}, \cdots$.

8. _____

9. Find the sum of the first five terms of the series
$\dfrac{2}{3} + \dfrac{4}{9} + \dfrac{8}{27} + \cdots$.

9. _____

10. Find the sum of the first 12 terms of the series
$-11 - 3 + 5 + \cdots$.

10. _____

~ Chapter 12 Test, Form 2A (continued)

11. Find the sum of the first 12 terms in the series
$-12 + 6 - 3 + \cdots$.

11. _____

12. Use the first five terms of the exponential series

$e^x = 1 + x + \dfrac{x^2}{2!} + \dfrac{x^3}{3!} + \dfrac{x^4}{4!} + \cdots$ to approximate $e^{2.7}$.

12. _____

13. Write $\displaystyle\sum_{k=0}^{2} 5\left(\dfrac{2}{7}\right)^k$ in expanded form and find the sum.

13. _____

14. Use the binomial theorem to expand $(2x - \sqrt{2})^4$.

14. _____

15. Prove $1 + 5 + 9 + \cdots + 4n - 3 = n(2n - 1)$ by using mathematical induction. Write your proof on a separate piece of paper.

Determine whether each series is convergent or divergent. Use the ratio test or the comparison test.

16. $\dfrac{2}{1^3} + \dfrac{2}{2^3} + \dfrac{2}{3^3} + \cdots$

16. _____

17. $\dfrac{2^1}{1} + \dfrac{2^2}{2} + \dfrac{2^3}{3} + \cdots$

17. _____

18. Express $\dfrac{1 \cdot 3}{2} + \dfrac{2 \cdot 4}{3} + \dfrac{3 \cdot 5}{4} + \cdots + \dfrac{9 \cdot 11}{10}$ using sigma notation.

18. _____

19. Find $\ln(-12.7)$.

19. _____

20. Write $\sqrt{3} - i$ in exponential form.

20. _____

Bonus

Find the sum of the coefficients of the expansion of $(x + y)^6$.

Bonus: _____

Chapter 12 Test, Form 2B

Sequences and Series

1. Find the sixth term of the geometric sequence
   $2\sqrt{5}, -10, 10\sqrt{5} \cdots$.

1. _____

Evaluate each limit, or state that the limit does not exist.

2. $\lim\limits_{n\to\infty} \dfrac{7n^3 + 4n^2}{7n^3 + n^2 + 3}$

3. $\lim\limits_{n\to\infty} \dfrac{-3n^4 + 7n}{9n^3 + 5n^2 - 1}$

2. _____

3. _____

4. Write $0.989898 \cdots$ as a fraction.

4. _____

5. Express $0.35 + 0.0035 + 0.000035 + \cdots$ using sigma notation.

5. _____

Find the sum of each infinite series, or state that the sum does not exist.

6. $\dfrac{3}{2} - \dfrac{3}{8} + \dfrac{3}{32} - \cdots$

6. _____

7. $\dfrac{11}{5} + \dfrac{33}{10} + \dfrac{99}{20} + \cdots$

7. _____

8. Find the tenth term in the sequence
   $-1 - \sqrt{3}, 0, 1 + \sqrt{3}, \cdots$.

8. _____

9. Find the sum of the first five terms of the series
   $\dfrac{2}{5} + \dfrac{4}{15} + \dfrac{8}{45} + \cdots$.

9. _____

10. Find the sum of the first 11 terms of the series
    $-20 + 3 + 26 + \cdots$.

10. _____

~ **Chapter 12 Test, Form 2B (continued)**

11. Find the seventh term of $(x + 4y)^9$.

11. _____

12. Use the first five terms of the exponential series
$e^x = 1 + x + \dfrac{x^2}{2!} + \dfrac{x^3}{3!} + \dfrac{x^4}{4!} + \cdots$ to approximate $e^{3.1}$.

12. _____

13. Write $\displaystyle\sum_{k=0}^{3} (k + 1)(k + 2)$ in expanded form and find the sum.

13. _____

14. Use the binomial theorem to expand $\left(2x + \sqrt{3}\right)^3$.

14. _____

15. Prove $1 + 5 + 25 + \cdots + 5^{n-1} = \dfrac{1}{4}(5^n - 1)$ by using mathematical induction. Write your proof on a separate piece of paper.

Determine whether each series is convergent or divergent. Use the ratio test or the comparison test.

16. $\dfrac{\sqrt{2}}{1^4} + \dfrac{\sqrt{2}}{2^4} + \dfrac{\sqrt{2}}{3^4} + \cdots$

16. _____

17. $\dfrac{3^1}{1} + \dfrac{3^2}{2} + \dfrac{3^3}{3} + \cdots$

17. _____

18. Express $\dfrac{1 \cdot 0}{2} + \dfrac{2 \cdot 1}{3} + \dfrac{3 \cdot 2}{4} + \cdots + \dfrac{10 \cdot 9}{11}$ using sigma notation.

18. _____

19. Find $\ln(-13.4)$.

19. _____

20. Write $4 - 4i$ in exponential form.

20. _____

Bonus

Find the sum of the coefficients of the expansion of $(x + y)^7$.

Bonus: _____

Chapter 12, Quiz A (Lessons 12-1 through 12-2)

1. Find the seventeenth term in the arithmetic sequence
   for which $a = 4.5$ and $d = 0.2$.

   1. _____

2. Form a geometric sequence that has one geometric mean between
   $\frac{1}{3}$ and $\frac{5}{27}$.

   2. _____

3. Find the sum of the first six terms of the geometric
   sequence $1, 1.5, 2.25 \cdots$.

   3. _____

4. Find the fifth term of the geometric sequence for which
   $a_3 = \sqrt{5}$ and $r = 3$.

   4. _____

5. Find the sum of the first eleven terms of the arithmetic
   sequence $\sqrt{3} + \sqrt{5}, 0, -\sqrt{3} - \sqrt{5}, \cdots$.

   5. _____

Chapter 12, Quiz B (Lessons 12-3 through 12-4)

Evaluate each limit, or state that the limit does not exist.

1. $\lim\limits_{n \to \infty} \dfrac{3n^4}{2n^2 + 5}$

   2. $\lim\limits_{n \to \infty} \dfrac{(2n + 1)(n - 2)}{2n^2}$

   1. _____

   2. _____

Find the sum of each infinite series, or state that the sum does not exist.

3. $-\dfrac{5}{3} + 1 - \dfrac{3}{5} + \cdots$

   3. _____

4. $0.002 + 0.02 + 0.2 + \cdots$

   4. _____

5. Determine whether $\dfrac{2}{3 \cdot 2} + \dfrac{3}{4 \cdot 3} + \dfrac{4}{5 \cdot 4} + \cdots$ is
   convergent or divergent. Use the ratio test or the
   comparison test.

   5. _____

Chapter 12, Quiz C (Lessons 12-5 through 12-6)

1. Write $\displaystyle\sum_{k=2}^{4}\left(2^{k-1}+\frac{1}{2}\right)$ in expanded form and find the sum.

1. _____

2. Use the binomial theorem to expand $(3a - d)^4$.

2. _____

3. Find the sixth term in the expansion of $(3a + \sqrt{2})^{12}$.

3. _____

4. Write $\dfrac{16}{81} + \dfrac{8}{27} + \dfrac{4}{9} + \cdots$ using sigma notation.

4. _____

5. Evaluate $\dfrac{7!}{3!4!}$.

5. _____

Chapter 12, Quiz D (Lessons 12-7 through 12-8)

1. Use the first five terms of the exponential series
$e^x = 1 + x + \dfrac{x^2}{2!} + \dfrac{x^3}{3!} + \dfrac{x^4}{4!} + \cdots$ to approximate $e^{4.1}$.

1. _____

2. Use mathematical induction to prove that
$1 + 3 + 5 + \cdots + 2n - 1 = n^2$. Write your proof on a
separate piece of paper.

2. _____

3. Find $\ln(-0.3675)$.

3. _____

4. Write $2\left(\cos\dfrac{2\pi}{3} + i\sin\dfrac{2\pi}{3}\right)$ in exponential form.

4. _____

5. Use mathematical induction to prove that
$-\dfrac{1}{3} - \dfrac{1}{9} - \dfrac{1}{27} - \cdots - \dfrac{1}{3^n} = \dfrac{1}{2}\left(\dfrac{1}{3^n} - 1\right)$. Write your
proof on a separate piece of paper.

Chapter 12 Mid-Chapter Test (Lessons 12-1 through 12-4)

1. Find the seventh term of the sequence
$$\frac{\sqrt{2}}{2}, \frac{1}{2}, \frac{\sqrt{2}}{4}, \cdots.$$

1. _____

Evaluate each limit, or state that the limit does not exist.

2. $\displaystyle\lim_{n\to\infty} \frac{(3n-5)(3n+5)}{n^2}$

3. $\displaystyle\lim_{n\to\infty} \frac{2n+(-1)n}{n^3}$

2. _____

3. _____

4. Find the sum of the first six terms of the series
$$\frac{5}{3} - \frac{25}{9} + \frac{125}{27} - \cdots.$$

4. _____

5. Use the ratio test to determine whether the series
$$5 + \frac{5^2}{1\cdot2} + \frac{5^3}{1\cdot2\cdot3} + \cdots \text{ is convergent or divergent.}$$

5. _____

6. Find the sum of the first one hundred terms of the series
$10 + 20 + 30 + \cdots.$

6. _____

7. Use the comparison test to determine whether the series
$$\frac{2^2}{2} + \frac{2^3}{3} + \frac{2^4}{4} + \cdots \text{ is convergent or divergent.}$$

7. _____

8. Find the twentieth term in the sequence
$-3 - \sqrt{11}, -3 + \sqrt{11}, -3 + 3\sqrt{11}, \cdots.$

8. _____

Find the sum of each infinite series, or state that the sum does not exist.

9. $12 + 2 + \dfrac{1}{3} + \cdots$

9. _____

10. $\dfrac{3}{7} + \dfrac{9}{7} + \dfrac{27}{7} + \cdots$

10. _____

~~ Standardized Test Questions (Chapters 1-12)

The questions on this page involve comparing two quantities, one in Column A and one in Column B. In certain questions, information related to one or both quantities is centered above them. All variables stand for real numbers.

Directions:
Write A if the quantity in Column A is greater.
Write B if the quantity in Column B is greater.
Write C if the quantities are equal.
Write D if there is not enough information to determine the relationship.

Column A	Column B	
1. $f(x) = x^5 + 5x^3 - 4x$ $\qquad$ $f(x)$	$-f(-x)$	**1.** _____
2. $a > b > 0$ the slope of $ax + by = c$	$-\dfrac{b}{a}$	**2.** _____
3. $x^4 + 4x^3 + 3x^2 - 4x - 4$	$(x + 1)(x - 1)(x + 2)^2$	**3.** _____
4. $\sin\left(\operatorname{Sin}^{-1}\dfrac{1}{2}\right)$	$\dfrac{1}{2}$	**4.** _____
5. $a < b < c < d$ the greatest root of $P(x) = (x - a)(x - b)(x - c)$	d	**5.** _____
6. $a < b$ area inside graph of $\dfrac{x^2}{a^2} + \dfrac{y^2}{b^2} = 1$	area inside graph of $\dfrac{x^2}{a^2} + \dfrac{y^2}{a^2} = 1$	**6.** _____
7. $\lvert 3a - 2bi \rvert$	$\sqrt{9a^2 - 4b^2}$	**7.** _____
8. n is an integer. $\cos\dfrac{n\pi}{2}$	$\sin\dfrac{n\pi}{2}$	**8.** _____
9. $x > 0$ $\dfrac{4x^2 + 3x - 1}{x}$	$4x + 3$	**9.** _____
10. $\vec{u}$ and $\vec{v}$ are nonzero vectors. $2\vec{u} + 3\vec{v}$	$3\vec{u} + 2\vec{v}$	**10.** _____
11. the frequency of $y = \cos(2x - \pi)$	the frequency of $y = \tan(3x - \pi)$	**11.** _____
12. n is a positive integer. $1 + 2 + 2^2 + \cdots + 2^{n-1}$	2^n	**12.** _____
13. $a > b$ and $c \neq 1$ ac^x	bc^x	**13.** _____
14. $a > b > 0$ $\begin{vmatrix} a & b \\ b & a \end{vmatrix}$	$\begin{vmatrix} b & a \\ a & b \end{vmatrix}$	**14.** _____

Chapter 13 Test, Form 1A

Write the letter for the correct answer in the blank at the right of each problem.

1. Find the first three iterates of the function $f(x) = x^2 + 1$ using $x_0 = 2$.
   A. 5, 10, 17   **B.** 5, 26, 677   **C.** 2, 5, 10   **D.** 2, 5, 26

   1. _____

2. Find the ninth iterate to the nearest ten thousandth for
   $f(x) = 0.5(1 + x)$ and $x_0 = 0.1$.
   A. 0.9995   **B.** 1.000   **C.** 0.9991   **D.** 0.9982

   2. _____

3. Which graph shows the first three iterates of the function
   $f(x) = 0.5x$ for the initial value −2?

   A. 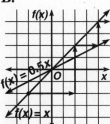 **B.** **C.** 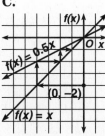 **D.**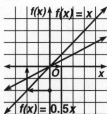

   3. _____

4. Describe the path that the iteration of the function $f(x) = 3x - 5$ forms.
   A. spiral in   **B.** staircase in
   C. spiral out   **D.** staircase out

   4. _____

5. Find the fixed point for the function $f(x) = 1.5x + 2$.
   A. (4, 4)   **B.** (1, 1)   **C.** (−4, −4)   **D.** (−1, −1)

   5. _____

6. For which function is the x-coordinate of the fixed point a repeller?
   A. $f(x) = -0.4x - 1$ **B.** $f(x) = 0.4x - 1$
   C. $f(x) = 0.4x + 1$ **D.** $f(x) = 4x + 1$

   6. _____

7. Find the coordinates of the vertex of the graph of the logistic function
   $f(x) = 2.8x(1 - x)$.
   A. (0, 0.7)   **B.** (0.5, 0.7)

   C. (0.5, 0.07)   **D.** $\left(\dfrac{1}{2}, \dfrac{1}{7}\right)$

   7. _____

8. Find the coordinates of the fixed points of the logistic function
   $f(x) = 0.6x(1 - x)$.

   A. (0, 0) and $\left(-\dfrac{2}{3}, -\dfrac{2}{3}\right)$ **B.** (0, 0) and $\left(\dfrac{3}{2}, \dfrac{3}{2}\right)$

   C. (0, 0) and $\left(\dfrac{2}{3}, \dfrac{2}{3}\right)$ **D.** (0, 0) and $\left(-\dfrac{3}{2}, -\dfrac{3}{2}\right)$

   8. _____

~~~ **Chapter 13 Test, Form 1A (continued)**

9. Which iterate pattern appears to be chaotic?
   A. 1.3, 2.5, 1.3, 2.5,...
   B. 1.39, 1.387, 1.380,...
   C. 1.325, 1.38, 1.325, 1.38,...
   D. 1.3, 6.7, 0.25, 10.2,...

   9. _____

10. Find the first two iterates of the function $f(z) = 2z - i$ if the
    initial point is $5 + 3i$.
    A. $2 - i, 4 - i$ **B.** $2 - i, 4 - 3i$
    C. $10 + 5i, 20 + 9i$ **D.** $10 + 4i, 20 + 7i$

    10. _____

11. Find the first three iterates of the function $f(z) = z^2 + c$
    for $c = 2 - i$ and $z_0 = 1 + i$.
    A. $3, 11 - i, 13 - 2i$ **B.** $2 + i, 5 + 3i, 18 + 29i$
    C. $i, 1 - i, 1 + i$ **D.** $-i, -1 + i, i$

    11. _____

12. Which point is in the prisoner set for the function $f(z) = z^2$?
    A. $0.2 - 0.2i$ **B.** $1 + 2i$
    C. $0.25 - 0.5\sqrt{15}i$ **D.** $-1 + 0.5i$

    12. _____

13. For which function is the Julia set connected?
    A. $f(z) = z^2 + (1 - i)$ **B.** $f(z) = z^2 + (1 + 0i)$
    C. $f(z) = z^2 + (-0.5 + 0.3i)$ **D.** $f(z) = z^2 + (2 - 0.5i)$

    13. _____

14. Determine which number is outside the Mandelbrot set.
    A. $c = 0.2 + 0.3i$ **B.** $c = 0.2 + 0.2i$
    C. $c = -0.2 - 1.4i$ **D.** $c = -0.3 - 0.2i$

    14. _____

Color a point:	**If its iterations:**
black	**fail to escape to infinity.**
dark blue	**exceed 80 in 1 to 3 iterations.**
orange	**exceed 80 in 4 to 6 iterations.**
light blue	**exceed 80 in 7 to 9 iterations.**

15. Use the color scheme above to assign a color to the point $0.5 + 0.5i$.
    A. black   **B.** dark blue   **C.** orange   **D.** light blue

    15. _____

Bonus

Which statement is true of a fixed point?
   A. A fixed point escapes to infinity.
   B. A fixed point is in the prisoner set.
   C. A fixed point is in the escape set.
   D. A fixed point is in the Julia set.

   Bonus: _____

Chapter 13 Test, Form 1B

Write the letter for the correct answer in the blank at the right of each problem.

1. Which set of numbers is the first three iterates
   of the function $f(x) = 2x$ using $x_0 = -3$?
   A. $-6, -12, -24$ **B.** $-6, 12, -24$
   C. $-6, -4, -2$ **D.** $0, 2, 4$

   1. _____

2. For which function is the tenth iterate approximately -9.9840 if $x_0 = -0.2$?
   A. $f(x) = 1.3(x - 1)$ **B.** $f(x) = 1.3(x + 1)$
   C. $f(x) = 1.3(1 - x)$ **D.** $f(x) = 1.3(-x)$

   2. _____

3. Which graph shows the first three iterates of the function
   $f(x) = -2x$ for the initial value 2?

   A.   **B.**   **C.**   **D.**

   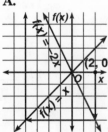 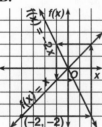 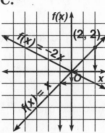 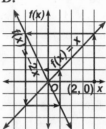

   3. _____

4. For which function does the path that the iteration forms staircase in?
   A. $f(x) = 0.5x + 2$ **B.** $f(x) = -0.5x + 2$
   C. $f(x) = 1.5x + 2$ **D.** $f(x) = -1.5x + 2$

   4. _____

5. Find the fixed point for the function $f(x) = -0.75x - 7$.

   A. $(4, 4)$ **B.** $(-4, -4)$ **C.** $\left(\dfrac{28}{3}, \dfrac{28}{3}\right)$ **D.** $\left(-\dfrac{28}{3}, -\dfrac{28}{3}\right)$

   5. _____

6. For which function is the x-coordinate of the fixed point an attractor?
   A. $f(x) = 1.7x + 3$ **B.** $f(x) = -0.7x + 3$
   C. $f(x) = 1.7x - 3$ **D.** $f(x) = -1.7x + 3$

   6. _____

7. Find the coordinates of the vertex of the graph of the
   logistic function $f(x) = 3.2x(1 - x)$.
   A. $(0.5, 0.8)$ **B.** $(0, 0.8)$

   C. $\left(\dfrac{1}{2}, \dfrac{1}{8}\right)$ **D.** $\left(\dfrac{1}{8}, \dfrac{1}{2}\right)$

   7. _____

8. Find the coordinates of the fixed points of the function $f(x) = 4x(1 - x)$.

   A. $(0, 0), \left(-\dfrac{3}{4}, -\dfrac{3}{4}\right)$ **B.** $\left(0, \dfrac{3}{4}\right), \left(0, -\dfrac{3}{4}\right)$

   C. $(0, 0), \left(\dfrac{4}{3}, \dfrac{4}{3}\right)$ **D.** $(0, 0), \left(\dfrac{3}{4}, \dfrac{3}{4}\right)$

   8. _____

Chapter 13 Test, Form 1B (continued)

9. Which iterate pattern suggests a period–2 attractor?
   A. 0.334, 0.145, 0.27, 0.334,...
   B. 0.334, 0.145, 0.334, 0.145,...
   C. 0.334, 0.145, 0.334, 0.27,...
   D. 0.334, 0.334, 0.145, 0.145,...

9. _____

10. Given the function $f(z) = 3z + i$ and $z_0 = 1 - 2i$,
    find the first three iterates of $f(z)$.
    A. $3 - 3i, 9 - 8i, 27 - 23i$ **B.** $9, 27 + i, 81 + 4i$
    C. $3 - 5i, 9 - 14i, 27 - 41i$ **D.** $3 + i, 6 + i, 9 + i$

10. _____

11. Find the next two iterates of the function
    $f(z) = z^2 + c$ for $c = 1$ and $z_0 = 1 - 2i$.
    A. $-1 + i, 1$ **B.** $-1, 1$
    C. $6 - 4i, 53 - 48i$ **D.** $-2 - 4i, -11 + 16i$

11. _____

12. Which point is in the escape set for the function $f(z) = z^2$?
    A. $0.3 - 0.3i$ **B.** $0.25 - 0.25\sqrt{15}i$
    C. $0.5 - 0.5\sqrt{3}i$ **D.** $2 + 3i$

12. _____

13. For which function is the Julia set disconnected?
    A. $f(z) = z^2 + (-0.5 + 0.3i)$
    B. $f(z) = z^2 + (2 - i)$
    C. $f(z) = z^2 + (-0.3 + 0.25i)$
    D. $f(z) = z^2 + (-0.4 - 0.1i)$

13. _____

14. Determine which number is inside the Mandelbrot set.
    A. $c = -0.5 + 0.75i$ **B.** $c = 0.2 + 0.1i$
    C. $c = 0.4 + 0.8i$ **D.** $c = -0.6 + 0.9i$

14. _____

Color a point:	If its iterations:
black	fail to escape to infinity.
dark blue	exceed 80 in 1 to 3 iterations.
orange	exceed 80 in 4 to 6 iterations.
light blue	exceed 80 in 7 to 9 iterations.

15. Using the color scheme above, which point would be assigned the color black?
    A. $1.2 - 0.3i$ **B.** $0.2 - 1.4i$
    C. $0.4 + 0.2i$ **D.** $0.3 - 0.8i$

15. _____

Bonus

A certain function of the form $f(z) = z^2 + c$ has a connected
prisoner set. Which color would you assign to the
point c?
   A. dark blue   **B.** light blue   **C.** black   **D.** orange

Bonus: _____

Chapter 13 Test, Form 2A

1. Find the first three iterates of the function
   $f(x) = -x^2$ using $x_0 = -\frac{1}{3}$.

   1. _____

2. Determine, to the nearest hundredth,
   the tenth iterate for $f(x) = 1.2x(x - 1)$ using $x_0 = 0.9$.

   2. _____

Graph each function and the function f(x) = x on the same set of axes. Then perform graphical iteration for the first four iterates for the given value of x_0.

3. $f(x) = -1.5x - 2$;
   $x_0 = 1$

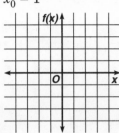

4. $f(x) = 2x$;
   $x_0 = 0.5$

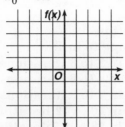

   3. _____

   4. _____

5. Determine the slope of the linear function $f(x) = 0.3x - 7$ and
   the type of path that the iteration forms.

   5. _____

6. Find the coordinates of the fixed point for the
   function $f(x) = -1.2x - 11$.

   6. _____

Determine whether the x-coordinate of the fixed point for each function is an attractor or a repeller.

7. $f(x) = -0.2x + 5$

8. $f(x) = 0.2x - 1$

   7. _____

   8. _____

9. Find the coordinates of the vertex of the graph of the
   logistic function $f(x) = 1.2x(1 - x)$.

   9. _____

10. One of the two fixed points for the function $f(x) = 0.5x(1 - x)$ is
    at $(0, 0)$. Find the other fixed point.

    10. _____

11. The iterates of a given function form the pattern
    1.215, 3.177, 1.215, 3.177, ... Describe the long-term iterative
    behavior of the function. Write *period-n attractor, fixed-point
    attractor,* or *chaos.*

    11. _____

12. Let $f(z) = 3z + 1$ and $z_0 = 2 + i$. Determine
    $z_1, z_2,$ and z_3.

    12. _____

Glencoe Division, Macmillan/McGraw-Hill

~~ **Chapter 13 Test, Form 2A (continued)**

13. Determine the next three iterates of the function $f(z) = z^2 + c$ for
$c = 1 + i$ and $z_0 = 1$.

13. _____

14. Determine whether the point $4 + 2i$ is in the prisoner set or the
escape set for the function $f(z) = z^2 + (-5 + 0i)$.

14. _____

15. Determine whether the Julia set for the function
$f(z) = z^2 + (-4 + 0i)$ is connected or disconnected.

15. _____

16. Is the point $-0.3 + 0.7i$ inside or ouside the Mandelbrot set?

16. _____

Color a point:	If its iterations:
black	fail to escape to infinity.
dark blue	exceed 80 in 1 to 3 iterations.
orange	exceed 80 in 4 to 6 iterations.
light blue	exceed 80 in 7 to 9 iterations.
red	exceed 80 in 10 to 12 iterations.
yellow	exceed 80 in 13 to 15 iterations.
purple	exceed 80 in 16 or more iterations.

*Use the color scheme above to assign a color to
each point.*

17. $c = -0.3 + 0.7i$

17. _____

18. $c = 0.6 + 0.5i$

18. _____

19. $c = -0.5 + i$

19. _____

20. The balance of a bank account using simple interest compounded
at the end of a period of time can be found by iterating the function
$P_{n+1} = P_n + rP_n$, where P_n is the principal after n periods of time
and r is the interest rate for a period of time. Find the balance of
an account after each of the first three years if the initial balance
is $4500 and the account has an annual yield of 5.8%.

20. _____

Bonus

Find one point in the prisoner set of the function
$f(z) = z^2 + (-0.4 + 0i)$.

Bonus: _____

Chapter 13 Test, Form 2B

1. For $f(x) = x(2 - x)$ and $x_0 = -1$, determine the first three iterates of
   the function.

   1. _____

2. If $x_0 = -0.1$ and $f(x) = -1.5(x + 1)$, find the tenth iterate to the
   nearest hundredth.

   2. _____

**Graph each function and the function $f(x) = x$ on the
same set of axes. Then perform graphical iteration for
the first four iterates for each value of x_0.**

3. $f(x) = 0.2x + 1$;
   $x_0 = -1$

4. $f(x) = 5 - x$;
   $x_0 = 1$

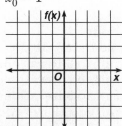

   3. _____

   4. _____

5. Determine the slope of the linear function $f(x) = -4x + 3$ and
   the type of path that the iteration forms.

   5. _____

6. Determine the coordinates of the fixed point for the function
   $f(x) = -3x + 2$.

   6. _____

**Determine whether the x-coordinate of the fixed point for
each function is an attractor or a repeller.**

7. $f(x) = -3x + 2$

8. $f(x) = -2x$

   7. _____

   8. _____

9. Find the coordinates of the vertex of the graph of the
   logistic function $f(x) = 0.4x(1 - x)$.

   9. _____

10. Determine the nonzero fixed point for the function
    $f(x) = 1.2x(1 - x)$.

    10. _____

11. Describe the long-term iterative behavior of a function whose
    iterates form the pattern 0.117, 0.235, 0.124, 0.117, 0.235, 0.124...
    Write *period-n attractor, fixed-point attractor,* or *chaos.*

    11. _____

12. Find the first three iterates of the function
    $f(z) = 0.5z$ if $x_0 = 4 - 2i$.

    12. _____

Glencoe Division, Macmillan/McGraw-Hill

~ Chapter 13 Test, Form 2B (continued)

13. Consider the function $f(z) = z^2 + c$. Determine the next
three iterates of the function if $z_0 = 0$ and $c = i$.

13. _____

14. Is the point $2 + i$ in the prisoner set or the escape set for
the function $f(z) = z^2 + (-4 + 0i)$?

14. _____

15. Is the Julia set for the function $f(z) = z^2 + (-0.1 + 0.5i)$ connected or
disconnected?

15. _____

16. Is the point $1 - i$ inside or outside the Mandelbrot set?

16. _____

Color a point:	If its iterations:
black	fail to escape to infinity.
dark blue	exceed 80 in 1 to 3 iterations.
orange	exceed 80 in 4 to 6 iterations.
light blue	exceed 80 in 7 to 9 iterations.
red	exceed 80 in 10 to 12 iterations.
yellow	exceed 80 in 13 to 15 iterations.
purple	exceed 80 in 16 or more iterations.

*Use the color scheme above to assign a color to
each point.*

17. $c = 1 - i$

17. _____

18. $c = 0.5 + 0.7i$

18. _____

19. $c = 0.5 - 0.4i$

19. _____

20. The balance of a bank account using simple interest compounded
at the end of a period of time can be found by iterating the
function $P_{n+1} = P_n + rP_n$, where P_n is the principal after n
periods of time and r is the interest rate for a period of time.
Find the balance of the account after each of the first three years
if the initial balance is $325 and the account has an annual yield
of 6.5%.

20. _____

Bonus

Find the coordinates of one point in the escape set of the
function $f(z) = z^2 + (0.5 + 0i)$

Bonus: _____

~Chapter 13, Quiz A (Lessons 13-1 through 13-2)

Find the first two iterates of each function using the initial value. If necessary, round your answers to the nearest tenth.

1. $f(x) = x^3 - 1$;
   $x_0 = -2.1$

2. $f(x) = 3.5(1 - x)$;
   $x_0 = 0.2$

1. _____

2. _____

3. Graph the function $f(x) = -0.25x$ and the function $f(x) = x$ on the same set of axes. Then perform graphical iteration for $x_0 = 2$. State the type of path the iteration forms.

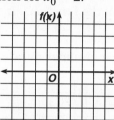

3. _____

4. Describe the iteration path of a linear staircase function whose slope is greater than 1.

4. _____

5. Is the x-coordinate of the fixed point for the function $f(x) = -2x + 1$ a repeller or an attractor?

5. _____

Chapter 13, Quiz B (Lesson 13-3)

Find the coordinates of the fixed points for each function.

1. $f(x) = 2.4x(1 - x)$

2. $f(x) = 1.8x(1 - x)$

1. _____

2. _____

3. Find the coordinates of the vertex of the graph of the logistic function $f(x) = -0.3x(1 - x)$.

3. _____

Use the program below to determine the long-term iterative behavior of the function $f(x) = ax(1 - x)$ for each value of a.

4. _____

4. $a = 3.14$

5. $a = 2.25$

5. _____

```
Line 1: ClrDraw        Line 14: DrawF X         Line 27: Lbl 3
Line 2: Fix 3          Line 15: 0 → M           Line 28: AI − AII → J
Line 3: 0 → Xmin       Line 16: 100 → C         Line 29: Line(I,I,I,J)
Line 4: 1 → Xmax       Line 17: If C = 0        Line 30: Line(I,J,J,J)
Line 5: 0.1 → Xscl     Line 18: Goto 2          Line 31: Pause
Line 6: 0 → Ymin       Line 19: Lbl 1           Line 32: Disp J
Line 7: 1 → Ymax       Line 20: AI − AII → I     Line 33: Pause
Line 8: 0.1 → Yscl     Line 21: M + 1 → M       Line 34: J → I
Line 9: Disp "A ="     Line 22: If M < C        Line 35: M + 1 → M
Line 10: Input A       Line 23: Goto 1          Line 36: If M < C + 15
Line 11: Disp "I ="    Line 24: Goto 3          Line 37: Goto 3
Line 12: Input I       Line 25: Lbl 2           Line 38: End
Line 13: DrawF AX(1 − X)  Line 26: Line(I,0,I,I)
```

Chapter 13, Quiz C (Lesson 13-4)

1. Find the first three iterates of the function
   $f(z) = 2z + i$ for $z_0 = 3 - i$.

   1. _____

2. Find the first three iterates of the function
   $f(z) = z^2 + c$ for $c = -1 + 2i$ and $z_0 = 0 + 0i$.

   2. _____

Let f(z) = z + (1 − 2i) and z₀ = 4 − i.

3. Find the first four iterates of the function.

   3. _____

4. Plot the orbit of the initial point under iteration of $f(z)$ for the
   first six iterations.

   4. _____

Chapter 13, Quiz D (Lessons 13-5 through 13-6)

1. Determine whether the point $c = 1 + 0.5i$ is in the prisoner set or
   the escape set for the function $f(z) = z^2 + (-1 + 0i)$.

   1. _____

Let c = −0.5 + i.

2. Is the Julia set associated with point c connected or disconnected?

   2. _____

3. Is point c inside or outside the Mandelbrot Set?

   3. _____

4. Is c in the prisoner set?

   4. _____

5. What happens to the iterates of point c between
   4 and 6 iterations?

   5. _____

Chapter 13 Mid-Chapter Test (Lessons 13-1 through 13-3)

Find the first three iterates of each function using the initial value. If necessary, round your answers to the nearest hundredth.

1. $f(x) = x^2$;
   $x_0 = 2$

2. $f(x) = 1.2(1 - x)$;
   $x_0 = 0.3$

1. _____

2. _____

Graph each function and the function $f(x) = x$ on the same set of axes. Then perform graphical iteration for $x_0 = -1$. State the slope of the linear function and the type of path that the iteration forms.

3. $f(x) = 2x + 5$

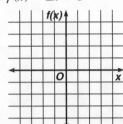

4. $f(x) = -0.5x$

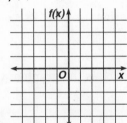

3. _____

4. _____

Find the nonzero fixed point for each function. Is the x-coordinate of the fixed point a repeller or an attractor?

5. $f(x) = -3.2x + 7$

6. $f(x) = 1.5x(1 - x)$

5. _____

6. _____

Find the coordinates of the vertex of the graph of each logistic function.

7. $f(x) = 1.4x(1 - x)$

8. $f(x) = 0.8x(1 - x)$

7. _____

8. _____

Use the program below to determine the long-term iterative behavior of the function $f(x) = ax(1 - x)$ for each value of a.

9. $a = 1.2$

10. $a = 3.3$

9. _____

10. _____

```
Line 1: ClrDraw          Line 14: DrawF X          Line 27: Lbl 3
Line 2: Fix 3            Line 15: 0 → M            Line 28: AI − AII → J
Line 3: 0 → Xmin        Line 16: 100 → C          Line 29: Line(I,I,I,J)
Line 4: 1 → Xmax        Line 17: If C = 0         Line 30: Line(I,J,J,J)
Line 5: 0.1 → Xscl      Line 18: Goto 2           Line 31: Pause
Line 6: 0 → Ymin        Line 19: Lbl 1            Line 32: Disp J
Line 7: 1 → Ymax        Line 20: AI − AII → I     Line 33: Pause
Line 8: 0.1 → Yscl      Line 21: M + 1 → M        Line 34: J → I
Line 9: Disp "A ="      Line 22: If M < C         Line 35: M + 1 → M
Line 10: Input A        Line 23: Goto 1           Line 36: If M < C + 15
Line 11: Disp "I ="     Line 24: Goto 3           Line 37: Goto 3
Line 12: Input I        Line 25: Lbl 2            Line 38: End
Line 13: DrawF AX(1 − X)  Line 26: Line(I,0,I,I)
```

Standardized Test Questions (Chapters 1-13)

Choose the best answer. Write A, B, C, or D.

1. Change $\dfrac{-5\pi}{6}$ to degree measure.

   A. $-200°$ **B.** $-150°$ **C.** $75°$ **D.** $105°$ 1. _____

2. Write the equation $5x - 2y = 10$ in parametric form.

   A. $x = t, 2y = -5t + 10$ **B.** $x = t, 2y = 5t + 10$

   C. $x = t, y = \dfrac{5}{2}t - 5$ **D.** $x = t, y = \dfrac{5}{2}t + 5$ 2. _____

3. Find the values of θ for which $\csc \theta = -1$ if k is any integer.

   A. $270° + 360k°$ **B.** $180° + 360k°$

   C. $270° + 180k°$ **D.** $315° + 180k°$ 3. _____

4. Which number is not a possible rational zero of $2x^3 - 5x^2 - 9x + 12 = 0$?

   A. 6   **B.** -3 **C.** $\dfrac{1}{3}$ **D.** $\dfrac{-3}{2}$ 4. _____

5. Using the parent graph $y = x^3$, which is the graph of $y = (x - 2)^3$?

   A.   **B.**   **C.**   **D.**   5. _____

 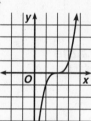 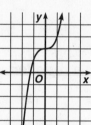 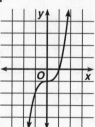

The questions below involve comparing two quantities, one in Column A and one in Column B. In certain questions, information related to one or both quantities is centered above them. All variables represent real numbers.

Directions:
Write A if the quantity in column A is greater.
Write B if the quantity in column B is greater.
Write C if the two quantities are equal.
Write D if there is not enough information to determine the relationship.

Column A	Column B	
6. the number of solutions of $\sin 2\alpha = -2$	the number of solutions of $\cos \alpha = 0.5$	6. _____
7. the second iterate of $f(z) = 2z + i$	the second iterate of $f(z) = -3z + 2i$	7. _____
8. the value of x for $9^{-x} = \dfrac{1}{27}$	the value of x for $2^{x+2} = 32$	8. _____
9. the positive x-intercept of the graph of $x^2 + 25y^2 = 100$	the positive x-intercept of the graph of $6x^2 + 4y^2 = 36$	9. _____

~ Chapter 14 Test, Form 1A

Write the letter for the correct answer in the blank at the right of each problem.

1. Find the value of $P(9, 4)$.
   A. 15,120   B. 5280   C. 3024   D. 120   1. _____

2. There are 6 finalists in the 100-meter hurdles. In how many ways can gold, silver, and bronze metals be awarded?
   A. 720   B. 120   C. 360   D. 90   2. _____

3. How many ways can the letters in the word *freeform* be arranged?
   A. 40,320   B. 5040   C. 10,080   D. 6720   3. _____

4. How many ways can 8 pins be arranged on a circular hat band?
   A. 5040   B. 40,320   C. 720   D. 2540   4. _____

5. How many ways can 5 people be seated around a circular table with 6 chairs if the chair by the door must be empty?
   A. 720   B. 360   C. 240   D. 120   5. _____

6. Three men and 3 women are to be selected to represent a group of 10 men and 11 women. How many ways can the representatives be selected?
   A. 1710   B. 59,400   C. 19,800   D. 712,800   6. _____

7. Evaluate the expression $C(5, 2) \cdot C(7, 3)$.
   A. 4200   B. 350   C. 210   D. 2100   7. _____

8. The probability that Bob's name will be drawn to win a door prize is 1 in 75. What are the odds that Bob's name will be drawn?
   A. $\frac{1}{74}$ B. $\frac{1}{75}$ C. $\frac{1}{76}$ D. $\frac{7}{6}$ 8. _____

9. Mr. Lim has 6 striped ties, 8 patterned ties, and 5 solid colored ties. If he selects 2 ties at random, what is the probability that both will be striped?
   A. $\frac{5}{57}$ B. $\frac{1}{8}$ C. $\frac{15}{128}$ D. $\frac{9}{64}$ 9. _____

10. If 3 cards are dealt from a standard deck of cards, what are the odds that all of the cards will be face cards?
    A. $\frac{11}{1094}$ B. $\frac{1}{18}$ C. $\frac{27}{2197}$ D. $\frac{2197}{132,600}$ 10. _____

11. A red die and a green die are tossed. What is the probability that both dice will show 4?
    A. $\frac{1}{3}$ B. $\frac{1}{18}$ C. $\frac{1}{6}$ D. $\frac{1}{36}$ 11. _____

Chapter 14 Test, Form 1A (continued)

12. There are 5 pens, 6 pencils, and 4 crayons in a jar. Robin selects three without replacement. What is the probability that she selects one of each?

    A. $\frac{1}{8}$ B. $\frac{24}{91}$ C. $\frac{24}{675}$ D. $\frac{91}{2730}$

    12. _____

13. Table-tennis balls numbered 1 to 20 are placed in a box. Three balls are drawn at random. What is the probability of drawing 3 numbers less than 10 if no replacement occurs?

    A. $\frac{7}{95}$ B. $\frac{729}{8000}$ C. $\frac{81}{760}$ D. $\frac{63}{1000}$

    13. _____

14. A card is drawn from a standard deck of cards. What is the probability that the card will be either a diamond or a face card?

    A. $\frac{1}{16}$ B. $\frac{25}{52}$ C. $\frac{11}{26}$ D. $\frac{3}{8}$

    14. _____

15. There are 12 seniors and 10 juniors on the prom committee. If 2 people are selected at random to be in charge of the decorations, what is the probability that at least one of them will be a senior?

    A. $\frac{62}{77}$ B. $\frac{5}{11}$ C. $\frac{11}{60}$ D. $\frac{5}{6}$

    15. _____

16. Jean has 5 blue shirts, 3 red shirts, and 5 white shirts. If she selects one shirt at random, what is the probability the shirt will be red or blue?

    A. $\frac{5}{8}$ B. $\frac{3}{8}$ C. $\frac{4}{5}$ D. $\frac{8}{13}$

    16. _____

17. A card is drawn at random from a standard deck of cards. If the card is black, what is the probability that it is the ace of clubs?

    A. $\frac{1}{52}$ B. $\frac{1}{26}$ C. $\frac{1}{13}$ D. $\frac{1}{4}$

    17. _____

18. 70% of the employees at Acme Wheels graduated from college, 50% have had 5 or more years of business experience. 20% have 5 or more years of business experience and have graduated from college. What is the probability that an employee selected at random has less than 5 years experience if the employee graduated from college?

    A. $\frac{5}{7}$ B. $\frac{1}{5}$ C. $\frac{2}{7}$ D. $\frac{3}{5}$

    18. _____

19. If three coins are tossed, find P(at least 2 tails).

    A. $\frac{3}{8}$ B. $\frac{1}{4}$ C. $\frac{1}{2}$ D. $\frac{5}{8}$

    19. _____

20. The probability that Julie will make a free throw is $\frac{2}{5}$ What is the probability that she will make exactly 4 out of her next 6 free throw shots?

    A. $\frac{4}{15}$ B. $\frac{6}{25}$ C. $\frac{108}{805}$ D. $\frac{432}{3125}$

    20. _____

Bonus

A test has 5 true and false questions and 5 multiple-choice questions. Each multiple-choice question has 4 possible answers. If Maria guesses on all 10 questions, what is the probability that she will get exactly 8 right answers?

    A. $\frac{189}{2048}$ B. $\frac{175}{32,768}$ C. $\frac{81}{16,384}$ D. $\frac{243}{1024}$

    Bonus: _____

Chapter 14 Test, Form 1B

Write the letter for the correct answer in the blank at the right of each problem.

1. How many 5-digit zip codes can begin with the digits 55?
   A. 3125   B. 100,000   C. 59,049   D. 1000

   1. _____

2. How many ways can 4 different numbers be drawn from the numbers 1 through 25?
   A. 303,600   B. 390,625   C. 100,000   D. 25,000

   2. _____

3. Find the value of $\dfrac{P(7, 4)}{P(5, 3)}$.

   A. 7   B. 14   C. 35   D. 49

   3. _____

4. How many five-letter patterns can be formed from the letters in the word *grateful* if g must appear followed directly by r?
   A. 5040   B. 1680   C. 840   D. 480

   4. _____

5. How many six-letter patterns can be formed from the letters in the word *roller*?
   A. 720   B. 360   C. 180   D. 120

   5. _____

6. In how many ways can 6 people be seated around a circular table with 6 chairs?
   A. 720   B. 360   C. 180   D. 120

   6. _____

7. How many ways can 7 people be seated around a circular table if Kelly and Tim must be seated next to each other?
   A. 5040   B. 720   C. 360   D. 240

   7. _____

8. How many different 5-member teams can be formed from 12 players?
   A. 248,832   B. 792   C. 95,040   D. 3125

   8. _____

9. Using a standard deck of cards, how many different 3-card hands can be dealt in which each card is from a different suit?
   A. 132,600   B. 8,788   C. 52,728   D. 140,608

   9. _____

10. Two cards are drawn at random from a standard deck of cards. What is the probability that both will be kings?

    A. $\dfrac{1}{221}$ B. $\dfrac{2}{169}$ C. $\dfrac{2}{2652}$ D. $\dfrac{1}{26}$

    10. _____

11. The probability that Lonnie will play in tomorrow's football game is $\dfrac{2}{5}$. What are the odds that he will not play in tomorrow's game?

    A. $\dfrac{5}{2}$ B. $\dfrac{3}{5}$ C. $\dfrac{3}{2}$ D. $\dfrac{2}{3}$

    11. _____

Glencoe Division, Macmillan/McGraw-Hill

12. Odds are 2 to 1 that Ms. Cone is home before 6 P.M. What is the probability that she will be home before 6 P.M. on the next three days?

   A. $\frac{1}{8}$ **B.** $\frac{8}{27}$ **C.** $\frac{1}{6}$ **D.** $\frac{3}{16}$

   12. _____

13. If three cards are drawn from a standard deck of cards with no replacement, find the probability that all of them will be face cards.

   A. $\frac{11}{1105}$ **B.** $\frac{2197}{132,600}$ **C.** $\frac{1716}{2197}$ **D.** $\frac{429}{35,152}$

   13. _____

14. Marcy has 7 dimes, 7 nickels, and 4 pennies in her pocket. If she takes one coin from her pocket at random, what is the probability that it is a dime or a penny?

   A. $\frac{11}{18}$ **B.** $\frac{7}{9}$ **C.** $\frac{4}{7}$ **D.** $\frac{9}{14}$

   14. _____

15. A die is tossed. What is the probability that it will show an even number or a 5?

   A. $\frac{1}{6}$ **B.** $\frac{1}{12}$ **C.** $\frac{5}{6}$ **D.** $\frac{2}{3}$

   15. _____

16. There are 9 men and 9 women on the school board. If a group of 4 randomly selected board members rides in a car, what is the probability that all 4 will be women?

   A. $\frac{2}{9}$ **B.** $\frac{4}{81}$ **C.** $\frac{7}{170}$ **D.** $\frac{13}{210}$

   16. _____

17. A card is drawn from a standard deck of cards. What is the probability that the card is a king if it is a face card?

   A. $\frac{1}{13}$ **B.** $\frac{1}{3}$ **C.** $\frac{4}{13}$ **D.** $\frac{1}{4}$

   17. _____

18. A four-digit number is formed using each of the digits 1, 2, 3, and 4 once. What is the probability that the number ends in the digits 41 given that it is odd?

   A. $\frac{1}{2}$ **B.** $\frac{1}{6}$ **C.** $\frac{1}{3}$ **D.** $\frac{1}{4}$

   18. _____

19. Five coins are tossed. What is the probability that at least 4 will show heads?

   A. $\frac{1}{16}$ **B.** $\frac{1}{4}$ **C.** $\frac{3}{16}$ **D.** $\frac{1}{8}$

   19. _____

20. Lee attends $\frac{1}{3}$ of the chorus concerts. What is the probability that he will attend exactly 2 of the next 5 concerts?

   A. $\frac{2}{15}$ **B.** $\frac{4}{27}$ **C.** $\frac{20}{81}$ **D.** $\frac{80}{243}$

   20. _____

Bonus

A pair of dice is thrown twice. What is the probability of getting a sum of at least ten on both throws?

   A. $\frac{1}{36}$ **B.** $\frac{1}{6}$ **C.** $\frac{100}{1296}$ **D.** $\frac{1}{144}$

   Bonus: _____

~ Chapter 14 Test, Form 2A

Write the answer in the blank at the right of the problem.

1. Find the number of permutations of 4 objects taken 4 at a time.

   1. _____

2. How many ways can 7 awards be displayed in a row on a shelf?

   2. _____

3. How many seven-letter patterns can be formed from the letters in the word *lessens*?

   3. _____

4. In how many ways can 4 children be seated on a 4-animal merry-go-round if Andy is seated on the giraffe?

   4. _____

5. In how many ways can 8 keys be arranged on a key ring?

   5. _____

6. From a group of 12 people, how many groups of 5 people can be chosen?

   6. _____

7. Find the value of n in the equation $C(n, 4) = C(n, 5)$.

   7. _____

8. A basket contains 9 blue ribbons, 7 red ribbons, and 6 white ribbons. What is the probability that a ribbon selected at random will be red?

   8. _____

9. There is an 80% chance that it will snow in Chicago tomorrow. What are the odds that it will not snow in Chicago tomorrow?

   9. _____

10. There are 7 blue chips and 9 green chips in a box. If Sally takes a chip out of the box and then Alex takes a chip, what is the probability that both select blue chips?

    10. _____

11. A rack contains 8 short-sleeved shirts and 6 long-sleeved shirts. Mr. Lemke selects one shirt, returns it to the rack and then selects another. What is the probability both shirts selected were short-sleeved?

    11. _____

12. There are 8 members of the women's basketball team and 7 members of the men's track team at an athletic club meeting. What is the probability that a committee of 3 selected at random will have at least 2 members of the basketball team?

    12. _____

Glencoe Division, Macmillan/McGraw-Hill

Chapter 14 Test, Form 2A (continued)

13. Six coins are tossed. What is the probability that at least 4 of them will show heads?

13. _____

14. Thirty people in a class just bought tickets to a dance. Twenty people just bought tickets to a concert. The remaining five people in the class bought tickets to both the dance and the concert. If one person from the class is selected at random, what is the probability that he or she has tickets to either the dance or the concert?

14. _____

15. A pair of dice is rolled. Find the probability that the numbers showing on the dice match, given that their sum is less than ten.

15. _____

16. A box contains 3 oranges and 3 apples. Another box contains 4 oranges and 6 apples. A piece of fruit is drawn from one of the boxes at random. If it is an orange, what is the probability that it is from the first box?

16. _____

17. Four coins are tossed. Find the probability that all of the coins landed heads up if it is known that two coins land heads up.

17. _____

18. Four cards are drawn from a standard deck of cards. What is the probability that exactly 4 hearts will be drawn if the cards are replaced after each draw?

18. _____

19. Jackie has been averaging 3 hits for every 10 times at bat. What is the probability that she will get exactly 2 hits in her next 5 times at bat?

19. _____

20. If four dice are tossed, find the probability that at least 3 fives will show.

20. _____

Bonus

30% of the members of the track team play musical instruments. 60% play other sports. 10% play both musical instruments and other sports. What is the probability that a member of the track team selected at random plays a musical instrument if that member does not play other sports?

Bonus: _____

Chapter 14 Test, Form 2B

Write the answer in the blank at the right of the problem.

1. Find the value of $P(7, 4)$.

   1. _____

2. How many ways can 9 students enter a room if they enter 1 at a time?

   2. _____

3. How many ways can 4 people sit in a row of 5 chairs?

   3. _____

4. How many five-letter patterns can be formed from the letters in the word *color*?

   4. _____

5. There are 40 people in a room. How many different groups of 2 people can be formed?

   5. _____

6. A bag contains 6 bottles, 3 cans, and 4 jars. How many ways can 2 bottles and 2 cans be selected from the bag?

   6. _____

7. If you select 2 letters at random from the word *dinosaur*, what is the probability that one will be a vowel and the other a consonant?

   7. _____

8. A die is thrown twice. What are the odds of getting 2 threes?

   8. _____

9. A grab bag contains 7 blue boxes, 8 green boxes, and 5 yellow boxes. What is the probability of drawing 2 yellow boxes if no replacement occurs?

   9. _____

10. Jennifer has 6 pairs of athletic shoes, 5 pairs of dress shoes, and 3 pairs of boots. What is the probability she will randomly select a pair of boots one day and a pair of dress shoes the next day, if she replaces them at night?

    10. _____

11. Glenn has 5 quarters, 4 dimes, and 7 pennies in his pocket. If he selects 3 coins at random, what is the probability that he will select 2 quarters and 1 penny?

    11. _____

Glencoe Division, Macmillan/McGraw-Hill

Chapter 14 Test, Form 2B (continued)

12. The Wellsville Fire Department knows that $\frac{1}{5}$ of its fire calls are brush fires and $\frac{1}{6}$ of its fire calls are chimney fires. What is the probability that the next fire call will be a brush fire or a chimney fire?

12. _____

13. Three dice are tossed. What is the probability that at least 2 of them will show numbers greater than 5?

13. _____

14. A card is chosen at random from a standard deck of cards. If the card is black, what is the probability that it is the two of hearts?

14. _____

15. Norton has two pens and two pencils in his pocket. He removes them one at a time. What is the probability that he removes a pencil last if he removes a pencil first?

15. _____

16. The computer club has 10 junior class members, 4 of whom are female. The remaining club members are 8 seniors class members, 4 of whom are male. A member is chosen at random. If the member chosen is a female, what is the probability that she is a junior?

16. _____

17. Eight coins are tossed. What is the probability that exactly 5 will show heads?

17. _____

18. If a coin is tossed 5 times, what is the probability that 2 heads will be tossed?

18. _____

19. Georgia attends stamp club meetings $\frac{2}{3}$ of the time. What is the probability that she will attend at least one of the next two meetings?

19. _____

20. 90% of the items in a store are on sale. What is the probability that all 4 of the items Julie selected at random are on sale?

20. _____

Bonus

In how many ways can 5 cups and 5 glasses be arranged on a shelf if all of the glasses must be together?

Bonus: _____

Chapter 14, Quiz A (Lessons 14-1 through 14-2)

Write the answer in the blank at the right of the problem.

1. In how many different orders can Andrea, Brian, Cody, and Donna play the piano?

   1. _____

2. How many ways can the letters in the word *scrap* be arranged if the first letter must be s?

   2. _____

3. In how many ways can 3 blue, 3 red, and 4 white baseball caps be arranged?

   3. _____

4. In how many ways can 7 differently colored chairs be arranged in a circle?

   4. _____

5. How many ways can 6 charms be arranged on a bracelet if the bracelet has a clasp?

   5. _____

Chapter 14, Quiz B (Lessons 14-3 through 14-4)

Write the answer in the blank at the right of the problem.

1. A box contains 5 roses, 8 carnations, and 4 lilies. How many ways can 2 roses, 2 carnations, and 1 lily be selected?

   1. _____

2. Find the value of n in the equation $C(12, 9) = C(n, 3)$.

   2. _____

3. How many 4-member committees can be formed from a group of 10 people?

   3. _____

4. Laura has 16 antique dolls in her collection. Four of the dolls have hats. If Laura selects 2 dolls at random, what is the probability that at least one of them will have a hat?

   4. _____

5. Of the 20 animals at the animal shelter, 12 are dogs. Two animals are chosen at random. What are the odds that both are dogs?

   5. _____

Chapter 14, Quiz C (Lessons 14-5 through 14-6)

Write the answers in the blank at the right of the problem.

1. Each of three students in an art class is given a box of 10 differently colored pencils. If each student selects one pencil at random from his or her box, what is the probability that all three will select orange pencils?

   1. _____

2. 70% of the time Willis waits for his ride to school. 20% of the time he waits for his ride home. Find the probability he will wait for his rides to and from school today.

   2. _____

3. Two dice are tossed. What is the probability that the sum will be either 2 or 11?

   3. _____

4. Two cards are drawn from a standard deck of cards. Find the probability that each is black or a queen.

   4. _____

5. Donna has 10 bottles of regular soft drink and 8 bottles of diet soft drink. If she selects three bottles at random to take to a party, what is the probability that she will take exactly 2 bottles of regular soft drink?

   5. _____

Chapter 14, Quiz D (Lessons 14-7 through 14-8)

Write the answer in the blank at the right of the problem.

1. Two coins are tossed. What is the probability that both coins show heads if one coin shows heads?

   1. _____

2. A pair of dice is rolled. Find the probability that the sum is 10 given that the sum is greater than or equal to 9.

   2. _____

3. Wally hit the bullseye with 4 of his last 12 darts. What is the probability that both of his next two darts will be bullseyes?

   3. _____

4. Suppose you guess at all 8 questions on a true/false test. What is the probability that you will get exactly 7 correct?

   4. _____

5. Yolanda guessed at all 8 questions on a true/false test. What is the probability that she will get at least 7 correct?

   5. _____

Chapter 14 Mid-Chapter Test (Lessons 14-1 through 14-4)

Write the answers in the blank at the right of the problem.

1. The model airplane club sold T-shirts and sweatshirts with either a Lockheed SR-71 or a North American p-51 Mustang print. The shirts came in small, medium, large, and extra large sizes. How many different selections are possible?

   1. _____

2. Find the value of $\dfrac{7!}{(7-3)!}$.

   2. _____

3. A penny, a dime, and a quarter are tossed simultaneously. How many different ways can the coins land?

   3. _____

4. In how many ways can 3 model cars and 3 model planes be arranged on a shelf if the cars and planes must alternate on the shelf?

   4. _____

5. Five charms are placed on a bracelet. How many ways can they be arranged if the bracelet has no clasp?

   5. _____

6. How many distinct triangles can be formed from 5 points on a plane if no 3 points are collinear?

   6. _____

7. Write an expression to represent the number of different 9-member baseball teams that can be formed from a 16-member team.

   7. _____

8. A surgical team of 2 doctors and 2 nurses is to be formed from a group of 8 doctors and 6 nurses. How many different teams are possible?

   8. _____

9. Suppose you select 2 different letters at random from the word *random*. What is the probability that both will be consonants?

   9. _____

10. If 4 cards are drawn at random from a standard deck of cards, what are the odds that the first three will be of the same suit and the fourth of another suit?

    10. _____

Glencoe Division, Macmillan/McGraw-Hill

~ Standardized Test Questions (Chapters 1-14)

Write the letter for the correct answer in the blank at the right of each problem.

1. Find the distance between $(2, 4)$ and $(-2, 7)$.
   A. 10   **B.** 3   **C.** 5   **D.** 25

   1. _____

2. Solve the system of equations. $y = x - 4$
                                      $y = 2x - 8$
   A. $(4, 0)$ **B.** $(2, 4)$ **C.** $(-4, 0)$ **D.** $(0, 4)$

   2. _____

3. The graph of $xy = 10$ is *not* symmetric with respect to
   A. the origin.   **B.** the y-axis.   C. the line $y = x$.   D. the line $y = -x$.

   3. _____

4. Find the length of the arc intercepted by a central angle measuring $\frac{\pi}{2}$ in a circle of radius 14 cm.
   A. $\frac{\pi}{7}$ cm   **B.** 14π cm   **C.** $\frac{7\pi}{2}$ cm   **D.** 7π cm

   4. _____

5. What is the equation for the inverse of $y = \cot x$?
   A. $y = \text{Csc } x$ **B.** $y = \text{arccot } x$ **C.** $y = \text{arcsec } x$ **D.** $y = \text{Sin } x$

   5. _____

6. For values between $0°$ and $90°$, find $\cos \theta$ if $\sin \theta = \frac{4}{5}$.

   A. $\frac{3}{5}$ **B.** 0   **C.** $\frac{3}{4}$ **D.** 1

   6. _____

7. Find the inner product of $(3, -2, 6)$ and $(1, -4, -3)$.
   A. -7 **B.** -25 **C.** 29   **D.** 0

   7. _____

8. Use a calculator to evaluate $e^{1.55}$.
   A. 2.0684   **B.** 7.6947   **C.** 4.7115   **D.** 4.4816

   8. _____

9. Find the 9th term of the sequence $36, -18, 9, \cdots$.
   A. $-\frac{3}{8}$ **B.** $\frac{1}{64}$ **C.** $-\frac{9}{64}$ **D.** $\frac{9}{64}$

   9. _____

10. Find the first three iterates of the function $f(x) = 3x + 2$ for an initial value of $x_0 = 0$.
    A. 0, 2, 8   **B.** 2, 8, 26   **C.** 2, 5, 8   **D.** $-1, 0, 8$

    10. _____

Chapter 15 Test, Form 1A

Write the letter for the correct answer in the blank at the right of each problem. Use the data in the table below for Exercises 1-11.

Number of Cars per 1000 People, 1988					
Country	Number	Country	Number	Country	Number
United States	559	Sweden	400	Finland	344
Australia	497	France	394	Denmark	321
Canada	454	Austria	370	United Kingdom	318
Switzerland	419	Belgium	349	Spain	263
Italy	408	Netherlands	348	Japan	241

1. What is the range of the data?
   A. 559   **B.** 318   **C.** 800   **D.** 241   1. _____

2. Which would be an appropriate class interval for displaying the data?
   A. 200   **B.** 100   **C.** 30   **D.** 5   2. _____

3. What is the mean of the data?
   A. 569   **B.** 379   **C.** 370   **D.** 349   3. _____

4. Find the mode of the data.
   A. 379   **B.** 370   **C.** 349   **D.** none   4. _____

5. What is the median of the data?
   A. 370   **B.** 379   **C.** 408   **D.** none   5. _____

6. What is the deviation from the mean for the number of cars in the United States?
   A. 180   **B.** 189   **C.** 270   **D.** 379   6. _____

7. Find the mean deviation of the data.
   A. 956   **B.** 63.1   **C.** 65.6   **D.** 63.7   7. _____

8. What is the upper quartile value of the data?
   A. 413.5   **B.** 419   **C.** 408   **D.** 379   8. _____

9. What is the lower quartile value of the data?
   A. 344   **B.** 305.5   **C.** 348   **D.** 321   9. _____

10. What is the interquartile range for the data?
    A. 98   **B.** 81   **C.** 140   **D.** 198   10. _____

11. What is the semi-interquartile range of the data?
    A. 40.5   **B.** 99   **C.** 70   **D.** 49   11. _____

~~~~

Chapter 15 Test, Form 1A (continued)

A set of data has a normal distribution with a mean of 180 and a standard deviation of 20.

12. What percent of the data is in the interval 140-220?
    A. 38.3%   **B.** 68.3%   **C.** 95.5%   **D.** 99.7%   12. _____

13. Find the probability that a value selected at random is less than 160.
    A. 15.9%   **B.** 19.1%   **C.** 2.2%   **D.** 31.7%   13. _____

14. Find the limit below which 80% of the data lies.
    A. 216   **B.** 206   **C.** 196   **D.** 154   14. _____

Suppose each of the families in a sample of 100 purchase an average of 5.4 magazines monthly. The standard deviation of the samples is 1.2 magazines.

15. Find the standard error of the mean.
    A. 1.0   **B.** 0.12   **C.** 0.45   **D.** 0.54   15. _____

16. Find the interval about the sample mean that has a 5% confidence level.
    A. 5.32–5.48   **B.** 4.34–6.46   **C.** 4.2–5.52   **D.** 5.16–5.64   16. _____

17. Find the interval about the sample mean that gives a 50% chance that the true mean lies within that interval.
    A. 5.32–5.48   **B.** 4.34–6.46   **C.** 4.2–5.52   **D.** 5.16–5.64   17. _____

18. Find the interval about the sample mean such that the probability is 0.90 that the true mean lies within the interval.
    A. 5.202–5.598   **B.** 7.05–3.75   **C.** 4.5–6.3   **D.** 4.2–6.6   18. _____

A study of the deer population in a certain forest yielded the following data.

Year	1964	1968	1972	1976	1980	1984	1988	1992
Number of Deer	756	702	643	512	396	304	235	172

19. Find an equation of the line of regression.
    A. $y = 3x$ **B.** $y = 22.5 - 449x$
    C. $y = 44946 - 22.5x$ **D.** $y = 22x - 449$ 19. _____

20. Describe the relationship.
    A. strongly negative   **B.** moderately negative
    C. moderately positive   **D.** strongly positive   20. _____

Bonus

Find the Pearson product-moment correlation value for the number of deer.
    A. 0.99368   **B.** −0.99368   **C.** 0.00632   **D.** −0.00632   Bonus: _____

Chapter 15 Test, Form 1B

Write the letter for the correct answer in the blank at the right of each problem.
Use the data in this table for questions 1-7.

Average Dinner Check per Person at 100 Restaurants	
Amount of Check	**Frequency**
$0.01 – $10.00	14
$10.01 – $20.00	24
$20.01 – $30.00	20
$30.01 – $40.00	23
$40.01 – $50.00	19

1. What is the class interval of the frequency distribution?
   A. less than $10   **B.** $10.00   **C.** $20.00   **D.** $50.00   1. _____

2. What is the class mark for the interval $40.01–$50.00?
   A. $40.00   **B.** $42.50   **C.** $45.00   **D.** $47.50   2. _____

3. In what percent of the restaurants shown is the average check per person $20.01 to $30.00?
   A. 10%   **B.** 20%   **C.** 30%   **D.** 40%   3. _____

4. In what percent of the restaurants is the average check per person at least $30.01?
   A. 20%   **B.** 23%   **C.** 42%   **D.** 62%   4. _____

5. What is the mean of the data?
   A. $20.50   **B.** $25.00   **C.** $25.90   **D.** $29.10   5. _____

6. What is the median class of the data?
   A. $27.50   **B.** $10.01–$30.00 **C.** $25.00   **D.** $20.01–$30.00   6. _____

7. What is the standard deviation for the data?
   A. $20.90   **B.** $19.10   **C.** $13.35   **D.** $10.90   7. _____

Use the data in this table for Exercises 8-11.

Cars Rented at Rob's Car Rental (in thousands)											
Jan	**Feb**	**March**	**April**	**May**	**June**	**July**	**Aug**	**Sept**	**Oct**	**Nov**	**Dec**
0.7	0.6	0.9	1.2	1.3	1.5	1.8	1.7	1.1	0.9	0.9	1.2

8. Find the lower quartile value for the data.
   A. 0.9   **B.** 1.05   **C.** 1.2   **D.** 1.25   8. _____

9. What is the interquartile range for the data?
   A. 0.3   **B.** 0.5   **C.** 0.9   **D.** 1.4   9. _____

Glencoe Division, Macmillan/McGraw-Hill

Chapter 15 Test, Form 1B (continued)

10. What is the mean of the data?

    A. 1.15   **B.** 1.25   **C.** 1.5   **D.** 1.65   **10.** _____

11. Find the deviation from the mean for February.

    A. 0.6   **B.** 1.1   **C.** 0.55   **D.** 0.65   **11.** _____

Suppose a sample of 300 values has a normal distribution with a mean of 50 and a standard deviation of 5.

12. What percent of the data is between 45 and 55?

    A. 38.3%   **B.** 50%   **C.** 68.3%   **D.** 95.5%   **12.** _____

13. Out of 100 values, how many will be between 40 and 60?

    A. 50   **B.** 68   **C.** 80   **D.** 95   **13.** _____

14. Find the interval about the mean that contains 90% of the data.

    A. 41.75–58.25   **B.** 42.5–57.5   **C.** 38.75–61.25   **D.** 40–60   **14.** _____

15. Find the standard error of the mean.

    A. 0.7   **B.** 0.29   **C.** 2.9   **D.** 0.17   **15.** _____

16. Find the interval about the sample mean that has a 50% confidence level.

    A. 49.5–50.5   **B.** 49.8–50.2   **C.** 48.43–52.57   **D.** 49.9–50.1   **16.** _____

17. Find the interval about the sample mean that gives a 95% chance that the true mean lies within the interval.

    A. 48.5–51.5   **B.** 49.8–50.2   **C.** 49.43–50.57   **D.** 49.9–50.1   **17.** _____

18. With what level of confidence can it be said that the true mean lies between 49.5 and 50.5?

    A. 91.1%   **B.** 96.5%   **C.** 85%   **D.** 50%   **18.** _____

Use the data in the table below for Exercises 19-20.

Age (in years)	1	2	4	5	7	8	10	11
Height (in cm)	73	80	96	104	115	121	132	136

19. Find an equation of the line of regression.

    A. $y = 99 + 69x$ **B.** $y = 73 + 2x$ **C.** $y = 6.3 + 69x$ **D.** $y = 69 + 6.3x$ **19.** _____

20. Find the Pearson product-moment correlation value for the data.

    A. 69   **B.** 6.34   **C.** 0.99   **D.** 9.95   **20.** _____

Bonus

Which is most affected by extreme values?

    A. mean   **B.** median   **C.** mode   **D.** frequency   **Bonus:** _____

Chapter 15 Test, Form 2A

Year	1900	1920	1940	1960	1980
Republican	292	404	82	219	489
Democratic	155	127	449	303	49

1. On a separate piece of paper, make a back-to-back bar graph to show the electoral votes cast for Democratic and Republican presidential candidates.

2. In which years was a Democrat elected president?

2. _____

3. In what year was the difference between the numbers of the electoral votes cast the greatest?

3. _____

The stem-and-leaf plot below shows the grades students received on a math test. Use the data in the stem-and-leaf plot for Exercises 4-11.

```
 6 |  8 9
 7 |  3 6 8 8 9
 8 |  0 4 5 7 7 8 9
 9 |  0 1 2 4 7
10 |  0 0          6 | 8 = 68
```

4. How many students took the test?

4. _____

5. What is the mean of the test scores?

5. _____

6. What is the median of the test scores?

6. _____

7. What is the deviation from the mean for a grade of 100?

7. _____

8. Find the standard deviation of the test grades.

8. _____

9. Find the values of the three quartiles.

9. _____

10. What is the interquartile range for the data?

10. _____

11. On a separate sheet of paper draw a box-and-whisker plot of the data.

Glencoe Division, Macmillan/McGraw-Hill

Chapter 15 Test, Form 2A (continued)

Suppose a set of 1000 values has a normal distribution with a mean of 400 and a standard deviation of 30.

12. What percent of the data is between 385 and 415?

12. _____

13. Find the probability that a value selected at random from the data is greater than 350.

13. _____

14. Find the interval about the mean that includes 50% of the data.

14. _____

A sample of 225 homes showed an average of 5.2 clocks in each home. The standard deviation was 0.8 clocks.

15. Find the standard error of the mean.

15. _____

16. Find the interval about the sample mean that has an 87% confidence interval.

16. _____

17. Find the probability that the mean of all homes will be more than one-tenth of a clock from the mean of the sample.

17. _____

Use the data in the table below for Exercises 18-20.

Experience (years)	6	1	12	9	10	4	8	3
Hourly Wage	$12	$7	$20	$17	$19	$10	$15	$10

18. On a separate sheet of paper, draw a scatter plot to show the relationship between experience and hourly wage.

19. Find an equation of the line of regression.

19. _____

20. Describe the relationship.

20. _____

Bonus

The life of calculator batteries is normally distributed with a mean of 50 hours and a standard deviation of 3 hours. Out of 1000 batteries, how many will last longer than 56 hours?

Bonus: _____

Chapter 15 Test, Form 2B

Fifty students recorded the number of hours the television was on in their homes during one week. The results are given in the chart below. Use the chart for Exercises 1-6.

Number of Hours (to the nearest hour)

54	28	9	15	3	54	35	32	0	34
72	57	62	33	58	23	57	53	24	27
36	63	34	58	53	13	12	75	66	57
18	53	53	46	77	26	32	42	43	88
44	71	22	57	45	73	44	11	45	34

1. On a separate sheet of paper, make a frequency polygon of the data.

2. What are the class limits in your frequency polygon?　　　　2. _____

3. In what percent of the homes was the television on fewer than 10 hours per week?　　　　3. _____

4. In what percent of the homes was the television on more than 50 hours per week?　　　　4. _____

5. Find the median of the data.　　　　5. _____

6. Find the mode of the data.　　　　6. _____

7. Find the value of x so that the mean of $\{x, 3x, 2x + 1 \text{ and } 2x - 5\}$ is 9.　　　　7. _____

The table below shows the percent pay raise given to 13 employees. Use the data for Exercises 8-10.

Percent Pay Raise												
3.2%	4.4%	4.1%	3.8%	1.5%	2.4%	3.3%	1.7%	9.2%	4.5%	4.2%	5.1%	4.6%

8. Find the mean of the percentages.　　　　8. _____

9. Find the mean deviation of the percentages.　　　　9. _____

10. On a separate sheet of paper, draw a box-and-whisker plot of the data. Name any outliers.

Chapter 15 Test, Form 2B (continued)

Suppose a set of 600 values has a normal distribution with a mean of 120 and a standard deviation of 10.

11. What percent of the data is between 100 and 140?

11. _____

12. Find the range about the mean that includes 80% of the data.

12. _____

13. Find the probability that a value selected at random from the data is between 105 and 135.

13. _____

In a random sample of 256 people, it was found that they each ate in a restaurant an average of 2.6 times a week with a standard deviation of 0.4.

14. Find the standard error of the mean.

14. _____

15. Find the interval about the sample mean that has a 1% confidence level.

15. _____

16. Find the interval about the sample mean such that a probability of 0.8 exists that the true mean will lie within the interval.

16. _____

17. Find the probability that the mean of the population will be less than 0.1 restaurant meal from the mean of the sample.

17. _____

Use the data in the table below for Exercises 18-20.

Hours of Practice	2	4	6	8	10	12	14	16
Number of Mistakes	30	25	22	19	15	9	4	1

18. On a separate sheet of paper, draw a scatter plot for the data.

19. Determine the Pearson product-moment correlation value for the data.

19. _____

20. Describe the relationship.

20. _____

Bonus

For the data above, find an equation for the line of regression.

Bonus: _____

Chapter 15, Quiz A (Lessons 15-1 through 15-2)

Use the data in the table below for Exercises 1-3.

Crude Oil Production (in millions of barrels per day)				
Year	1960	1970	1980	1990
OPEC	8.7	23.4	27	23.7
USA	7	9.6	8.6	7.3
USSR	2.9	7	11.5	11.7

1. On a separate sheet of paper, make a three-dimensional bar graph of the data in the table.

2. In what year did OPEC produce about twice as many barrels of oil per day as the USSR?

2. _____

3. What is the range of the data in the table?

3. _____

4. Find the difference between the mean and the median of the heights. Heights (in inches): 54, 67, 57, 67, 56, 52, and 60.

4. _____

5. Find the value of x so that the mean of {4.6, 5.4, 6 and x} is 5.2.

5. _____

Chapter 15, Quiz B (Lesson 15-3)

Games Won by Each Team in the Mid-State League in 1993											
64	63	58	58	47	45	64	64	58	53	53	45

1. Find the mean number of games won.

1. _____

2. Find the mean deviation of the games won.

2. _____

3. What is the interquartile range of the data?

3. _____

4. What is the standard deviation of the data?

4. _____

5. On a separate sheet of paper, make a box-and-whisker plot of the data.

Chapter 15, Quiz C (Lesson 15-4)

A set of 900 values has a normal distribution with a mean of 150 and a standard deviation of 8.

1. What percent of the data is in the interval 134−166?

   1. _____

2. How many values are within one standard deviation of the mean?

   2. _____

3. How many values are between one and two standard deviations greater than the mean?

   3. _____

4. Find the probability that a value selected at random from the data is greater than 162.

   4. _____

5. Find the interval within which 90% of the data lies.

   5. _____

Chapter 15, Quiz D (Lessons 15-5 through 15-6)

In a sample of 100 adults, the average time they kept a car was 6.2 years. The standard deviation was 1.1 years.

1. Find the standard error of the mean.

   1. _____

2. Find the interval about the mean that has a 5% confidence level.

   2. _____

3. Find the probability that the mean of the population will be less than 0.1 year from the mean of the sample.

   3. _____

The table below shows the crude steel production and the car production of nine countries in 1989.

Steel (in millions of tons)	80.9	17.2	11.5	97.9	35.9	17.7	22.7	16.9	2.6
Cars (in millions)	7.1	1.2	1.4	7.9	4.3	3	1.7	1.3	0.9

4. On a separate sheet of paper draw a scatter plot of the data.

5. Find an equation for the line of regression.

   5. _____

Chapter 15 Mid-Chapter Test (Lessons 15-1 through 15-4)

The table below shows the amount of money 13 families spent on food in one year. Use the data for Exercises 1-10. Use a separate sheet of paper for Exercises 1-3.

Food Costs (in thousands of dollars)												
4.5	5.2	6.5	2.9	2.7	4.6	3.9	6	4.7	4.2	5.2	4.6	7.2

1. Organize the data into a frequency distribution table.

2. Make a stem-and-leaf plot of the data.

3. Make a box-and-whisker plot of the data.

4. Find the mean of the data.

4. _____

5. What is the median of the data?

5. _____

6. Find the mode of the data.

6. _____

7. What is the interquartile range for the data?

7. _____

8. What is the mean deviation for the data?

8. _____

9. What is the standard deviation for the data?

9. _____

10. Find the interval about the mean that includes 68.3% of the data.

10. _____

Glencoe Division, Macmillan/McGraw-Hill

Standardized Test Questions (Chapters 1-15)

Choose the best answer. Write A, B, C, or D.

1. Find the zero of $f(x) = 6x + 5$

   A. $\dfrac{5}{6}$ **B.** $-\dfrac{5}{6}$ **C.** $-\dfrac{6}{5}$ **D.** $\dfrac{6}{5}$

   1. _____

2. Find an equation for the vertical asymptote for $f(x) = \dfrac{1}{x+1}$

   A. $x = -1$ **B.** $x = 0$ **C.** $x = 1$ **D.** $x = 2$

   2. _____

3. Find the roots of $x^2 - 169 = 0$

   A. 0, 169   **B.** 0, 13   **C.** 0, −13   **D.** 13, −13

   3. _____

4. Find the measure of a in right $\triangle ABC$ if $c = 10$ and $A = 65°$.

   A. 9.1   **B.** 4.2   **C.** 6.5   **D.** 35

   4. _____

5. Evaluate $\cos\left(\arccos \dfrac{1}{2}\right)$.

   A. $\dfrac{\sqrt{3}}{2}$ **B.** 0   **C.** $\dfrac{1}{2}$ **D.** $\dfrac{\sqrt{2}}{2}$

   5. _____

6. Find the ordered pair that represents the vector from $L\,(6, 2)$ to $M(-3, 0)$.

   A. (9, 2)   **B.** (−9, −2)   **C.** (9, −2)   **D.** (−9, 2)

   6. _____

7. Find the polar coordinates of the point with rectangular coordinates (0, 3).

   A. $(0, 3)$ **B.** $\left(-3, \dfrac{\pi}{2}\right)$ **C.** $\left(3, \dfrac{\pi}{2}\right)$ **D.** $\left(-6, \dfrac{\sqrt{3}}{2}\right)$

   7. _____

8. Identify the conic section represented by the equation $x^2 + 6x + 2y = 6 - y^2$.

   A. circle   **B.** ellipse   **C.** parabola   **D.** hyperbola

   8. _____

9. Use logarithms to evaluate $\sqrt{\dfrac{7.2^3}{5.5}}$.

   A. 0.9158   **B.** 8.2379   **C.** 2.5719   **D.** 1.8316

   9. _____

10. In the detective game Clue™, there are 6 suspects, 6 weapons, and 9 rooms. What is the probability that the crime was committed by Mrs. White, in the library, with a candlestick?

    A. $\dfrac{1}{108}$ **B.** $\dfrac{1}{216}$ **C.** $\dfrac{1}{324}$ **D.** $\dfrac{1}{54}$

    10. _____

Chapter 16 Test, Form 1A

Write the letter for the correct answer in the blank at the right of each problem.

1. Which statement is *not* true of a simple graph?
   A. A simple graph has no loops.
   B. A simple graph can have parallel edges.
   C. A simple graph does not have edges connecting a vertex to itself.
   D. A simple graph can be described by the number of its vertices and the number of its edges.

   1. _____

2. Which diagram represents a graph with 4 vertices, each with degree 2?
   A.   B.   C.   D.

   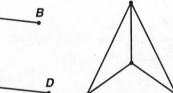 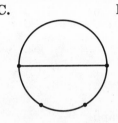 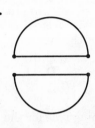

   2. _____

3. Determine how many edges K_9 has.
   A. 45   B. 40   C. 36   D. 31

   3. _____

4. Which graph is not complete?
   A. $G(6, 15)$ B. $G(12, 66)$ C. $G(8, 28)$ D. $G(25, 325)$

   4. _____

5. Determine the most specific name of the walk $a, b, g, f, e,$ in the graph to the right.

   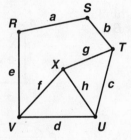

   A. circuit   B. path
   C. trail   D. cycle

   5. _____

6. Which statement best describes $G(9, 36)$?
   A. The graph is disconnected.
   B. The graph may be connected.
   C. The graph is connected.
   D. The graph is both connected and complete.

   6. _____

For Exercises 7-9, refer to the multigraphs below.

A.   B.   C.   D.

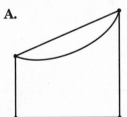  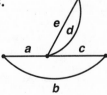 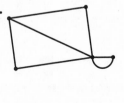

7. Identify any simple graphs.
   A. A, C   B. B   C. A, C, D   D. There are none.

   7. _____

8. Which path in graph C is an Euler circuit?
   A. a, e, d, c, b, a B. a, b, c, d, e
   C. c, d, e, a, c, b D. There are none.

   8. _____

Chapter 16 Test, Form 1A (continued)

9. Identify any graph with an Euler path.

   A. B   **B.** A and D   **C.** C   **D.** There are none.

                                          9. _____

10. Use the breadth-first search algorithm to determine the distance of the shortest path from A to Z in the multigraph at the right.

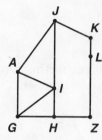

   A. 5   **B.** 4

   C. 3   **D.** 2   10. _____

11. Use Dijkstra's algorithm to find the minimal distance from A to Z in the multigraph at the right.

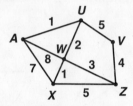

   A. 6   **B.** 7

   C. 10   **D.** 11   11. _____

12. Find a spanning tree for the graph at the right.

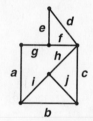

   A. g, e, h **B.** a, b, c, d, e, f

   C. a, g, e, d, f **D.** g, e, d, h, i, b 12. _____

13. Which number represents the weight of a minimal spanning tree from vertex B for the graph at the right?

   A. 15   **B.** 12

   C. 19   **D.** 11   13. _____

14. Find the entry in the second column of the third row of $M(G)$ for the digraph at the right.

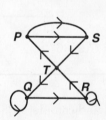

   A. 0   **B.** 1

   C. 2   **D.** 3   14. _____

15. Find the number of directed edges from Z to Y in the digraph described by the matrix below.

$$\begin{array}{c} \\ W \\ X \\ Y \\ Z \end{array}\begin{array}{c} W\ X\ Y\ Z \\ \left[\begin{array}{cccc} 0 & 0 & 1 & 2 \\ 0 & 1 & 2 & 1 \\ 2 & 0 & 0 & 1 \\ 1 & 1 & 3 & 0 \end{array}\right] \end{array}$$

   A. 0   **B.** 1   **C.** 2   **D.** 3   15. _____

Bonus

How many edges are there in $K_{2x + 1}$?

   A. $2x^2 + x$ **B.** $\dfrac{4x^2 + 5x + 2}{2}$

   C. $4x^2 + 2x$ **D.** $\dfrac{2x^2 + 4x + 1}{2}$ Bonus: _____

Chapter 16 Test, Form 1B

Write the letter for the correct answer in the blank at the right of each problem.

1. Which statement is true of a multigraph?
   A. A multigraph has no loops.
   B. A multigraph has no parallel edges.
   C. A multigraph has at least one edge connecting the same pair of vertices.
   D. A multigraph may be described by indicating the number of vertices and the number of edges.

   1. _____

2. Which diagram represents the graph described by $V = \{P, Q, R, S\}$ and $E = \{\{P, Q\}, \{P, R\}, \{R, S\}, \{P, S\}, \{S, Q\}\}$?

   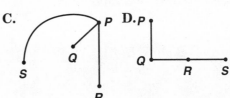

   2. _____

3. Find the number of edges in K_3.
   A. 4   B. 3   C. 6   D. 2

   3. _____

4. Choose the graph that is complete.
   A. $G(6, 21)$ B. $G(4, 5)$ C. $G(10, 45)$ D. $G(7, 18)$

   4. _____

5. Refer to the graph at the right to determine the most specific name for the walk f, g, e, c.
   A. circuit   B. path
   C. trail   D. walk

   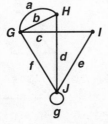

   5. _____

6. Which statement best describes $G(7, 5)$?
   A. The graph is disconnected.
   B. The graph may be connected.
   C. The graph is connected.
   D. The graph is both connected and complete.

   6. _____

For Exercises 7-9, refer to the multigraphs below.

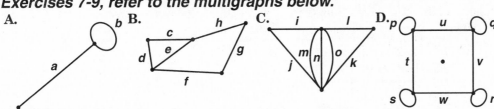

7. Which path in graph B is an Euler path?
   A. There are none.   B. d, c, h, g, f, e
   C. f, e, c, d, e, h, g D. h, c, d, f, g, e

   7. _____

8. Identify any connected multigraphs.
   A. A, B, C, D   B. A, B, C   C. A   D. B, C

   8. _____

Glencoe Division, Macmillan/McGraw-Hill

9. Name any graphs that have Euler circuits.
   A. There are none **B.** D   **C.** A, C   **D.** B, C   9. _____

10. Use the breadth-first search algorithm
    to find the distance of a shortest path
    from A to Z in the graph at the right.
    A. 5   **B.** 6
    C. 4   **D.** 3   10. _____

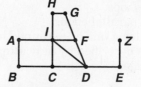

11. Use Dijkstra's algorithm to find a minimal
    path from A to Z in the multigraph at
    the right.

    A. A, L, J, I, Z **B.** A, G, H, Z
    C. A, L, K, I, Z **D.** A, M, J, I, Z 11. _____

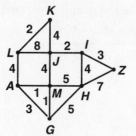

12. Find a spanning tree for the graph
    at the right.
    A. a, b, c, d, e **B.** b, g, h, c, i, e
    C. g, h, i, d, e **D.** b, c, d, e 12. _____

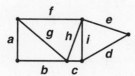

13. Which number represents the weight of a
    minimal spanning tree from vertex E in
    the graph at the right?

    A. 11   **B.** 15
    C. 9   **D.** 12   13. _____

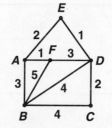

14. Find the entry in the fourth column
    of the first row of $M(G)$ for the
    digraph at the right.
    A. 0   **B.** 1
    C. 2   **D.** 3   14. _____

15. Find the number of directed edges from G to H in the digraph described by
    the matrix below.

$$\begin{array}{c} \\ E \\ F \\ G \\ H \end{array} \begin{array}{c} E\ F\ G\ H \\ \left[\begin{array}{cccc} 0 & 2 & 1 & 2 \\ 1 & 3 & 0 & 0 \\ 2 & 1 & 1 & 2 \\ 0 & 1 & 1 & 1 \end{array}\right] \end{array}$$

    A. 0   **B.** 1   **C.** 2   **D.** 3   15. _____

Bonus

If K_x has $\dfrac{n^2 - 3n + 2}{2}$ edges, how many vertices does it have?

    A. $n - 2$ **B.** $n - 1$ **C.** $n + 2$ **D.** $n + 1$ Bonus: _____

Chapter 16 Test, Form 2A

1. True or false? A multigraph must have more than one edge connecting the same pair of vertices.

   1. _____

2. Draw a graph with 3 vertices such that deg(A) = 1, deg(B) = 0, and deg (C) = 2.

   2. _____

3. How many edges does K_{20} have?

   3. _____

4. Determine whether G(15, 105) is complete. Write *yes* or *no*.

   4. _____

5. Refer to the graph at the right to determine whether the walk g, h, d, c, a is a circuit, a cycle, a path, or a trail. Use the most specific name.

   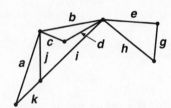

   5. _____

6. Is G(10, 8) connected? Write *yes* or *no*.

   6. _____

For Exercises 7-9, refer to the multigraph below.

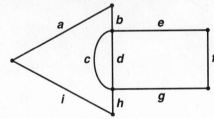

7. Is the graph a simple graph? Write *yes* or *no*.

   7. _____

8. If possible, find an Euler circuit.

   8. _____

9. Is there an Euler path? Why or why not?

   9. _____

Chapter 16 Test, Form 2A (continued)

10. Determine the distance and a shortest path from A to Z in the graph at the right by using the breadth-first search algorithm.

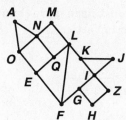

10. _____

11. Find a minimal path and the minimal distance from A to Z for the graph at the right by using Dijkstra's algorithm.

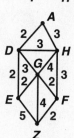

11. _____

12. Find a spanning tree for the graph below.

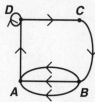

12. _____

13. Find a minimal spanning tree for the graph below. Then state the weight of the tree.

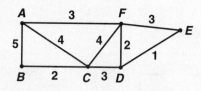

13. _____

14. Find $M(G)$ for the digraph below.

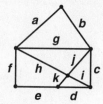

14. _____

15. Draw a graph for which $M(G)$ is

$$\begin{array}{c} \quad R \ S \ T \\ \begin{array}{c} R \\ S \\ T \end{array} \left[\begin{array}{ccc} 1 & 0 & 2 \\ 0 & 0 & 1 \\ 1 & 0 & 1 \end{array} \right] \end{array}$$

15. _____

Bonus

Draw a graph with 5 vertices that contains an Euler path.

Bonus: _____

Chapter 16 Test, Form 2B

1. True or false? A multigraph does not necessarily have a vertex
   where two edges of the multigraph cross.

   1. _____

2. Draw a graph represented by $G(4, 2)$.

   2. _____

3. How many edges does K_{11} have?

   3. _____

4. Determine whether $G(9, 45)$ is complete. Write *yes* or *no*.

   4. _____

5. Refer to the graph at the right
   to determine whether the walk
   b, a is a circuit, a cycle, a path,
   or a trail. Use the most
   specific name.

   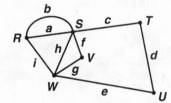

   5. _____

6. Is $G(15, 105)$ connected? Write *yes* or *no*.

   6. _____

For Exercises 7-8, refer to the multigraph below.

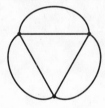

7. Is the graph connected? Write *yes* or *no*.

   7. _____

8. Does the graph have an Euler circuit? Why or why not?

   8. _____

9. If possible, find an Euler path
   in the graph at the right.

   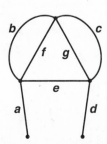

   9. _____

Glencoe Division, Macmillan/McGraw-Hill

~~Chapter 16 Test, Form 2B (continued)

10. Determine the distance and a
    shortest path from A to Z in
    the graph at the right by using
    the breadth-first
    search algorithm.

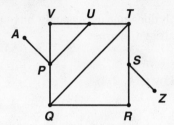

10. _____

11. Find a minimal path and the
    minimal distance from A to Z
    for the graph at the right by
    using Dijkstra's algorithm.

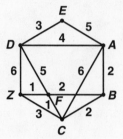

11. _____

12. Find a spanning tree for the graph below.

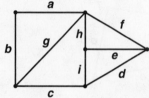

12. _____

13. Find a minimal spanning tree for the graph below.
    Then state the weight of the tree.

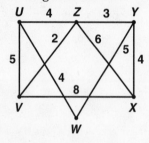

13. _____

14. Find $M(G)$ for the digraph below.

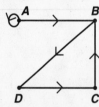

14. _____

15. Draw a digraph for which $M(G)$ is

$$
\begin{array}{c}
\begin{array}{ccc} A & B & C \end{array} \\
\begin{array}{c} A \\ B \\ C \end{array}
\left[\begin{array}{ccc}
0 & 2 & 1 \\
0 & 0 & 1 \\
1 & 0 & 1
\end{array}\right].
\end{array}
$$

15. _____

Bonus

Draw a graph with 4 vertices that contains an Euler circuit.

Bonus: _____

Chapter 16, Quiz A (Lessons 16-1 through 16-2)

1. Draw a simple graph with 5 vertices and 4 edges.

1. _____

2. Draw a multigraph with 3 vertices and 4 edges.

2. _____

3. Determine whether $G(2, 3)$ is complete. Write *yes* or *no*.

3. _____

4. Find a *J-J* circuit of length 4 in the multigraph below.

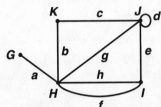

4. _____

5. Is it possible to determine if $G(7, 21)$ is connected? Why or why not?

5. _____

NAME _____ DATE _____

Chapter 16, Quiz B (Lesson 16-3)

Determine whether each multigraph is a simple graph.
Write yes or no.

1.

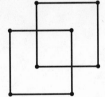

2.

1. _____

2. _____

3. Is the multigraph at
the right connected?
Write *yes* or *no*.

3. _____

For Exercises 4 and 5, refer to the graph below.

4. _____

4. Does the graph have an Euler circuit? Why or why not?

5. Does the graph have an Euler path? Why or why not?

5. _____

Glencoe Division, Macmillan/McGraw-Hill

Chapter 16, Quiz C (Lesson 16-4)

Determine the distance and a shortest path from A to Z in the graphs below by using the breadth-first search algorithm.

1.

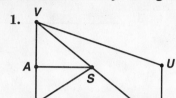

2.

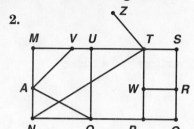

1. _____

2. _____

3.

3. _____

Find a minimal path and the distance in each weighted multigraph from A to Z by using Dijkstra's algorithm.

4.

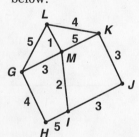

5.

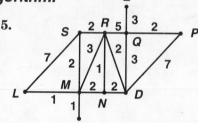

4. _____

5. _____

Chapter 16, Quiz D (Lessons 16-5 through 16-6)

1. Is the graph at the right a tree? Write *yes* or *no*. If no, explain.

2. Find a spanning tree for the graph below.

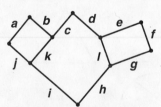

1. _____

3. Find the weight of a minimal spanning tree for the graph below.

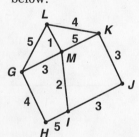

4. Find $M(G)$ for the digraph below.

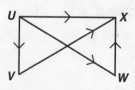

2. _____

3. _____

5. Draw a graph for which $M(G)$ is $Y \begin{bmatrix} X & Y & Z \\ 0 & 2 & 1 \\ 2 & 0 & 1 \\ 1 & 2 & 0 \end{bmatrix}$.

4. _____

5. _____

Chapter 16 Mid-Chapter Test(Lessons 16-1 through 16-3)

1. True or false? A multigraph may have many loops.

1. _____

2. In the multigraph below, name the parallel edges.

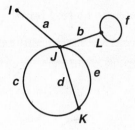

2. _____

3. Draw a graph with 3 vertices such that degree $(A) = 1$, degree $(B) = 2$, and degree $(C) = 0$.

3. _____

4. How many edges does K_8 have?

4. _____

5. Is $G(10, 45)$ connected? Write *yes* or *no*.

5. _____

For Exercises 6-8, refer to the graph below.

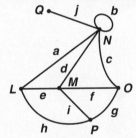

6. What is the shortest L-Q path?

6. _____

7. Is d, b, c, f a circuit, a cycle, or neither?

7. _____

8. Name an M-L walk of length 5.

8. _____

For Exercises 9-10, refer to the graph below.

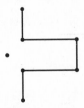

9. Is the graph a simple graph? Write *yes* or *no*.

9. _____

10. Does the graph have an Euler circuit? Why or why not?

10. _____

Glencoe Division, Macmillan/McGraw-Hill

Standardized Test Questions (Chapters 1-16)

Choose the best answer. Write A, B, C, or D.

1. Between which successive integers is a real zero of the
   function $f(x) = x^3 - x^2 + 1$ located?
   A. 0 and 1   **B.** −1 and 0   **C.** −1 and 1   **D.** There are no real zeros.   1. _____

2. Simplify $(3 - 2i)(3 + 2i)$.
   A. $13 - i$ **B.** 11   **C.** $13 + 12i$ **D.** 13   2. _____

3. Which diagram represents the multigraph $G(3, 4)$?
   A.   **B.**   **C.** 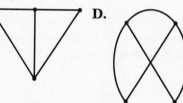   **D.**

   3. _____

4. Find the seventh term in the arithmetic sequence $3\sqrt{2}, \sqrt{2}, -\sqrt{2},\ldots$
   A. $-\sqrt{2}$ **B.** $-13\sqrt{2}$ **C.** $-9\sqrt{2}$ **D.** $12\sqrt{2}$ 4. _____

5. Write the polar form of $-4 + 4i$.
   A. $4\sqrt{2}(\cos 135° + i \sin 135°)$
   B. $4\sqrt{2}(\cos 135° - i \sin 135°)$
   C. $6(\cos 45° + i \sin 45°)$
   D. $6(\cos 45° - i \sin 45°)$ 5. _____

The questions below involve comparing two quantities, one in Column A,
and one in Column B. In certain questions, information related to one
or both quantities is centered above them. All variables represent
real numbers.

Directions:
Write A if the quantity in column A is greater.
Write B if the quantity in column B is greater.
Write C if the two quantities are equal.
*Write D if there is not enough information to determine
the relationship.*

Column A	Column B	
6. $\vec{s} = (5, 2)$ and $\vec{t} = (-4, 3)$		
the x-coordinate of $2(\vec{s} + \vec{t})$	the y-coordinate of $3\vec{t} - 2\vec{s}$	6. _____
7. the slope of the tangent to the graph of		
$y = x^2 + 5x - 2$ at $(1, 4)$	$y = x^2$ at $(2, 4)$	7. _____
8. the value of x for		
$2^x = 1.263$	$e^x = 2.014$	8. _____
9. $\lim\limits_{x \to 2} \dfrac{x^3 - 8}{x - 2}$	$\lim\limits_{x \to \infty} \dfrac{x - 3}{x^2 - 1}$	9. _____
10. $\tan(\text{Tan}^{-1} x)$	x	10. _____

Unit Test, Chapters 12-16

1. Determine whether the Julia set for the the function
$f(z) = z^2 + (-0.2 + 0i)$ is connected or disconnected.

1. _____

2. A set of data has a normal distribution with a mean of 16
and a standard deviation of 0.3. What percent of the
data is in the interval $15.2 - 16$?

2. _____

3. Is the multigraph at the right
a simple graph? Write *yes* or *no*.

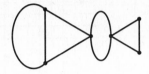

3. _____

4. Find the twelfth term of the geometric
sequence $\dfrac{1}{16}, \dfrac{1}{8}, \dfrac{1}{4}, \dots$.

4. _____

5. There are 21 wrapped packages in a grab bag at an office
holiday party. Five of the packages contain \$20 bills, 7
packages contain \$5 bills, and 9 packages contain \$1 bills.
What is the probability that the first two people choose
packages with \$20 bills inside them?

5. _____

6. Write $1 + i$ in exponential form.

6. _____

7. Find the coordinates of the vertex of the graph of the
logistic function $f(x) = 1.9x(1 - x)$.

7. _____

8. *True* or *false*: Choosing an entrée and choosing an
appetizer from a dinner menu are independent events.

8. _____

9. Find a minimal path and the
minimal distance from A to Z in
the graph at the right by using
Dijkstra's algorithm.

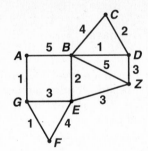

9. _____

10. Graph the functions $f(x) = -5x$ and
$f(x) = x$ on the same set of axes. Then
perform graphical iteration for $x_0 = 1$.
State the type of path that the
iteration forms.

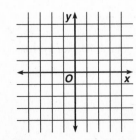

10. _____

Unit Test, Chapters 12-16 (continued)

11. The marketing manager for a company that sells office equipment recorded the amount spent on advertising and the amount of sales for 12 consecutive quarters. His results are recorded in the chart below. Draw a scatter plot to show how the expenditures for advertising are related to the income from sales. Describe the relationship.

Quarter	Advertising	Sales
1	$900	$20,000
2	$1000	$28,000
3	$1600	$22,000
4	$2000	$25,000
5	$2200	$34,000
6	$2700	$20,000
7	$3000	$30,000
8	$3000	$38,000
9	$4000	$30,000
10	$4000	$40,000
11	$4000	$50,000
12	$4600	$46,000

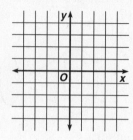

11. _____

12. How many different ways can the letters of the word *circular* be arranged?

12. _____

13. Use the ratio test to determine whether the series $\frac{1}{3} + \frac{1}{3^2} + \frac{1}{3^3} + \cdots$ is convergent or divergent.

13. _____

14. Find the first three iterates of the function $f(z) = z^2 + (z - i)$ if $z_0 = i$.

14. _____

15. How many edges does the graph of K_{14} have?

15. _____

16. Eight out of ten people surveyed prefer to observe Veterans Day on November 11 rather than on the second Monday of November. Use the binomial theorem to determine the probability that each of the first 3 people surveyed preferred to observe Veterans Day on November 11.

16. _____

17. Use the binomial theorem to expand $(x - 2y)^3$.

17. _____

18. Find a spanning tree for the graph at the right.

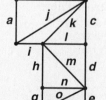

18. _____

Unit Test, Chapters 12-16 (continued)

19. Find the x-coordinate of the fixed point for the function $f(x) = 0.5x - 1$. Is it a repeller or an attractor?

19. _____

20. Find n for the arithmetic sequence for which $a_n = 129, a = 15,$ and $d = 6$.

20. _____

21. The set of class marks of a frequency distribution is $\{25.5, 35.5, 45.5, 55.5\}$. Find the class interval and the class limits.

21. _____

22. Find the value of n if $C(15, 2) = C(n, 13)$.

22. _____

23. Find the first three iterates of the function $f(x) = x^2 - 2$ for $x_0 = -2$.

23. _____

24. Use the graph at the right to determine whether a, g, j, i is a circuit, cycle, path, trail, or walk. Use the most specific name.

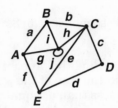

24. _____

25. Evaluate $\lim\limits_{n \to \infty} \dfrac{n^2 - 1}{n}$, or state that the limit does not exist.

25. _____

26. Twenty slips of paper are numbered from 1 to 20 and placed in a box. What is the probability of drawing a number that is odd or a multiple of 5?

26. _____

27. Find the adjacency matrix, $M(G)$, for the graph at the right.

27. _____

28. _____

28. True or false: A linear function whose slope is greater than one forms a graphical iteration path that staircases out.

The table below shows the number of gallons of heating oil delivered to a residential customer in December between 1986 and 1993.

Year	'86	'87	'88	'89	'90	'91	'92	'93
Gallons of oil	42	61	53	59	53	51	75	100

29. _____

29. Make a stem-and-leaf plot of the data.

30. Find the mean, median, and mode of the data.

30. _____

Glencoe Division, Macmillan/McGraw-Hill

Unit Test, Chapters 12-16 (continued)

31. Two cards are drawn at random from a standard deck of 52 cards. What is the probability that both cards are kings?

31. _____

32. Write the repeating decimal 0.3636 ... as a fraction.

32. _____

33. The scores on a company's employment exam are normally distributed with a mean of 50 points and a standard deviation of 10 points. What percent of the applicants taking the exam score 61 points or higher?

33. _____

34. Determine whether the graph below is a tree. Write *yes* or *no*. If not, explain.

34. _____

35. Find the 50th term in the arithmetic sequence 2, 5, 8, $\cdots$.

35. _____

36. A red die and a white die are thrown. Find the probability that the red die shows a 2, given that the sum of the numbers showing on the two dice is less than or equal to 5.

36. _____

37. Find the standard error of the mean for a sample in which $\sigma = 3.6$, $N = 100$, and $\overline{X} = 36$. Then use $t = 2.58$ to find the range for a 1% level of confidence. Round your answer to the nearest hundreth

37. _____

38. *True* or *false*: The point $2.1i$ is in the escape set for the function $f(z) = z^2 + (-1 + 0i)$.

38. _____

39. Is the graph $G(5, 9)$ complete? Write *yes* or *no*.

39. _____

40. The table below shows a frequency distribution of the number of pickup trucks sold at 85 truck dealerships in Maine over an 18-month period.

Number of Trucks Sold	70-90	90-110	110-130	130-150	150-170	170-190
Number of Dealerships	2	11	39	17	9	7

Find the interval about the sample mean such that the probability is 0.90 that the true mean lies within the interval. (When $P = 90\%$, $t = 1.65$.)

40. _____

Chapter 17 Test, Form 1A

Write the letter for the correct answer in the blank at the right.

Evaluate each limit.

1. $\lim\limits_{x \to -1} (x^2 - 3x + 1)$

    A. 3   **B.** –3   **C.** 5   **D.** –1   **1.** _____

2. $\lim\limits_{x \to 4} \dfrac{x^2 - 9x + 20}{x - 4}$

    A. 0   **B.** –1   **C.** 1   **D.** –4   **2.** _____

3. Evaluate $\lim\limits_{x \to 2} [5g(x)]$ if $g(x) = 2x$.

    A. 10   **B.** 9   **C.** 3   **D.** 20   **3.** _____

Find the derivative of each function.

4. $f(x) = 3x^3 - x$

    A. $9x^2 - 1$ **B.** $9x^2$ **C.** $6x^2 - 1$ **D.** $6x^2 - x$ **4.** _____

5. $f(x) = x^{-\frac{1}{3}}$

    A. $-\dfrac{\sqrt[3]{x^2}}{3x}$ **B.** $-\dfrac{\sqrt[3]{x}}{3x}$ **C.** $-\dfrac{\sqrt[3]{x^2}}{3x^2}$ **D.** $-\dfrac{1}{3\sqrt[3]{x^2}}$ **5.** _____

6. $f(x) = x^2(x + 4)^{-3}$

    A. $-\dfrac{3x^2}{(x + 4)^2}$ **B.** $-\dfrac{3x^2}{(x + 4)^4}$

    C. $\dfrac{-x^2 + 8x}{(x + 4)^4}$ **D.** $\dfrac{x^3 - 6x^2 - 24x}{(x + 4)^3}$ **6.** _____

Use a limit to find the area between each curve and the x-axis for the given interval.

7. $y = x^2$ from $x = 0$ to $x = 3$

    A. $\dfrac{27}{2}$ **B.** 9   **C.** 12   **D.** $\dfrac{27}{4}$ **7.** _____

8. $y = x^4$ from $x = 1$ to $x = 5$

    A. $\dfrac{15624}{5}$ **B.** 1562   **C.** $\dfrac{3124}{5}$ **D.** $\dfrac{1562}{3}$ **8.** _____

9. Find the area of the shaded region in the graph at the right.

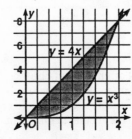

    A. 12   **B.** $\dfrac{1}{4}$ **C.** 2   **D.** 4   **9.** _____

Chapter 17 Test, Form 1A (continued)

Find each integral.

10. $\int \frac{1}{4}x^2\, dx$

    A. $\frac{1}{12}x^3 + C$ **B.** $\frac{1}{2}x^3 + C$ **C.** $\frac{1}{8}x^3 + C$ **D.** $\frac{1}{8}x + C$ 10. _____

11. $\int \sqrt{2 + x}\, dx$

    A. $\frac{1}{2\sqrt{1 + x}} + C$ **B.** $\frac{3\sqrt{(2 + x)^3}}{2} + C$

    C. $\frac{2\sqrt{(2 + x)^3}}{3} + C$ **D.** $\frac{2\sqrt[3]{(2 + x)^2}}{3} + C$ 11. _____

12. $\int \frac{1}{x - 3}\, dx$

    A. $\frac{1}{(x - 3)^2} + C$ **B.** $\ln |x - 3| + C$

    C. $\ln \frac{1}{|x - 3|^2} + C$ **D.** $\frac{1}{(x - 3)^2} + x + C$ 12. _____

Evaluate each definite integral.

13. $\int_1^4 (x^2 + 4x + 5)\, dx$

    A. 20   **B.** 6   **C.** 66   **D.** 23   13. _____

14. $\int_0^6 x^2(6 - x)\, dx$

    A. 756   **B.** 108   **C.** 36   **D.** 180   14. _____

15. Use integration to find the area of the shaded region at the right.

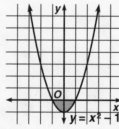

    A. $-\frac{4}{3}$ **B.** 0   **C.** $\frac{2}{3}$ **D.** $\frac{4}{3}$ 15. _____

Bonus

Acceleration is a measure of the rate of change of the velocity of an object. The velocity, in m/s, of a particle moving along a straight line is given by the function $v(t) = 3t^2 - 6t + 5$, where t is the time in seconds. Find the acceleration in m/s^2 of the particle after 5 seconds.

    A. 29 m/s^2 **B.** 24 m/s^2 **C.** 75 m/s^2 **D.** 50 m/s^2 **Bonus:** _____

Chapter 17 Test, Form 1B

**Write the letter for the correct answer in the blank
at the right of each problem.**

Evaluate each limit.

1. $\lim\limits_{x \to -2} x^3$

   A. 8 **B.** −8 **C.** −6 **D.** 6 1. _____

2. $\lim\limits_{x \to 3} \dfrac{x^3 - 27}{x - 3}$

   A. 0 **B.** 24 **C.** −18 **D.** 27 2. _____

3. Evaluate $\lim\limits_{x \to 1} [f(x) - g(x)]$ if $f(x) = x^2 + 1$ and $g(x) = 5 - x$.

   A. −2 **B.** −4 **C.** 3 **D.** 0 3. _____

Find the derivative of each function.

4. $f(x) = 17x$

   A. $17x^2$ **B.** 17 **C.** 0 **D.** $17x$ 4. _____

5. $f(x) = x^6 - 4x^2$

   A. $6x^5 - 8x$ **B.** $5x^6 - 8x$ **C.** $6x^5 - 6x$ **D.** $5x^6 - 6x$ 5. _____

6. $f(x) = \dfrac{3x - 8}{2x + 1}$

   A. $\dfrac{3}{2}$ **B.** $\dfrac{13}{(2x + 1)^2}$ **C.** $\dfrac{19}{(2x + 1)^2}$ **D.** 19 6. _____

Use a limit to find the area between each curve and the x-axis for the given interval.

7. $y = x^3$ from $x = 0$ to $x = 2$

   A. $\dfrac{1}{4}$ **B.** $\dfrac{1}{2}$ **C.** 2 **D.** 4 7. _____

8. $y = x^2$ from $x = b$ to $x = a$, $b < a < 0$

   A. $\dfrac{a^3 + b^3}{3}$ **B.** $\dfrac{b^3 - a^3}{3}$ **C.** $\dfrac{a^3 - b^3}{3}$ **D.** $-\dfrac{a^4}{3}$ 8. _____

9. Find the area of the shaded region
   in the graph to the right.

   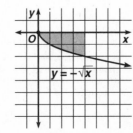

   $y = -\sqrt{x}$

   A. $\dfrac{2}{3}$ **B.** $\dfrac{4}{3}$ **C.** 2 **D.** $\dfrac{16}{3}$ 9. _____

~ **Chapter 17 Test, Form 1B (continued)**

Find each integral.

10. $\int (12x + 5)\, dx$

   A. $6x^2 + 5x$ **B.** $12x^2 + 5 + C$

   C. $12x^2 + 5x$ **D.** $6x^2 + 5x + C$ **10.** _____

11. $\int (x^3 - 2x)\, dx$

   A. $\dfrac{3x^4}{4} - x^2 + C$ **B.** $\dfrac{x^4}{4} - x^2 + C$

   C. $3x^2 - 2$ **D.** $3x^2 - 2 + C$ **11.** _____

12. $\int \dfrac{1}{x + 2}\, dx$

   A. $\dfrac{C}{(x + 2)^2}$ **B.** $\dfrac{\ln}{|x + 2|^2} + C$

   C. $\ln |x + 2| + C$ **D.** $\dfrac{C - 1}{(x + 2)^2}$ **12.** _____

Evaluate each definite integral.

13. $\int_{1}^{5} (2x - 1)\, dx$

   A. 8   **B.** 21   **C.** 22   **D.** 20   **13.** _____

14. $\int_{-2}^{2} (x^3 + 1)\, dx$

   A. 4   **B.** 2   **C.** 10   **D.** 12   **14.** _____

15. Use integration to find the area of the shaded region at the right.

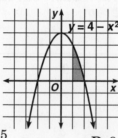

   A. $\dfrac{32}{3}$ **B.** $\dfrac{16}{3}$ **C.** $\dfrac{5}{3}$ **D.** 9   **15.** _____

Bonus

Find the area in square units of the region bounded by the curve $y = 8x^3 - 48x^2 + 72x$, the x-axis, and the lines $x = 3$ and $x = 4$.

   A. 54   **B.** 32   **C.** 10   **D.** 21   **Bonus:** _____

Chapter 17 Test, Form 2A

Evaluate each limit.

1. $\lim\limits_{x \to 3} x^4 - 3x$

2. $\lim\limits_{x \to 0} (x + 1)^2$

1. _____

2. _____

3. $\lim\limits_{x \to 1} \dfrac{x^2 - 4x + 3}{x^2 - 1}$

3. _____

4. Evaluate $\lim\limits_{x \to -1} f[g(x)]$ for $f(x) = 4x + 3$ and $g(x) = x - 2$.

4. _____

5. Evaluate $\lim\limits_{x \to -1} [f(x)]^2$ for $f(x) = 2x^2 - 7x$.

5. _____

Find the derivative of each function.

6. $f(x) = 5x^5 - 4x^4 - 3x^3$

7. $f(x) = 8x^3$

6. _____

7. _____

8. $f(x) = (x^4 - 3x)(2x^3)$

9. $f(x) = \sqrt{3x}$

8. _____

9. _____

10. $f(x) = \dfrac{5x^2 - 3x + 1}{4x}$

10. _____

Write a limit to find the area between each curve and the x-axis for the given interval. Then find the area.

11. $y = x^4$ from $x = 0$ to $x = 1$

11. _____

12. $y = \dfrac{1}{2}x^2$ from $x = 0$ to $x = 4$

12. _____

13. $y = x^3$ from $x = 0$ to $x = 3$

13. _____

Find the area of each shaded region.

14.

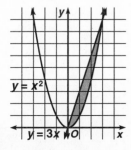

15.

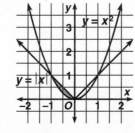

14. _____

15. _____

Glencoe Division, Macmillan/McGraw-Hill

Chapter 17 Test, Form 2A (continued)

Find each integral.

16. $\int 15\,dx$

16. _____

17. $\int (3x^2 + 4x - 1)\,dx$

17. _____

18. $\int (7x^3 + \pi)\,dx$

18. _____

19. Find the antiderivative of $f(x) = 9x^5$

19. _____

20. If a function $f(x) = 6x - \dfrac{162}{x^2}$ describes the dimensions of a box of given

volume constructed so as to minimize the amount of material used, then the functon $g(x)$ that describes the amount of material needed to construct the box can be found by integrating $f(x)$. Write an equation that describes the amount of material needed to construct the box.

20. _____

Evaluate each definite integral.

21. $\int_0^1 \sqrt{x}\,dx$

21. _____

22. $\int_{-2}^2 x(x-2)(x+2)\,dx$

22. _____

23. $\int_0^2 (x^2 - 2x)\,dx$

23. _____

Use integration to find the area of each shaded region.

24.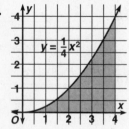

25.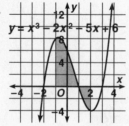

24. _____

25. _____

Bonus

Find the derivative of $f(x) = 4\sqrt{x} + \dfrac{5}{\sqrt{x}}$.

Bonus: _____

Chapter 17 Test, Form 2B

Evaluate each limit.

1. $\lim\limits_{x \to 0} (-3x^2 - 2x + 5)$

1. _____

2. $\lim\limits_{x \to -1} \dfrac{x + 5}{x - 2}$

2. _____

3. $\lim\limits_{x \to 0} \dfrac{x^3 + 5x^2 + 6x}{2x}$

3. _____

4. Evaluate $\lim\limits_{x \to -2} [f(x) + g(x)]$ for $f(x) = x^2$ and $g(x) = 5x - 2$.

4. _____

5. Evaluate $\lim\limits_{x \to 0} f[g(x)]$ for $f(x) = \dfrac{1}{x^2}$ and $g(x) = x^3 - 2$.

5. _____

Find the derivative of each function.

6. $f(x) = x^6 + 2x^4 + 3x^2$

6. _____

7. $f(x) = 3x + 5$

7. _____

8. $f(x) = \sqrt{x^2 + 6x + 4}$

8. _____

9. $f(x) = (x^3 + 4x)(x^4)$

9. _____

10. $f(x) = \dfrac{1}{4x^4}$

10. _____

Write a limit to find the area between each curve and the x-axis for the given interval. Then find the area.

11. $y = x^2$ from $x = 0$ to $x = 4$

11. _____

12. $y = x^4$ from $x = -2$ to $x = 0$

12. _____

13. $y = \dfrac{1}{4}x^2$ from $x = 0$ to $x = 4$

13. _____

Find the area of each shaded region.

14.

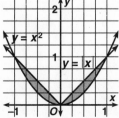

15.

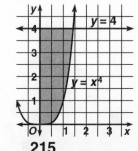

14. _____

15. _____

Glencoe Division, Macmillan/McGraw-Hill

~ **Chapter 17 Test, Form 2B (continued)**

Find each integral.

16. $\int 100x^3\,dx$

16. _____

17. $\int (x-7)^{10}\,dx$

17. _____

18. $\int (-9x^2 + 4x)\,dx$

18. _____

19. Find the antiderivative of $f(x) = \dfrac{1}{x^4} - x^2$.

19. _____

20. If the velocity of a ball thrown upward is given by $v(t) = -10t + 30$, then the function $h(t)$ that descibes the height of the ball after t seconds can be found by integrating $v(t)$. Write an equation that describes the height of the ball after t seconds.

20. _____

Evaluate each definite integral.

21. $\int_0^4 \frac{1}{4}\,x^2\,dx$

21. _____

22. $\int_0^3 (x^2 + 1)\,dx$

22. _____

23. $\int_{-3}^{2} (6 - x - x^2)\,dx$

23. _____

Use integration to find the area of each shaded region.

24.

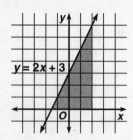

25.

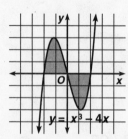

24. _____

25. _____

Bonus

If $f(x) = \dfrac{1}{\sqrt{2x-1}}$, find the value of $f'(x)$ at $x = 3$.

Bonus: _____

Chapter 17, Quiz A (Lessons 17-1 through 17-2)

Evaluate each limit.

1. $\lim\limits_{x \to 1} \left(x^4 - 2x^2 + x + 3\right)$

2. $\lim\limits_{x \to 0} (3x - 4)$

3. $\lim\limits_{x \to 5} \dfrac{(x + 4)(x - 4) - 9}{x - 5}$

Evaluate each limit for f(x) = 3x + 2 and g(x) = 5x.

4. $\lim\limits_{x \to -1} f[g(x)]$

5. $\lim\limits_{x \to 0} \dfrac{g(x)}{f(x)}$

Find the derivative of each function.

6. $f(x) = -7$

7. $f(x) = x^3 - 2x$

8. $f(x) = (x^2 - 1)(2x^2)$

9. $f(x) = \sqrt{x}$

10. $f(x) = \sqrt{3x + 4}$

1. _____

2. _____

3. _____

4. _____

5. _____

6. _____

7. _____

8. _____

9. _____

10. _____

Chapter 17, Quiz B (Lesson 17-3)

Write a limit to find the area between each curve and the x-axis for the given interval. Then find the area.

1. $y = x^2$ from $x = 0$ to $x = 6$

1. _____

2. $y = x^3$ from $x = -1$ to $x = 1$

2. _____

3. $y = x^4$ from $x = 0$ to $x = a, a > 0$

3. _____

Find the area of each shaded region.

4.

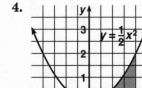

5.

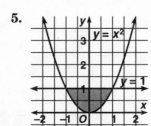

4. _____

5. _____

Chapter 17, Quiz C (Lesson 17-4)

Find each integral.

1. $\int -5\,dx$

1. _____

2. $\int \left(\dfrac{1}{3}x^3 - 2x^2 + 10 \right) dx$

2. _____

3. $\int \dfrac{-2x}{\sqrt{1 + x^2}}\,dx$

3. _____

4. Find the antiderivative of $f(x) = 3\sqrt[5]{x}$.

4. _____

5. If a function $a(t) = 6t - 6$ describes the acceleration of a moving object after t seconds, then the function $v(t)$ that describes the velocity of the object can be found by integrating $a(t)$. Write the function that describes the velocity of the object after t seconds.

5. _____

Chapter 17, Quiz D (Lesson 17-5)

Evaluate each definite integral.

1. $\int_0^3 \dfrac{1}{2}x^2\,dx$

1. _____

2. $\int_{-1}^2 (x + 1)\,dx$

2. _____

3. $\int_{-3}^3 (3x^2 + 2)\,dx$

3. _____

Use integration to find the area of each shaded region.

4.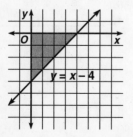

5.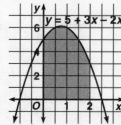

4. _____

5. _____

Chapter 17 Mid-Chapter Test (Lessons 17-1 through 17-3)

Evaluate each limit.

1. $\lim\limits_{x \to 1} 3x^2$

2. $\lim\limits_{x \to 0} (x^3 - 3x^2 + 1)$

3. $\lim\limits_{x \to 3} \dfrac{x - 3}{x^2 - 9}$

4. $\lim\limits_{x \to -1} \dfrac{x^4 - 1}{x^2 - 1}$

Evaluate the limit of f[g(x)] as x approaches 2 for each f(x) and g(x).

5. $f(x) = -x^2$
$g(x) = 2x + 1$

6. $f(x) = 5x + 3$
$g(x) = x - 4$

Find the derivative of each function.

7. $f(x) = 6x^2$

8. $f(x) = -10x + 1$

9. $f(x) = x^{-\frac{1}{3}}$

10. $f(x) = 3x^3 - 4x^2 + 2$

11. $f(x) = (5x - 2)(3x^2)$

12. $f(x) = (x^3 - 6)^3$

13. $f(x) = \dfrac{4}{\sqrt{x}}$

14. $f(x) = \dfrac{4x^2 - 1}{x + 2}$

Use a limit to find the area between each curve and the x-axis for the given interval.

15. $y = x^3$ from $x = 0$ to $x = 3$

16. $y = x^2$ from $x = 2$ to $x = 5$

17. $y = \dfrac{1}{2}x^2$ from $x = -3$ to $x = 3$

18. A particle accelerates over a period of 10 seconds. Its velocity, in feet per second, over that time is given by $v(t) = 0.36t^2$ and the function that describes the distance that it travels in t seconds can be found by integrating $v(t)$. Find the distance the particle traveled in the first 10 seconds.

Find the area of each shaded region.

19.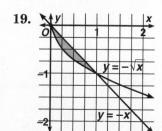

20.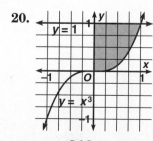

1. _____

2. _____

3. _____

4. _____

5. _____

6. _____

7. _____

8. _____

9. _____

10. _____

11. _____

12. _____

13. _____

14. _____

15. _____

16. _____

17. _____

18. _____

19. _____

20. _____

Standardized Test Questions (Chapters 1-17)

The questions below involve comparing two quantities, one in Column A and one in Column B. In certain questions, information related to one or both quantities is centered above them. All variables used stand for real numbers.

Directions:
Write A if the quantity in column A is greater.
Write B if the quantity in column B is greater.
Write C if the two quantities are equal.
Write D if there is not enough information to determine the relationship.

	Column A	Column B	
1.	3,5,6,7,9		
	the standard deviation	the mean	**1.** _____
2.	the sum of the series		
	$1 - \dfrac{1}{3} + \dfrac{1}{9} - \dfrac{1}{27} + \ldots$	$5 + 5^{-1} + 5^{-3} + \ldots$	**2.** _____
3. $\sin^2 30° + \cos^2 30°$		$\csc^2 45° - \sec^2 45°$	**3.** _____
4.	the x-coordinate of the vertex of		
	$y^2 + 4y = -3 - x$	$x = y^2 + 4y + 5$	**4.** _____
5.	$(a + b)^{12}$		
	the coefficient of $a^8 b^4$	the coefficient of $a^4 b^8$	**5.** _____
6.	the value of k when the vectors in		
	each pair are perpendicular for		
	$(2, 5, -3)$ and $(4, 2, k)$	$(3, k, 1)$ and $(6, 3, 3)$	**6.** _____

Choose the best answer. Write A, B, C, or D.

7. Write $\log_5 \dfrac{1}{125} = -3$ in exponential form.

A. $\left(\dfrac{1}{\sqrt{5}}\right)^3 = \dfrac{1}{125}$ **B.** $\left(\dfrac{1}{5}\right)^{-3} = \dfrac{1}{125}$ **C.** $\sqrt[3]{5} = \dfrac{1}{125}$ **D.** $5^{-3} = \dfrac{1}{125}$ **7.** _____

8. Find $\lim\limits_{n \to 0} \dfrac{2n^2}{n^2 + 1}$.

A. 2   **B.** 1   **C.** 0   **D.** no limit   **8.** _____

9. Identify the domain of $f(x) = \sqrt{1 - x^2}$.
  A. $\{x \mid 0 \leq x \leq 1\}$ **B.** $\{x \mid -1 \leq x \leq 0\}$
  C. $\{x \mid -1 \leq x \leq 1\}$ **D.** {all reals, $x \neq \pm 1$}   **9.** _____

10. For which values of r does the circle $x^2 + y^2 = r^2$ intersect the line $2x + y = 6$?

  A. $r \leq \dfrac{6\sqrt{5}}{5}$ **B.** $r \geq \dfrac{6\sqrt{5}}{5}$ **C.** $r = \dfrac{6\sqrt{5}}{5}$ **D.** $r = -\dfrac{6\sqrt{5}}{5}$ **10.** _____

Semester Test, Chapters 1-8

**Write the letter for the correct answer in the blank at the right of
each problem.**

1. Which angle is not coterminal with −30°?

   A. $-\dfrac{\pi}{6}$ **B.** −750°   **C.** $\dfrac{35\pi}{6}$ **D.** 750°

   1. _____

2. Write the equation of the line that passes through (−7, −5) and is parallel to
   the line $2x + 3y + 6 = 0$.

   A. $2x - 3y - 29 = 0$ **B.** $2x + 3y + 29 = 0$
   C. $2x + 3y - 29 = 0$ **D.** $3x - 2y + 29 = 0$

   2. _____

3. Which ordered triple represents $\overrightarrow{CD}$ for $C(5, 0, -1)$ and $D(3, -2, 6)$?

   A. (8, −2, 5)   **B.** (−2, −2, 7)
   C. (−2, 2, −7)   **D.** (2, 2, −5)

   3. _____

4. Choose the graph of $|x - 2| > 3 + y$.

   A.   **B.**   **C.**   **D.**

   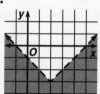 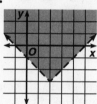 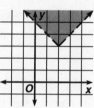 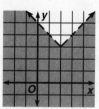

   4. _____

5. Evaluate $\cos\left(\sin^{-1}\dfrac{\sqrt{3}}{2}\right)$. Assume that the angle is in Quadrant I.

   A. $\dfrac{\sqrt{3}}{2}$ **B.** $\dfrac{1}{2}$ **C.** $\sqrt{3}$ **D.** $\dfrac{\sqrt{2}}{2}$

   5. _____

6. Write the polynomial equation of least degree with roots $7i$ and $-7i$.

   A. $x^2 + 49 = 0$ **B.** $x^2 - 49x = 0$
   C. $x^2 = 7$ **D.** $x^2 + 7 = 0$

   6. _____

7. Find the angle to the nearest degree that the normal to the line $3x - y + 4 = 0$
   makes with the positive x-axis.

   A. −18°   **B.** 18°   **C.** 162°   **D.** 108°

   7. _____

8. Find the x-intercept(s) of the graph of the function $f(x) = (x - 3)(x^2 + 4x + 3)$.

   A. 3, 1   **B.** −9   **C.** −3, 3, −1   **D.** 9, −9

   8. _____

Semester Test, Chapters 1-8 (continued)

9. Solve the system of equations using augmented matrices.
   $x - 2y = 6$
   $-3x - 4y = -8$
   A. $(-1, 4)$ **B.** $(4, -1)$ **C.** $(8, 1)$ **D.** $(1, -2.5)$ 9. _____

10. Solve $\sin \theta = -1$ for all values of θ. Assume k is any integer.
    A. $90° + 360k°$ **B.** $180° + 360k°$
    C. $360k°$ **D.** $270° + 360k°$ 10. _____

11. Which expression best describes
    the situation graphed at the right?

    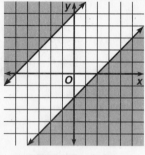

    A. has an optimal solution   **B.** has alternate optimal solutions
    C. is infeasible   **D.** is unbounded   11. _____

12. A section of highway is 4.2 km long and rises at a uniform grade making a
    3.2° angle with the horizontal. What is the change in elevation of this section
    of highway to the nearest thousandth?
    A. 0.235 km   **B.** 0.013 km   **C.** 4.193 km   **D.** 0.234 km   12. _____

13. Use the remainder theorem to find the remainder for
    $(2x^3 - 5x^2 + 3x + 4) \div (x - 2)$.
    A. -6 **B.** 6   **C.** 2   **D.** 0   13. _____

14. Find the magnitude of $\overrightarrow{AB}$ for $A(8, 8)$ and $B(-7, 3)$.
    A. $5\sqrt{10}$ **B.** $\sqrt{26}$ **C.** $10\sqrt{2}$ **D.** $\sqrt{123}$ 14. _____

15. The graph of $y = 4x^4 - 2x^2 + 1$ is symmetric with respect to
    A. the x-axis.   **B.** the y-axis.
    C. the line $y = x$.   **D.** the line $y = -x$.   15. _____

16. Find the zero of the function $f(x) = 5x + 7$.
    A. $-\dfrac{7}{5}$ **B.** $-\dfrac{5}{7}$ **C.** $\dfrac{7}{5}$ **D.** no zero   16. _____

Semester Test, Chapters 1-8 (continued)

17. Simplify $\sec\theta - \tan\theta\sin\theta$.

    A. $\cos\theta$ **B.** $\sin\theta$ **C.** $\sec\theta$ **D.** $\csc\theta$ 17. _____

18. Find the slope of the line passing through $P(-z, 5-w)$ and $Q(-z, w)$.

    A. $\dfrac{5-2w}{-2z}$ **B.** 0 **C.** $\dfrac{-2z}{5-2w}$ **D.** undefined   18. _____

19. If $\sin\theta = -\dfrac{1}{2}$ and θ lies in Quadrant III, find $\cot\theta$.

    A. $-\dfrac{\sqrt{3}}{3}$ **B.** $\dfrac{\sqrt{3}}{3}$ **C.** $\sqrt{3}$ **D.** $-\sqrt{3}$ 19. _____

20. Which relation is the inverse of the function $y = (x-2)^3$?

    A. $y = \sqrt[3]{x} - 2$ **B.** $y = \sqrt[3]{x} - 2$

    C. $y = \sqrt[3]{x} + 2$ **D.** $y = \sqrt[3]{x} + 2$ 20. _____

21. Find the value of $\mathrm{Cos}^{-1}\left(\sin\dfrac{\pi}{2}\right)$.

    A. 0 **B.** $\dfrac{\pi}{2}$ **C.** π **D.** $\dfrac{3\pi}{2}$ 21. _____

22. Given $f(x) = [x] - 5$, find $f(-4.5)$.

    A. -9 **B.** -0.5 **C.** -10 **D.** -1 22. _____

23. If α is a first quadrant angle and $\cos\alpha = \dfrac{\sqrt{10}}{10}$, find $\sin 2\alpha$.

    A. $\dfrac{3\sqrt{10}}{5}$ **B.** $\dfrac{3}{5}$ **C.** $-\dfrac{4}{5}$ **D.** $-\dfrac{3}{4}$ 23. _____

24. How many solutions does the system of equations have?

$$y = -2x + 3$$
$$y = 0.5x + 7$$

    A. 1 **B.** 2 **C.** 0 **D.** infinitely many   24. _____

25. Solve $3\sqrt{2x-1} \le 4$.

    A. $x \ge \dfrac{25}{18}$ **B.** $x \ge \dfrac{5}{9}$ **C.** $\dfrac{1}{2} \le x \le \dfrac{19}{6}$ **D.** $\dfrac{1}{2} \le x \le \dfrac{25}{18}$ 25. _____

Glencoe Division, Macmillan/McGraw-Hill

Semester Test, Chapters 1-8 (continued)

26. Determine the slant asymptote for the graph of $f(x) = \dfrac{x^2 - 3x + 2}{x}$.

26. _____

27. Write an equation in slope-intercept form of the line with parametric equations $x = 2t + 1$ and $y = -3t - 4$.

27. _____

28. Solve $2 \cos x - \sec x = 1$ for $0° \le x \le 180°$.

28. _____

29. If $A = \begin{bmatrix} 1 & -3 \\ -3 & 1 \end{bmatrix}$, find A^2.

29. _____

30. $\vec{v}$ has a magnitude of 20 and an amplitude of 140°. Find the magnitude of its vertical and horizontal components.

30. _____

31. Find the equation of the line tangent to the graph of $y = x^2 - 3x + 5$ at $(2, 3)$. Write the equation in slope-intercept form.

31. _____

32. Solve $5x^2 + 10x + 6 = 3$ by using the quadratic formula.

32. _____

33. Write the equation for the inverse of $y = \text{arccot } x$. Then graph the function and its inverse.

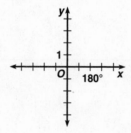

33. _____

34. Use a calculator to approximate the value of sec 8° to four decimal places.

34. _____

35. Write the slope-intercept form of the equation of the line passing through $(4, 1)$ and $(-5, 4)$.

35. _____

36. Find the length of an arc, to the nearest thousandth, that a central angle of 56° subtends in a circle of radius 6 cm.

36. _____

37. If $\vec{v} = (-5, 1)$ and $\vec{w} = (4, -6)$, find $\vec{v} - 2\vec{w}$.

37. _____

38. Determine whether the graph of $y = \dfrac{3}{x^2} - 1$ has infinite discontinuity, jump discontinuity, point discontinuity, or is continuous.

38. _____

Semester Test, Chapters 1-8 (continued)

39. Find the distance between the lines with equations $6y - 8x = 18$ and $4x - 3y = 7$.

39. _____

40. Determine the rational zeros of $f(x) = 2x^3 - 3x^2 - 18x - 8$.

40. _____

41. State the amplitude and period for $y = -4 \cos x$.

41. _____

42. Solve the system of inequalities by graphing. Name the coordinates of the vertices of the polygonal convex set. Then, find the maximum and minimum values for the function $f(x, y) = 4x - 2y$.

$y \geq 1$
$y \geq 2x$
$y \leq x + 3$

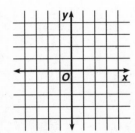

42. _____

43. Are $f(x) = 0.5x + 1$ and $g(x) = 2(x - 1)$ inverses of each other? Write *yes* or *no*.

43. _____

44. Write an equation with phase shift zero to represent simple harmonic motion when the initial position is -5, the amplitude is 5, and the period is 6.

44. _____

45. If $\sin \alpha = \dfrac{1}{3}$ and $\cos \beta = \dfrac{3}{4}$, find $\cos(\alpha - \beta)$ if α is a first quadrant angle and β is a fourth quadrant angle.

45. _____

46. Approximate the positive real zero of the function $f(x) = x^3 + 3x - 8 = 0$ to the nearest tenth.

46. _____

47. Evaluate $(1, 5, -3) \times (2, 1, 1)$.

47. _____

48. Use the law of cosines to solve $\triangle ABC$ if $a = 10$, $b = 40$, and $C = 120°$.

48. _____

49. Describe the transformation that relates the graph of $g(x) = [x - 1]$ to the parent graph $f(x) = [x]$.

49. _____

50. If $A = \begin{bmatrix} 2 & -3 \\ 4 & -5 \end{bmatrix}$, find A^{-1}.

50. _____

~~~ **Semester Test,** (Chapters 9-17)

Write the letter for the correct answer in the blank at the right of each problem.

1. Solve $6^{2x+3} = 34.7$. Round your answer to the nearest hundredth.
   A. 2.49   **B.** −1.37   **C.** −0.51   **D.** −1.25   1. _____

2. Evaluate $\lim\limits_{x \to 5} \dfrac{x^2 - 5}{x^3 - 25}$.

   A. $\dfrac{1}{5}$ **B.** 5   **C.** $\dfrac{1}{10}$ **D.** $\dfrac{1}{25}$ 2. _____

3. If the probability that it will rain on the day of the senior class picnic is 0.4, what are the odds that it will not rain on that day?
   A. $\dfrac{3}{5}$ **B.** $\dfrac{2}{3}$ **C.** $\dfrac{3}{2}$ **D.** $\dfrac{1}{2}$ 3. _____

4. Simplify $i^{32} - i^{17}$.
   A. 0   **B.** −2   **C.** $1 - i$ **D.** $-2i$ 4. _____

5. Find the 4th iterate of $f(x) = (x + 1)^2$ for $x_0 = -1$.
   A. 25   **B.** 1   **C.** 36   **D.** 9   5. _____

6. Find the standard error of the mean for a sample with $N = 400$ and $\sigma = 15$.
   A. 0.75   **B.** 0.0375   **C.** 26.67   **D.** 1.33   6. _____

7. Which equation represents an ellipse?
   A. $2x^2 + 4x + 2y^2 + 6y = 66$ **B.** $x^2 + 2y^2 = 8$
   C. $2x^2 - 5x + y - 19 = 0$ **D.** $3x^2 - 5x = y - 17$ 7. _____

8. Which graph is not a spanning tree for the graph at the right?

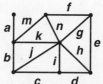

A. 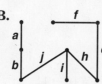   **B.**   **C.** 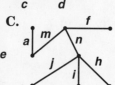   **D.** 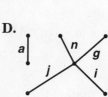   8. _____

9. Find the twenty-first term in the arithmetic sequence 8, 3, −2, −7, ⋯.
   A. −97   **B.** −95   **C.** −105   **D.** −92   9. _____

Semester Test, Chapters 9-17 (continued)

10. A band director checking the overnight rates at six area hotels found the following prices: $80, $51, $72, $89, $68, and $60. What is the standard deviation in price?

A. $18.60   **B.** $12.45   **C.** $83.64   **D.** $56.36   10. _____

11. Identify the equation of the line tangent to the graph of
$\dfrac{x^2}{25} + \dfrac{y^2}{4} = 1$ at (3, 1.6).

A. $3x + 10y - 25 = 0$ **B.** $15x - 20y - 13 = 0$
C. $3x - 10y + 25 = 0$ **D.** $20x - 15y - 36 = 0$ 11. _____

12. A landscaper has 4 rose bushes and 4 peony bushes that are all different colors. In how many different ways can she plant the 8 bushes in a circular bed if she plants roses and peonies alternately?

A. 288   **B.** 2520   **C.** 5040   **D.** 144   12. _____

13. Evaluate $\displaystyle\int_{-2}^{2} (x^3 + 1)\, dx$.

A. 4   **B.** 8   **C.** 2   **D.** 0   13. _____

14. Write the polar equation $4r = \dfrac{8}{\cos \theta}$ in rectangular form.

A. $y = 2$ **B.** $x = 2$ **C.** $x = \dfrac{1}{2}$ **D.** $y = \dfrac{1}{2}$ 14. _____

15. Which series is divergent?

A. $1 + \dfrac{1}{2^3} + \dfrac{1}{3^3} + \dfrac{1}{4^3} + \cdots$ **B.** $\dfrac{1}{5} + \dfrac{1}{5^2} + \dfrac{1}{5^3} + \cdots$

C. $\dfrac{4}{5} + \dfrac{4}{6} + \dfrac{4}{7} + \dfrac{4}{8} + \cdots$ **D.** $2 + \dfrac{2}{3} + \dfrac{2}{9} + \dfrac{2}{27} + \cdots$ 15. _____

16. Find the median of the set {175, 235, 210, 256, 215, 198}.

A. 212.5   **B.** 235.5   **C.** 214.8   **D.** 210   16. _____

17. Refer to the graph at the right to determine which walk is a closed path.

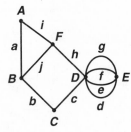

A. b, c, d, e, h, j **B.** b, c, h, j
C. a, j, h, c, b, j, i **D.** h, g, e, c, b, j 17. _____

Semester Test, Chapters 9-17 (continued)

18. If you are proving "for all positive integers n, if $n \geq 4$, then $n! > 2^n$" by mathematical induction, what must you prove in the second part of the proof?

A. If $k! > 2^k$, then $(k + 1)! > 2^{k+1}$.
B. If $1! > 2!$, then $4! > 2^4$.
C. If $2! > 2^4$, then $5! > 2^5$.
D. If $n! > 2^n$, then $k! > 2^k$.

18. _____

19. From a group of 5 science teachers and 3 mathematics teachers, 3 teachers will be selected to attend a conference on chaos theory. Determine the probability that exactly 1 mathematics teacher is chosen.

A. $\dfrac{5}{28}$ **B.** $\dfrac{15}{28}$ **C.** $\dfrac{15}{56}$ **D.** $\dfrac{1}{56}$

19. _____

20. Choose the equation of a circle with center at $(-2, 1)$ and radius 3.

A. $x^2 - 6x + y^2 + 8y = -9$ **B.** $x^2 + y^2 = 3$
C. $(x + 2)^2 + (y - 1)^2 = 3$ **D.** $x^2 + 4x + y^2 - 2y = 4$

20. _____

21. For which function is the x-coordinate of the fixed point an attractor?

A. $f(x) = 10x - 6$ **B.** $f(x) = -0.6x$
C. $f(x) = -5x - 1$ **D.** $f(x) = 2x + 4$

21. _____

22. Express $(x^3y^2)^{\frac{7}{n}}$ using radicals.

A. $\sqrt[n]{x^{21}y^{14}}$ **B.** $\sqrt[n]{x^{10}y^9}$ **C.** $\sqrt[7]{x^{3n}y^{2n}}$ **D.** $\sqrt[7n]{x^3y^2}$

22. _____

23. Find $f'(x)$ for $f(x) = \dfrac{5x}{1 + 2x^2}$.

A. $\dfrac{-20x}{(1 + 2x^2)^2}$ **B.** $\dfrac{5}{-4x(1 + 2x^2)}$

C. $\dfrac{5(1 - 2x^2)}{1 + 2x^2}$ **D.** $\dfrac{5(1 - 2x^2)}{(1 + 2x^2)^2}$

23. _____

24. Which equation represents a spiral of Archimedes?

A. $r = 3\theta$ **B.** $r = 3 + 3 \sin \theta$
C. $r = 3 \cos 2\theta$ **D.** $r = 3 + 2 \cos \theta$

24. _____

25. Solve $\log_6 5(2y - 3) = \log_6 25$.

A. 2   **B.** 4   **C.** $\dfrac{7 + 3\sqrt{5}}{2}$ **D.** 1

25. _____

Semester Test, Chapters 9-17 (continued)

26. Is the point $2 + 4i$ in the escape set for the function
$f(z) = z^2 + (0 - i)$? Write *yes* or *no*.

26. _____

27. Determine the distance and a shortest
path from A to Z in the graph at the right
by using the breadth-first search algorithm.

27. _____

28. Use a calculator to find antilog 0.0783 to the nearest
hundredth.

28. _____

29. A coin is tossed 8 times. What is the probability that exactly 3
heads will occur?

29. _____

30. Find the rectangular coordinates of the point whose polar
coordinates are (20, 140°). Round to the nearest hundredth.

30. _____

31. Write a limit to find the area of the region bounded by the curve
$y = x^2$, the positive x-axis, and the line $x = 3$. Then find the area.

31. _____

32. Find the first four terms of the geometric sequence for which
$a_{10} = 128$ and $r = 2$.

32. _____

33. Write a prediction equation for the data given in the chart below.
Let x represent the number of pounds per square foot of fertilizer
and let y represent the number of pounds of carrots.

Organic fertilizer in lb/100 ft²	0	10	20	30	40
Yield of carrots in pounds	8	11	23	28	34

33. _____

34. Write the equation in general form of a parabola that passes
through the point (0, 3), has a vertex at (1, 4), and opens down.

34. _____

35. The iterates of a function form the pattern 0.5361, 0.2334, 0.5361,
0.2334, ⋯. Describe the long-term iterative behavior of the function.

35. _____

36. Find $\int (x - 2)^{10} \, dx$.

36. _____

37. What is the probability that a card drawn from a standard deck of
52 cards is a jack, a king, or a queen?

37. _____

Semester Test, Chapters 9-17 (continued)

38. Evaluate $\dfrac{13!}{8!5!}$.

38. _____

39. True or false? A simple graph can have parallel edges.

39. _____

40. Find the quotient $\dfrac{\cos \dfrac{5\pi}{12} + i \sin \dfrac{5\pi}{12}}{2\left(\cos \dfrac{\pi}{12} + i \sin \dfrac{\pi}{12}\right)}$. Then write the result in rectangular form.

40. _____

41. Evaluate $C(6, 2) \cdot C(4, 1) \cdot P(3, 2)$.

41. _____

42. Determine whether the point $c = 0.2 - 1.4i$ is inside or outside the Mandelbrot set.

42. _____

43. Evaluate $\displaystyle\sum_{k=2}^{7} (3 - 5k)$.

43. _____

44. Express $4\left(\cos \dfrac{\pi}{6} + i \sin \dfrac{\pi}{6}\right)$ in rectangular form.

44. _____

45. Determine whether the graph at the right contains an Euler circuit, an Euler path, or neither.

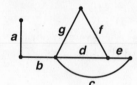

45. _____

46. Solve $250 = 5e^{0.45t}$. Round your answer to the nearest hundredth.

46. _____

47. The annual salaries obtained from a random sample of 50 school superintendents ranged from $51,000 to $135,000. Name the class limits of a frequency distribution with 5 class intervals drawn to represent the data.

47. _____

48. A speed walker accelerates from a resting position to a velocity of 7.2 feet per second in 6 seconds. His velocity is given by $v(t) = 0.2t^2$. Find the distance that the speed walker traveled in the first 6 seconds.

48. _____

49. Determine the eccentricity of the conic section represented by $9x^2 - 16y^2 = 144$.

49. _____

50. Graph the equation $y = 2^{x+1}$.

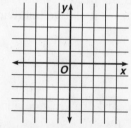

50. _____

Final Test, Chapters 1-17

Write the letter for the correct answer in the blank at the right of each problem.

1. A 10-lb force and a $10\sqrt{3}$-lb force act on the same object. The angle between the forces measures 90°. Find the measure of the angle that the resultant force makes with the $10\sqrt{3}$-lb force.

    A. 270°   **B.** 30°   **C.** 300°   **D.** 60°

1. _____

2. Find the sum of the odd integers greater than 15 but less than 241.

    A. 14,336   **B.** 28,672   **C.** 14,448   **D.** 28,896

2. _____

3. Choose the graph of the relation whose inverse is a function.

  A.   **B.**   **C.**   **D.**

 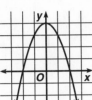 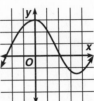 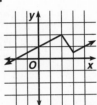

3. _____

4. Identify the conic section represented by the equation $x^2 - 2x + y^2 - 6y - 26 = 0$.

    A. circle   **B.** hyperbola   **C.** ellipse   **D.** parabola

4. _____

5. For which measures does triangle ABC have no solution?

    A. $A = 30°, a = 5, b = 10$

    B. $B = 126°, b = 12, c = 7$

    C. $B = 40°, a = 12, b = 6$

    D. $A = 75°, B = 45°, c = 3$

5. _____

6. Find $\int \dfrac{1}{x^5}\, dx$.

    A. $-\dfrac{4}{x^4} + C$ **B.** $-4x^{-6} + C$ **C.** $4x^{-5} + C$ **D.** $-\dfrac{1}{4x^4} + C$

6. _____

7. If $f(x) = 2x^2 - 3$ and $g(x) = \sqrt{x + 1}$, find $[g \circ f](x)$.

    A. $2x^2 - 2$ **B.** $2x - 1$ **C.** $\sqrt{2x - 1}$ **D.** $\sqrt{2x^2 - 2}$

7. _____

Glencoe Division, Macmillan/McGraw-Hill

Final Test, Chapters 1-17 (continued)

8. Which equation represents simple harmonic motion with phase shift 0, an initial position of –6, an amplitude of 6, and a period of 12?

   A. $y = -6 \cos \dfrac{\pi t}{6}$

   B. $y = -6 \sin \dfrac{\pi t}{6}$

   C. $y = 6 \cos \dfrac{\pi t}{12}$

   D. $y = 6 \cos \dfrac{\pi t}{3}$

   8. _____

9. In how many ways can 5 students be chosen from a group of 4 juniors and 6 seniors to be on the prom committee if exactly 3 students must be seniors?

   A. 720   **B.** 1440   **C.** 60   **D.** 120

   9. _____

10. Solve $\sin 2x = 3 \cos x$ for all values of x. Assume that k is any integer.

    A. $180° + 360k°$

    B. $180° + 180k°$

    C. $90° + 360k°$

    D. $90° + 180k°$

    10. _____

11. Write $\log_5 \dfrac{1}{125} = -3$ in exponential form.

    A. $\left(\dfrac{1}{\sqrt{5}}\right)^3 = \dfrac{1}{125}$

    B. $\left(\dfrac{1}{5}\right)^{-3} = \dfrac{1}{125}$

    C. $\sqrt[3]{5} = \dfrac{1}{125}$

    D. $5^{-3} = \dfrac{1}{125}$

    11. _____

12. Which statement is true for a polynomial function with odd degree?

    A. Its graph must cross the x-axis exactly once.
    B. Its graph must cross the x-axis less than once.
    C. Its graph must cross the x-axis more than once.
    D. Its graph must cross the x-axis at least once.

    12. _____

13. Find the $(2, 3)$th entry in $M(G)$ for the digraph at the right.

    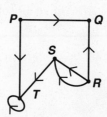

    A. 0   **B.** 1   **C.** 2   **D.** 3

    13. _____

14. Identify the polar form of the linear equation $4x + 3y = 10$.

    A. $5 = r \cos(\theta - 37°)$

    B. $2 = r \cos(\theta - 53°)$

    C. $2 = r \cos(\theta + 53°)$

    D. $2 = r \cos(\theta - 37°)$

    14. _____

Final Test, Chapters 1-17 (continued)

15. Identify the equation of a parabola whose focus is at $(5, -1)$ and whose directrix is $x = 3$.

A. $x^2 + 2x - 4y + 17 = 0$

B. $x^2 - 2x - 4y + 5 = 0$

C. $y^2 + 2y - 4x + 17 = 0$

D. $y^2 - 2y - 4x + 5 = 0$

15. _____

16. Find the area of triangle ABC to the nearest tenth if $B = 30°$, $C = 120°$, and $a = 4$.

A. 4 units^2

B. 6.9 units^2

C. 3.5 units^2

D. 13.9 units^2

16. _____

17. The line with equation $2x - 4y + 5 = 0$ is perpendicular to the line that passes through

A. $(3, 7)$ and $(0, 1)$.

B. $(-3, 7)$ and $(0, 1)$.

C. $(7, 3)$ and $(1, 0)$.

D. $(7, -3)$ and $(1, 0)$.

17. _____

18. For which point is the Julia set connected?

A. $0.5 + 0.8i$ B. $0.2 + 0.1i$ C. $1 - i$ D. $4 - 2i$

18. _____

19. Find the interquartile range for $\{38, 26, 37, 61, 38, 51, 28, 32, 9, 20\}$.

A. 33.75   B. 12   C. 10   D. 34

19. _____

20. What are the dimensions of the product of an $m \times n$ matrix and an $n \times r$ matrix?

A. $m \times r$

B. $r \times m$

C. $m \times n$

D. $n \times m$

20. _____

21. Find the probability of getting a sum of 5 on the first toss of two dice and a sum of 6 on the second toss.

A. $\dfrac{5}{324}$ B. $\dfrac{1}{54}$ C. $\dfrac{1}{4}$ D. $\dfrac{5}{18}$

21. _____

22. Choose the graph of $y = \sec x$ on the interval $0° \le x \le 360°$.

22. _____

A.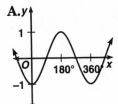

B.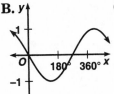

C.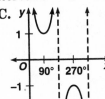

D.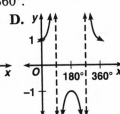

Glencoe Division, Macmillan/McGraw-Hill

~ **Final Test, Chapters 1-17 (continued)**

23. Which point is a point of inflection for the graph of $y = x^4 - 4x^3 + 14$?
    A. $(3, -13)$ **B.** $(0, 14)$ **C.** $(2, 0)$ **D.** $(4, 14)$

23. _____

24. Find the 5th term in the binomial expansion of $(2x - y^3)^6$.
    A. $15x^2y^{12}$ **B.** $60x^2y^{12}$ **C.** $60x^2y^7$ **D.** $-12xy^{15}$

24. _____

25. Evaluate $\lim\limits_{x \to 0} \dfrac{2 - \sqrt{4 - x}}{x}$ or state that the limit does not exist.

    A. does not exist   **B.** 0 **C.** 4 **D.** $\dfrac{1}{4}$

25. _____

26. Find the magnitude of $\overrightarrow{AB}$ for $A(2, 3, 5)$ and $B(-1, 0, 4)$.
    A. $\sqrt{11}$ **B.** $\sqrt{19}$ **C.** $\sqrt{163}$ **D.** $\sqrt{91}$

26. _____

27. Solve $e^{\sqrt{x}} = 4$. Round your answer to the nearest hundredth.
    A. 1.18 **B.** 1.92 **C.** 0.69 **D.** 7.39

27. _____

28. Which is the graph of $G(3, 4)$?
    A.   **B.**   **C.**   **D.**

28. _____

29. Approximate the greatest real root of $f(x) = x^3 - 2x - 5$ to the nearest tenth.
    A. 1.8 **B.** 2.0 **C.** 2.1 **D.** -0.6

29. _____

30. Find $\sqrt[3]{-8i}$.
    A. $2 + i$ **B.** $-2 + i$ **C.** $2i$ **D.** $-2i$

30. _____

Final Test, Chapters 1-17 (continued)

31. Evaluate $\lim\limits_{n \to \infty} \dfrac{(-1)^n 2^n}{5n^4}$, or state that the limit does not exist.

31. _____

32. To the nearest tenth, find the area of a sector of a circle with central angle measuring 24° in a circle of radius 36 cm.

32. _____

33. Is the point $1 - 0.5i$ inside or outside the Mandelbrot set?

33. _____

34. Solve the system of equations algebraically.
$2x + 5y = 10$
$3x + 4y = 12$

34. _____

35. Find the length of the normal, p, of the equation $x + y = 3\sqrt{2}$. Then find the angle, θ, that the graph of the line makes with the positive x-axis.

35. _____

36. The weekly salaries of a sample of 100 recent graduates of a private women's college are normally distributed with a mean of $600 and a standard deviation of $80. Determine the interval about the sample mean that has a 1% confidence level. Use $t = 2.58$.

36. _____

37. Graph $y < |x + 1| + 3$ on the grid at the right.

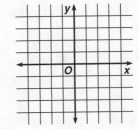

37. _____

38. Write the equation of the conic section with eccentricity of 0.8 and foci at $(1, -3)$ and $(9, -3)$.

38. _____

39. Find the area of the shaded region in the graph at the right.

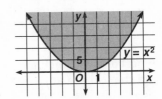

39. _____

40. True or false? $\operatorname{Sin}^{-1}(-x) = -\operatorname{Sin}^{-1} x$.

40. _____

41. A serial number is formed from the digits 1, 2, and 3 and the letters A and B. What is the probability that the serial number ends in 2A given that it ends in a letter?

41. _____

~ **Final Test, Chapters 1-17 (continued)**

42. Find the number of possible positive real zeros and the number of possible negative real zeros for $f(x) = x^3 + 2x^2 - 13x + 10$. Then determine all of the rational zeros.

42. _____

43. During one year, the cost of tuition, room, and board at a state university increased 5%. If the cost continues to increase at the rate of 5% a year, how long will it take, to the nearest year, to double the cost of tuition, room, and board?

43. _____

44. A football is kicked with an initial velocity of 42 ft/s at an angle of 35° to the horizontal. How far has it traveled horizontally after 0.5 seconds? Round your answer to the nearest tenth.

44. _____

45. True or false? If a connected graph contains n vertices, then a spanning tree for the graph contains $n - 1$ vertices from the graph.

45. _____

46. Name four different pairs of polar coordinates that represent the point A.

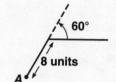

46. _____

47. Find the distance between $(4, -1)$ and $(-2, -5)$.

47. _____

48. Use a calculator to approximate the value of csc $(-145°)$ to four decimal places.

48. _____

49. The table below represents the deposits in the credit unions of a certain state. Find the median class of the data.

Deposits in Millions of Dollars	0-25	25-50	50-75	75-100
Number of Credit Unions	15	3	1	2

49. _____

50. Write the equation of the hyperbola for which the length of the transverse axis is 6 units and the foci are at $(0, 5)$ and $(0, -5)$.

50. _____

51. Find the values of x in the interval $0° \leq x \leq 360°$ that satisfy the equation $x = \arcsin \dfrac{\sqrt{2}}{2}$.

51. _____

52. Write a limit to find the area between the x-axis and the graph of $y = x^3$ from $x = 1$ to $x = 4$. Then find the area.

52. _____

Final Test, Chapters 1-17 (continued)

53. Describe the end behavior of the graph of $f(x) = 3 - x^2$.

53. _____

54. In the summer, Jill Pearson hires junior high school students for her lawn-mowing and garden-weeding service. In a given week, the total number of lawns mowed and gardens weeded cannot exceed 30. Three times the number of gardens weeded must be at least 25. If Ms. Pearson makes a profit of \$3 on each job, how many lawns should she contract to mow and how many gardens should she contract to weed? If the solution is not possible, state whether the problem is infeasible, has alternate optimal solutions, or is unbounded.

54. _____

55. Use a double-angle identity to find the value of cos 240°.

55. _____

56. In how many different ways can nine people be lined up to hit a piñata?

56. _____

57. Write $-1 - i$ in exponential form.

57. _____

58. Find the first three iterates of the function $f(z) = z + (2 - i)$ for $z_0 = -2i$.

58. _____

59. Express $5 - 2i$ in polar form. Round your answer to the nearest tenth.

59. _____

60. Solve $\sqrt{x + 1} - 6 = \sqrt{x + 8}$.

60. _____

61. Write an equation of the sine function with amplitude 4, period $\dfrac{3\pi}{2}$, and phase shift 0.

61. _____

62. Graph the system of equations. Then solve.
$4x - y = 3$
$y^2 - x^2 = 9$

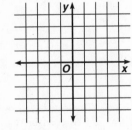

62. _____

63. Given that x is an integer, state the relation represented by $|y| = \dfrac{x}{2}$ and $0 \le x \le 2$ by listing a set of ordered pairs. Then state whether the relation is a function. Write *yes* or *no*.

63. _____

Final Test, Chapters 1-17 (continued)

64. Write the vector $(-6, 2, 3)$ as the sum of unit vectors.

64. _____

65. Make a histogram of the data below using a class interval of $7.50 on a seperate sheet of paper.

$15	$50	$24	$63	$18.50	$25	$35
$23	$70	$20	$32	$40	$20	$25.50
$60.50	$74.25	$28.50	$63	$13.75	$62	$32

66. Solve the system of equations by using matrices.
$2x - 3y + 2z = 13$
$3x + y - z = 2$
$x - 2y - z = 1$

66. _____

67. Two cards are drawn from a standard deck of 52 cards. What is the probability of having drawn both twos or both red?

67. _____

68. Use the graph at the right to determine the most specific name for the walk e, f, g, c, h.

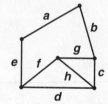

68. _____

69. Use a calculator to evaluate $3^{\sqrt{0.5}}$ to the nearest hundredth.

69. _____

70. Simplify $\sin x + \dfrac{\cot x}{\sec x}$.

70. _____

71. If a ball is thrown vertically upward with an initial speed of 32 ft/s, its instantaneous velocity at any time, t, is given by the formula $g(t) = 1600 - 32t$. The height of the ball in feet after t seconds can be found by integrating $g(t)$. Write a formula for the height in feet of the ball after t seconds.

71. _____

72. Find the coordinates of P' if $P(-1, 9)$ and P' are symmetric with respect to $M(1.5, 3)$.

72. _____

73. A paper company clear-cuts 20% of its 40,000 acres of timberland, leaving 32,000 acres of timber. If the company continues to clear-cut at the same rate, how many acres of timber will it have remaining at the end of 4 years?

73. _____

74. Express $\tan 315°$ as a function of an angle in Quadrant I.

74. _____

75. Describe the slope of a linear function whose iterations staircase out.

75. _____

Answers, Chapter 1 Test Form 1A & 1B

1. __A__
2. __B__
3. __D__
4. __B__
5. __D__
6. __C__
7. __C__
8. __B__
9. __D__
10. __C__
11. __C__

12. __D__
13. __D__
14. __A__
15. __B__
16. __A__
17. __D__
18. __B__
19. __C__
20. __C__

Bonus: __B__

1. __B__
2. __A__
3. __C__
4. __C__
5. __D__
6. __A__
7. __A__
8. __D__
9. __B__
10. __D__
11. __A__

12. __B__
13. __B__
14. __B__
15. __A__
16. __C__
17. __C__
18. __D__
19. __A__
20. __D__

Bonus: __C__

Glencoe Division, Macmillan/McGraw-Hill

Answers, Chapter 1 Test Form 2A

1. $D=\{-1,2,3,4\}$
$R=\{4, 6, 12\};$
yes

2. 0

3. $x = \pm 5$

4. $\dfrac{10}{x+1}$

5. $\dfrac{10x+10}{x}; \dfrac{10}{10+x}$

6. no;
$f^{-1}(x) = \dfrac{4+7x}{x}$

7. $f^{-1}(x) = x^2 + 3;$
yes

8. See students' work.

9. See students' work.

10. See students' work.

11. See students' work.

12. $x = \dfrac{7}{2}$

13. $3\sqrt{5}$

14. $-\dfrac{9}{2}$

15. $0; 0$

16. $y = -3x + 10$

17. $y = -\dfrac{7}{3}x + \dfrac{19}{3}$

18. $2x + y + 9 = 0$

19. $x - 2y + 8 = 0$

20. $\dfrac{10}{3}; 4$

21. $-\dfrac{p}{m}; \dfrac{q}{m}$

22. Yes, there is only one y-value for every x-value.

23. $-2 < x - y \leq 4$

24. $y = 4.8x$

25. See students' work.

Bonus: $f^{-1}(x) = \sqrt[3]{x^{20}}$

Glencoe Division, Macmillan/McGraw-Hill

Answers, Chapter 1 Test Form 2B

1. $D = \{-8,1,6,9\}$
   $R = \{-8, 1, 3, 4, 9\}$; no

2. 6

3. $x = \pm 2$

4. $x - 3, x \neq -2$

5. $x^2 + 3x - 4;$
   $x^2 - x - 4$

6. yes

7. $f^{-1}(x) = \dfrac{3x + 5}{x}$; yes

8. See students' work.

9. See students' work.

10. See students' work.

11. See students' work.

12. $x = -\dfrac{1}{4}$

13. $7\sqrt{2}$

14. $-\dfrac{1}{5}$

15. undefined; none

16. $y = \dfrac{1}{3}x - \dfrac{10}{3}$

17. $y = -\dfrac{11}{3}x - \dfrac{4}{3}$

18. $x - 2y + 1 = 0$

19. $4x - y - 12 = 0$

20. $-\dfrac{9}{4}; \dfrac{1}{4}$

21. $\dfrac{k}{h}; \dfrac{d}{h}$

22. Yes, there is only one y-value for every x-value.

23. $-6 \leq x + 2y < 1$

24. $y = 0.78x$

25. See students' work.

Bonus: $f^{-1}(x) = \sqrt{x^{15}}$

Glencoe Division, Macmillan/McGraw-Hill

Answers, Chapter 1 Quizzes

1. $D = \{-2, 6, 7, 9\}$
   $R = \{1, 2, 3, 4, 5\}$
2. no
3. $\{(-2, 14), (-1, 11), (0, 8)\}$; yes
4. $\dfrac{16}{11}$
5. $\dfrac{4n - 8}{2n - 1}$
6. $\dfrac{43x - 4}{6}$
7. $\dfrac{x + 2}{42x - 6}$
8. $\dfrac{7x + 1}{6}$
9. $\dfrac{7x + 8}{6}$
10. yes

1. $y \geq \dfrac{1}{3}x + 2$
2. $-\dfrac{3}{2}$
3. See students' work.
4. See students' work.
5. See students' work.

1. $11\sqrt{2}$
2. 1
3. no
4. 5
5. See students' work.

1. $y = -x$
2. $y = \dfrac{1}{12}x + \dfrac{5}{4}$
3. $x - 4y - 9 = 0$
4. $2x + 3y - 16 = 0$
5. $y = 0.5x + 1$

1. $D = \{-4, 0, 1, 2, 6\}$
   $R = \{-2, 1, 3, 5, 9\}$

2. $(6, 3)$ and $(6, 1)$

3. 35

4. $6k^2 + 8k + 5$

5. $x = \frac{1}{3}$

6. $-\sqrt{2} < x < \sqrt{2}$

7. $-x^2 - x + 6$

8. $-x^2 + 2x + 2$

9. no;
   $f^{-1}(x) = 4x - 7$

10. $f^{-1}(x) = \frac{2}{x}$

11. $g^{-1}(x) = \frac{6x + 7}{3}$

12. $-3 < -x + y \le 0$

13. 15

14. See students' work.

15. See students' work.

1. C

2. A

3. D

4. C

5. D

6. D

7. A

8. B

9. A

10. B

Answers, Chapter 2 Test Form 1A & 1B

1. C

2. A

3. D

4. A

5. B

6. B

7. C

8. A

9. A

10. D

11. B

12. A

13. D

14. A

15. C

Bonus: B

1. B

2. A

3. D

4. B

5. B

6. B

7. C

8. C

9. D

10. B

11. A

12. C

13. C

14. B

15. D

Bonus: B

1. consistent and dependent

2. (2, −1); See students' graphs.

3. no solution

4. $\begin{bmatrix} -1 & -5 \\ -7 & -4 \\ -1 & 10 \end{bmatrix}$

5. $\begin{bmatrix} -6 & 15 & 3 \\ 9 & 12 & -18 \end{bmatrix}$

6. (−5, −1)

7. 11

8. $\begin{bmatrix} \dfrac{1}{2} & 0 \\ -\dfrac{1}{6} & \dfrac{1}{3} \end{bmatrix}$

9. (5, 0)

10. $\dfrac{1}{2}$ pound

11. (4, 1, −7)

12. See students' work. Vertices: (0, 0), (0, 6), (6, 0); minimum: 0; maximum: 30

13. See students' work. no minimum; maximum: 0

14. $150

15. $2500

Bonus: $x = \dfrac{ce - bf}{ae - bd}$

1. **consistent and independent**

2. **(2, 1); See students' graphs.**

3. $\left(-\dfrac{5}{13}, \dfrac{19}{13}\right)$

4. $\begin{bmatrix} 5 & 4 \\ -5 & 9 \\ 9 & -2 \end{bmatrix}$

5. $\begin{bmatrix} 9 & -16 & 9 \\ 0 & 25 & -30 \\ -18 & 7 & 12 \end{bmatrix}$

6. $\left(-\dfrac{5}{4}, \dfrac{3}{4}\right)$

7. **101**

8. $\begin{bmatrix} -\dfrac{1}{38} & \dfrac{7}{38} \\ \dfrac{5}{38} & \dfrac{3}{38} \end{bmatrix}$

9. **(3, −4)**

10. **Infinitely many solutions; the system is consistent and dependent.**

11. **(2, 4, −3)**

12. **1 oz of each**

13. **See students' work. vertices: (0, 0), (−4, 0), (−4,−4); maximum: 0; minimum: −32**

14. **20 Giverny benches and 40 Kensington benches**

15. **not possible; unbounded**

Bonus: $x + y = 3$

1. <u>**one solution**</u>

2. <u>**See students' graphs.**</u>

$$\left(\frac{1}{2}, -\frac{2}{3}\right)$$

3. <u>**infinitely many solutions**</u>

4. $\begin{bmatrix} -8 & 12 \\ 0 & -10 \end{bmatrix}$

5. $\begin{bmatrix} -32 & 36 & 1 \\ -10 & 8 & 19 \\ 62 & -68 & -12 \end{bmatrix}$

1. <u>**−28**</u>

2. <u>**33**</u>

3. $\begin{bmatrix} \dfrac{3}{14} & \dfrac{4}{7} \\ -\dfrac{2}{7} & -\dfrac{3}{7} \end{bmatrix}$

4. $\left(\dfrac{2}{9}, -\dfrac{1}{3}\right)$

5. <u>**(−1, 2)**</u>

1. $\begin{bmatrix} 2 & -1 & 1 & \vdots & 6 \\ 1 & 3 & 5 & \vdots & 10 \\ 4 & -4 & 2 & \vdots & -3 \end{bmatrix}$

2. <u>**(2, 3)**</u>

3. <u>**(−1, 4, 2)**</u>

4. <u>**(3, −2, 4)**</u>

5. <u>**37.5°, 67.5°, 75°**</u>

1. <u>**21**</u>

2. <u>**See students' work.**
(1, 3), (0, 3)
(0, 0), (2, 0)</u>

3. <u>**6**</u>

4. <u>**−6**</u>

5. <u>**infeasible**</u>

1. **See students' graphs.**
$(1, -3)$

2. $(2, -1)$

3. $\begin{bmatrix} 0 & 0 & -3 \\ 1 & 3 & 5 \\ -10 & -3 & 8 \end{bmatrix}$

4. $(1, -5)$

5. $\left(-5, -\dfrac{20}{3}\right)$

6. $\begin{bmatrix} 6 & 0 \\ -12 & -4 \end{bmatrix}$

7. $\begin{bmatrix} 28 & 2 & -15 \\ 30 & 29 & -53 \\ -26 & -15 & 32 \end{bmatrix}$

8. **107**

9. **64**

10. $(29, -18)$

1. **D**

2. **A**

3. **D**

4. **B**

5. **A**

6. **A**

7. **C**

8. **D**

Answers, Chapter 3 Test Form 1A & 1B

1. __D__

2. __A__

3. __B__

4. __C__

5. __B__

6. __D__

7. __A__

8. __A__

9. __B__

10. __C__

11. __C__

12. __A__

13. __B__

14. __C__

15. __A__

Bonus: __B__

1. __C__

2. __B__

3. __A__

4. __A__

5. __D__

6. __B__

7. __A__

8. __C__

9. __A__

10. __C__

11. __D__

12. __A__

13. __A__

14. __D__

15. __B__

Bonus: __B__

Glencoe Division, Macmillan/McGraw-Hill

1. **y-axis**

2. **See students' work.**

3. **neither**

4. **(0, 2)**

5. **See students' work.**

6. $y = \pm \sqrt{x + 2} - 1$

7. **no**

8. **See students' work.**

9. **vert: $x = 0$,**
   slant:
   $y = x - \frac{5}{2}$

10. **See students' work.**

11. **See students' work.**

12. $\{x \mid x > 5 \text{ or } x < -7\}$

13. $3.6x^2 - 1.4x + 5$

14. $y = 13x + 11$

15. **(0, −1), rel. max.;**
    (2, −13), min.;
    $\left(-\frac{5}{4}, -4.4\right)$, **rel. min;**
    (1.2, -7.8), (-0.7, -2.9),
    pts. of inflection

16. **(0, 0); pt. of inflection**

17. **x: 0, −1; y: 0**

18. **infinite discontinuity**

19. **See students' graphs.**
    $x > 0$

20. **As $x \to \infty$,**
    $f(x) \to -\infty$.
    As $x \to -\infty$,
    $f(x) \to \infty$.

Bonus: **$x < -3$ and $x > 1$**

1. **x-axis**

2. **See students' work.**

3. **even**

4. **(0, 1)**

5. **See students' work.**

6. $y = \pm \sqrt{x - 2}$

7. **yes**

8. **See students' work.**

9. **vert: $x = -5$
   horiz: $y = -2$**

10. **See students' work.**

11. **See students' work.**

12. $\{x | 4 \leq x \leq 5\}$

13. $6x^2 - 6x$

14. $y = 10x - 11$

15. **(−1, 1), rel. max.;
    (1, −3), rel. min.
    (0, −1), pt. of infl.**

16. **one; (0, 1)**

17. **x: 0, 3, −2;
    y: 0**

18. **jump discontinuity**

19. **increase**

20. **As $x \to \infty$,
    $y \to \infty$.
    As $x \to -\infty$,
    $y \to \infty$.**

Bonus **See students' work.**

1. **both lines**

2. **odd**

3. **no**

4. **See students' work; translates the graph 2 units down**

5. **reflects over x-axis, translates 1 unit right**

----

1. **no**

2. **See students' work; yes.**

3. **vert: $x = -6$, $x = 6$; horiz: $y = 0$**

4. **vertical stretch**

5. **asymptotes: $x = 1$, $y = 0$; hole: $\left(4, \frac{1}{3}\right)$**

1. **See students' work.**

2. **$\{x \mid x < -\frac{1}{2}$ or $x > \frac{7}{2}\}$**

3. **$12x^2 - 4x - 1$**

4. **-2**

5. **$y = -6x - 11$**

1. **$(0, 0)$, pt. of infl; $(-1, 2)$, rel. max.; $(1, -2)$, rel. min.**

2. **x: -1, 0, 1; y: 0**

3. **$x < 0$, $x > 0$**

4. **jump discontinuity**

5. **See students' graphs; as $x \to \infty$, $f(x) \to 0$**

1. origin

2. y-axis

3. even

4. neither

5. Shrinks vertically, translates 5 units left.

6. Shrinks horizontally, translates 1 unit down.

7. yes

8. $y = \pm \sqrt{x + 3}$

9. $y = \frac{1}{2}\sqrt[3]{4(x - 5)}$

10. See students' work; yes.

11. See students' work; no.

12. vert: $x = 0$; slant: $y = x + 1$

13. vert: $x = 1$ horiz: $y = 0$

14. See students' work.

15. See students' work.

1. B

2. C

3. A

4. B

5. A

6. C

7. B

8. D

9. A

Answers, Chapter 4 Test Form 1A & 1B

1. __C__

2. __C__

3. __A__

4. __B__

5. __A__

6. __C__

7. __A__

8. __D__

9. __C__

10. __D__

11. __A__

12. __D__

13. __B__

14. __C__

15. __B__

16. __C__

17. __D__

18. __C__

19. __A__

20. __D__

Bonus: __D__

1. __C__

2. __A__

3. __A__

4. __C__

5. __C__

6. __D__

7. __D__

8. __B__

9. __C__

10. __B__

11. __D__

12. __A__

13. __C__

14. __A__

15. __C__

16. __C__

17. __B__

18. __D__

19. __B__

20. __A__

Bonus: __B__

Glencoe Division, Macmillan/McGraw-Hill

1. $12, -\dfrac{13}{2}$

2. 4

3. $\dfrac{-5 \pm \sqrt{89}}{8}$

4. 0.5

5. $-3 \le x \le 1$

6. $-2.5, -3$

7. no solution

8. $a \le -\dfrac{13}{4}, a > -2$

9. $-3, 1.5$

10. $1 \le x < 65$

11. $0, 1, 2$

12. $x^3 - x^2 - 10x - 8 = 0$

13. See students' work.

14. See students' work.

15. $x^3 + 2x^2$ R4

16. 0; yes

17. -12; imaginary

18. $\pm 1, \pm 2, \pm 3,$ $\pm 6, \pm 0.5, \pm 1.5$

19. none

20. 3 or 1; 0

21. -1 and 0

22. 0.9

23. 2

24. $\dfrac{4}{x} + \dfrac{3}{x+1} - \dfrac{1}{x-2}$

25. $2'' \times 10'' \times 14''$

Bonus: 4 or -4

1. $-\dfrac{13}{8}, 1$

2. $\dfrac{\pm\sqrt{6}}{6}$

3. $\dfrac{9 \pm \sqrt{105}}{4}$

4. 7

5. $2 \pm 3i$

6. $q \le -\dfrac{3}{4}, q > 0$

7. -1

8. $0 < x < 2, x > 6$

9. $3 \pm \sqrt{6}$

10. $-\dfrac{5}{2} \le x \le 10$

11. $0, 1, -4$

12. $x^3 - x^2 - 17x - 15 = 0$

13. **See students' work.**

14. **See students' work.**

15. $x^2 - 4x + 15$ R-65

16. -1; no

17. 0; one real root

18. $\pm 1, \pm 2, \pm 0.25, \pm 0.5$

19. -3

20. 1; 2 or 0

21. 1 and 2

22. 3.5

23. 0

24. $\dfrac{2}{x} - \dfrac{2}{x-4} + \dfrac{3}{x+3}$

25. $\dfrac{1}{2}$ or 3

Bonus: 6 or -6

1. $\pm 6i$

2. $0, 4, -1.5$

3. $2x^3 - x^2 - 2x + 1 = 0$

4. $12, -7$

5. $\dfrac{1}{3}, \dfrac{1}{4}$

6. 73; 2 distinct real roots

7. $2, 0.5$

8. $\dfrac{1 \pm i\sqrt{119}}{6}$

9. See students work.

10. See students work.

---

1. $x^2 - 7x - 3$

2. 55; no

3. 18; no

4. $\pm 1, \pm 3, \pm 1.5, \pm 0.5$; 1

5. 2 or 0; 1

---

1. -5 and -4; -1 and 0; 1 and 2

2. no real zeros

3. 1.2

4. $-0.9, 2.8$

5. upper 4; lower -1

6. $2, -5$

7. $y \le -\dfrac{21}{25}$

8. $-1 \le w < 0$; $\dfrac{2}{5} \le w < 1$

9. $4 \pm 2\sqrt{3}$

10. $\dfrac{6}{p} + \dfrac{5}{p-2} - \dfrac{7}{p+1}$

---

1. 7

2. no real solution

3. 7

4. -13

5. $t > 14$

1. $\pm 2\sqrt{5}$

2. $0, 1$

3. $x^3 - 4x^2 + 9x - 36 = 0$

4. $-14, 6$

5. $\dfrac{2}{3}, -1$

6. -23, no real roots

7. $\dfrac{1 \pm i\sqrt{29}}{10}$

8. $\dfrac{2}{3}, -\dfrac{3}{2}$

9. See students' work.

10. See students' work.

11. $x^2 - x - 8$ R -12

12. 22; no

13. 0; yes

14. $\pm 1, \pm 2, \pm 3, \pm 6, \pm 1.5, \pm 0.5$; none

15. 3 or $1; 0$

1. B

2. A

3. C

4. A

5. A

6. D

7. B

8. D

9. A

10. C

Glencoe Division, Macmillan/McGraw-Hill

ax: 6;
n: 3

$+ 10x^2 +$
$= 0$

$^2 - 9x + 25$
.e students'
aphs;
1, 1)

.e students'
aphs.

$\begin{bmatrix} -1 & -1 & | & 2 \\ 1 & 2 & -2 & | & 3 \\ 3 & -2 & -4 & | & 5 \end{bmatrix};$

, 1, 2)

$\dfrac{5}{+6} - \dfrac{3}{4n-1}$

oth axes

s $x \to \infty, f(y) \to$
∞; as $x \to -\infty,$
$y) \to -\infty$

finitely many

$\dfrac{2}{3}, 3$

$\dfrac{2 - \sqrt{10}}{3} \le$

$\le \dfrac{-2 + \sqrt{10}}{3}$

13. $-\dfrac{1}{2x^2}$

14. no

15. $y = \pm\sqrt{10x};$ no

16. yes; 8

17. moved 2 units right

18. $y = -x - 1$

19. yes

20. 20 mph

21. no solution

22. 64

23. $(4, 2)$

24. 1.5

25. See students' graphs.

26. $y = -6x - 11;$ See students' graphs.

27. $x + 3y - 18 = 0$

28. 5; no

29. 12

30. 11

31. $y = x - 5$

32. -41

33. D: {−5, −2, 4}; R: {0, 1, 2, 3}; no

34. neither

35. 1

36. $\left\{ x \middle| -\dfrac{2}{3} \le x \le 2 \right\}$

37. $\begin{bmatrix} 3 & 11 \\ 4 & 18 \end{bmatrix}$

38. -5

39. $y = -x - 2$

40. {(−1, 1), (0, 2), (1, 1)}; yes

41. infeasible

42. $\dfrac{-2 \pm 3\sqrt{2}}{2}$

43. infinite discontinuity

44. $-\dfrac{8}{3a}$

45. 2000; 3500

46. 3ft, 4ft, 7ft

47. $(4, -1, 3)$

48. $\dfrac{1}{2}, -\dfrac{7}{2}$

49. $(1, -3);$ maximum

50. $(1, 2)$

Glencoe Division, Macmillan/McGraw-Hill

Answers, Chapter 5 Test Form 1A & 1B

1. D

2. D

3. C

4. A

5. B

6. A

7. C

8. B

9. C

10. A

11. D

12. B

13. D

14. C

15. A

16. B

17. D

18. A

19. A

20. C

21. D

22. B

23. B

24. A

25. A

Bonus: A

1. A

2. B

3. B

4. D

5. A

6. D

7. A

8. D

9. D

10. C

11. B

12. A

13. B

14. A

15. C

16. D

17. A

18. C

19. D

20. C

21. B

22. D

23. A

24. B

25. D

Bonus: A

Glencoe Division, Macmillan/McGraw-Hill

1. $42°$

2. $\dfrac{\pi}{4}$

3. **Quadrant IV**

4. $\dfrac{15\pi}{4}$

5. $220°$

6. 4.299

7. $66.8°$

8. 29.0 cm^2

9. π **in.**

10. $\dfrac{12}{13}$

11. $-\dfrac{5}{12}$

12. $-\dfrac{12}{5}$

13. $\dfrac{13}{12}$

14. $-\dfrac{13}{5}$

15. **undefined**

16. $-\dfrac{2\sqrt{3}}{3}$

17. 0.0872

18. 1.1850

19. $38°$

20. 3.1

21. 5.1

22. **no solutions**

23. 26.3

24. 27.1

25. 11.1

26. $76°$

27. $48°$

28. 18.7 units^2

29. 10.2 units^2

30. 20.71 **feet**

Bonus: $-\sqrt{5}$

Glencoe Division, Macmillan/McGraw-Hill

1. _____ 16° _____

2. _____ $\dfrac{\pi}{3}$ _____

3. __ Quadrant I __

4. _____ $\dfrac{13\pi}{4}$ _____

5. _____ −690° _____

6. _____ 3.555 _____

7. _____ 36.8° _____

8. ___ 88.0 yd² ___

9. _____ $\dfrac{15\pi}{4}$ cm _____

10. _____ $-\dfrac{15}{17}$ _____

11. _____ $\dfrac{15}{8}$ _____

12. _____ $\dfrac{8}{15}$ _____

13. _____ $-\dfrac{17}{8}$ _____

14. _____ $-\dfrac{17}{15}$ _____

15. _____ $-\dfrac{2\sqrt{3}}{3}$ _____

16. _____ 1 _____

17. _____ −1.1106 _____

18. _____ −0.9589 _____

19. _____ 72° _____

20. _____ 3.9 _____

21. _____ 12.6 _____

22. __ 1 solution __

23. _____ 5.1 _____

24. _____ 6.6 _____

25. _____ 10.0 _____

26. _____ 52° _____

27. _____ 30° _____

28. __ 10.4 units² __

29. __ 6.1 units² __

30. __ 21.65 feet __

Bonus: _____ $\sqrt{10}$ _____

Glencoe Division, Macmillan/McGraw-Hill

1. __30°__

2. $\dfrac{\pi}{3}$

3. __Quadrant II__

4. $\dfrac{35\pi}{9}$

5. __−15°__

6. __0.874__

7. __76.4°__

8. __6.2m²__

9. __84.3 yd²__

10. $\dfrac{8\pi}{15}$m

1. $-\dfrac{\sqrt{6}}{3}$

2. $-\dfrac{\sqrt{3}}{3}$

3. $\dfrac{\sqrt{2}}{2}$

4. $-\sqrt{3}$

5. $-\dfrac{\sqrt{6}}{2}$

6. __0__

7. $\dfrac{\sqrt{3}}{3}$

8. __2__

9. __0.4067__

10. __−225.9508__

1. $\dfrac{24}{7}$

2. $\dfrac{25}{24}$

3. __47°__

4. __10.2__

5. __9.5__

6. __2 solutions__

7. __65° 50'__

8. __4.0__

9. __5.6__

10. __more than 30.6 feet away__

1. __34° 42'__

2. __22° 27'__

3. __122° 51'__

4. __33.7 units²__

5. __3.9 units²__

Glencoe Division, Macmillan/McGraw-Hill

Answers, Chapter 5 Mid-Chapter Test, Standardized Test

1. $80°$

2. $\dfrac{\pi}{6}$

3. Quadrant II

4. $-\dfrac{7\pi}{30}$

5. $\dfrac{5\pi}{12}$

6. $48°$

7. $-162°$

8. 0.246

9. $97.4°$

10. 15.4 cm^2

11. 260.1 m^2

12. $2\pi \text{ yd}$

13. $520°$ and $-200°$

14. 17.0 cm

15. 103.9 cm^2

16. $-\dfrac{2\sqrt{2}}{3}$

17. $\dfrac{1}{3}$

18. $-2\sqrt{2}$

19. $-\dfrac{\sqrt{2}}{4}$

20. $-\dfrac{3\sqrt{2}}{4}$

1. A

2. C

3. C

4. D

5. B

6. A

7. B

8. D

9. B

10. C

Glencoe Division, Macmillan/McGraw-Hill

Answers, Chapter 6 Test Form 1A & 1B

1. __D__

2. __A__

3. __B__

4. __B__

5. __D__

6. __B__

7. __A__

8. __C__

9. __A__

10. __A__

11. __A__

12. __C__

13. __D__

14. __D__

15. __B__

16. __B__

17. __A__

18. __C__

Bonus: __C__

1. __C__

2. __D__

3. __A__

4. __A__

5. __D__

6. __B__

7. __C__

8. __A__

9. __B__

10. __D__

11. __C__

12. __A__

13. __C__

14. __B__

15. __D__

16. __D__

17. __C__

18. __C__

Bonus: __C__

Glencoe Division, Macmillan/McGraw-Hill

Answers, Chapter 6 Test Form 2A

1. $180° + 360k°$

2. $90° + 180k°$

3. D = all $x \ne 90°$ + $180k°$, where k is any integer R = all real numbers

4. $6; 4\pi; -2\pi$

5. none; $2\pi; 2\pi$

6. $y = \pm 5 \cos (8x + 1440°)$

7. $y = \pm\frac{2}{3}\sin\left(\frac{1}{2}x - \frac{\pi}{4}\right)$

8. $0°, 180°, 360°$

9. $-45°, 45°$

10. See students' work.

11. $\frac{\sqrt{3}}{2}$

12. $45°$

13. 1

14. $\frac{7}{25}$

15. $\frac{\sqrt{3}}{2}$

16. $\frac{3}{4}$

17. 0

18. $D = 0° \le x \le 180°$ $R = -1 \le y \le 1$

19. $x = \frac{\sqrt{2}}{2}$

20. $2; 1; 1; \frac{3}{4}$

21. $y = \frac{1}{2} \cos \frac{\pi}{2} t$

22. $h = 4 \cos \frac{2\pi}{5} t$

23. See students' work.

24. See students' work.

25. See students' work.

Bonus: amplitude = $|a|$
period = $\frac{2\pi}{|b|}$
phase shift = $-c$

266

1. $90° + 360k°$

2. $135° + 180k°$

3. $D =$ all $x \neq 180k°$, where k is any integer $R =$ all real numbers

4. $\frac{1}{2}; \frac{2\pi}{3}; -\frac{4\pi}{9}$

5. none; $\frac{\pi}{2}; \frac{\pi}{2}$

6. $y = \pm\, 4 \sin\left(\frac{8}{3}x + 160°\right)$

7. $y = \pm\frac{1}{4}\cos\left(\frac{2}{3}x - \frac{\pi}{3}\right)$

8. $0°, 360°$

9. $30°, 150°$

10. See students' work.

11. $\frac{\sqrt{3}}{2}$

12. $0°$

13. $\frac{\sqrt{3}}{3}$

14. $\frac{24}{25}$

15. 0

16. $\frac{4}{3}$

17. $\sqrt{3}$

18. $D = -1 \leq x \leq 1$ $R = 0° \leq y \leq 180°$

19. $x = -\frac{\sqrt{2}}{2}$

20. $4; 4; \frac{1}{4}; -\frac{1}{3}$

21. $y = \frac{1}{4}\cos\frac{\pi}{3}t$

22. $h = -6\cos\frac{2\pi}{15}t$

23. See students' work.

24. See students' work.

25. See students' work.

Bonus: amplitude = none

period = $\frac{\pi}{|b|}$

phase shift = c

Glencoe Division, Macmillan/McGraw-Hill

1. $45° + 180k°$

2. $D = $ all $x \neq 180k°$, where k is any integer; $R = y \leq -1, y \geq 1$

3. See students' work.

4. See students' work.

5. $\frac{1}{3}$; 2π; $-\frac{\pi}{6}$

6. $y = \pm 7\cos(2x - 3\pi)$

1. See students' work.

2. See students' work.

3. $-150°, 30°$

4. $\frac{1}{2}$

5. 1

1. $\frac{1}{2}$

2. $\sqrt{3}$

3. 0

4. $\frac{2}{3}$

5. -1

6. $D = $ all $x \neq 90° + 180k°$, where k is any integer; $R = $ all reals

7. $D = -1 \leq x \leq 1$
$R = -90° \leq y \leq 90°$

8. See students' work.

9. See students' work.

10. $x = -1$

1. 0.4; 0.1; 10; $-\frac{1}{40}$

2. 100; 12; $\frac{1}{12}$; 0

3. $y = \pm 5 \sin \frac{2\pi}{3} t$

4. $y = -12 \cos 4\pi t$

5. $h = -8 \cos \frac{2\pi}{3} t + 7$

Answers, Chapter 6 Mid-Chapter Test, Standardized Test

1. $180k°$, where k is any integer
2. $45° + 180k°$, where k is any integer
3. D = all reals
   $R = -1 \leq y \leq 1$

4. See students' work.
5. $2; \frac{2\pi}{3}; \frac{\pi}{4}$
6. $1; \pi; -\frac{\pi}{8}$
7. $y = \pm 3 \cos\left(\frac{12}{5}x - 432°\right)$
8. $y = \pm\frac{1}{6} \sin(12x + 6\pi)$
9. $225°, 315°$
10. $-30°, -150°$
11. 1
12. 1
13. 1
14. See students' work.
15. See students' work.

1. D
2. A
3. B
4. B
5. C
6. D
7. A
8. A
9. D
10. D

Glencoe Division, Macmillan/McGraw-Hill

Answers, Chapter 7 Test Form 1A & 1B

1. C

2. D

3. A

4. D

5. A

6. D

7. D

8. B

9. A

10. A

11. B

12. C

13. C

14. A

15. B

16. B

17. D

18. B

19. B

20. B

Bonus: B

1. A

2. D

3. D

4. C

5. D

6. A

7. B

8. A

9. D

10. B

11. A

12. A

13. C

14. B

15. D

16. A

17. C

18. D

19. C

20. A

Bonus: C

1. $-\dfrac{5}{3}$

2. $-\dfrac{4}{5}$

3. $-\sin 30°$

4. $\tan^2\theta$

5. II, III

6. 2

7. See students' work.

8. $\dfrac{\sqrt{6}-\sqrt{2}}{4}$

9. $\dfrac{84}{85}$

10. $-\dfrac{1}{2}\sqrt{2+\sqrt{3}}$

11. $-\dfrac{3}{5}$

12. infinitely many

13. 90°

14. $45° + 180k°$, $120° + 360k°$, $240° + 360k°$

15. $\sqrt{3}x + y + 14 = 0$

16. $\dfrac{-2x}{\sqrt{5}} + \dfrac{y}{\sqrt{5}} - \dfrac{3}{\sqrt{5}} = 0$

17. 37°

18. $\dfrac{2\sqrt{5}}{5}$ or about 0.89 units

19. $\dfrac{3\sqrt{2}}{4}$ or about 1.06 units

20. $\left(3\sqrt{5} + 2\sqrt{10}\right)x + \left(\sqrt{5} - \sqrt{10}\right)y + 6\sqrt{5} - \sqrt{10} = 0$

Bonus: They are perpendicular to each other.

1. for all θ except multiples of 180°

2. $\dfrac{-3\sqrt{7}}{7} \approx -1.13$

3. $\tan 65°$

4. $\tan x$

5. I, II

6. Sample answer: $\csc x = 1$

7. See students' work.

8. $\dfrac{\sqrt{2} - \sqrt{6}}{4}$

9. $\dfrac{56}{65}$

10. $\sqrt{2} - 1$

11. $-\dfrac{120}{169}$

12. See students' work.

13. 45°, 135°

14. 60° + 180k°, 120° + 180k° where k is any integer

15. $\sqrt{34}$

16. $\dfrac{-5x}{\sqrt{26}} + \dfrac{y}{\sqrt{26}} - \dfrac{3}{\sqrt{26}} = 0$

17. 1 unit

18. $\dfrac{9\sqrt{5}}{10}$ or about 2.01 units

19. $\dfrac{\sqrt{5}}{5}$ or about 0.45 units

20. $\left(5\sqrt{5} + \sqrt{26}\right)x - \left(\sqrt{5} - 2\sqrt{26}\right)y - 6\sqrt{5} + 2\sqrt{26} = 0$

Bonus: See students' work.

Answers, Chapter 7 Quizzes

1. $\dfrac{\sqrt{53}}{7}$

2. $-\cos 60°$

3. $\cos x,\ \sin x \neq 0$

4. Sample answer: $\tan \theta = \dfrac{\sqrt{3}}{3}$

5. See students' work.

---

1. $-\dfrac{\sqrt{2}}{2}$

2. $\dfrac{117}{125}$

3. $\dfrac{24}{25}$

4. $\dfrac{\sqrt{2} - \sqrt{2}}{2}$

5. See students' work.

---

1. $0°,\ 90°$

2. $180°$

3. $45° + 180k°,\ -45° + 180k°$

4. $\sqrt{3}x + y - 2\sqrt{2} = 0$

5. $\dfrac{x}{\sqrt{2}} - \dfrac{y}{\sqrt{2}} - \dfrac{5}{\sqrt{2}} = 0$

---

1. $\dfrac{11\sqrt{17}}{17}$ or about 2.67 units

2. 0; the point is on the line

3. $\dfrac{\sqrt{10}}{10}$ or about 0.32 units

4. $d_1 = -d_2$

5. $\left(\sqrt{2} - \sqrt{5}\right)x - \left(2\sqrt{2} + \sqrt{5}\right)y + 2\sqrt{2} + \sqrt{5} = 0$

Glencoe Division, Macmillan/McGraw-Hill

1. **1**

2. **undefined**

3. **sin 60°**

4. **tan 45°**

5. **1, cos $A \neq 0$**

6. **Sample answer: cos $x = \frac{1}{2}$**

7. **Sample answer: cos $x = -1$**

8. **$\dfrac{\sqrt{2} - \sqrt{6}}{4}$**

9. **$\dfrac{\sqrt{6} - \sqrt{2}}{4}$**

10. **$\dfrac{220}{221}$**

11. **$\dfrac{56}{33}$**

12. **See students' work.**

13. **$-\dfrac{527}{625}$**

14. **$2 - \sqrt{3}$**

15. **See students' work.**

1. **A**

2. **C**

3. **B**

4. **A**

5. **B**

6. **C**

7. **A**

8. **D**

Glencoe Division, Macmillan/McGraw-Hill

Answers, Chapter 8 Test Form 1A & 1B

1. __B__

2. __A__

3. __D__

4. __B__

5. __C__

6. __C__

7. __A__

8. __A__

9. __A__

10. __C__

11. __C__

12. __D__

13. __B__

14. __A__

15. __B__

16. __D__

17. __C__

18. __C__

19. __C__

20. __D__

Bonus: __A__

1. __A__

2. __C__

3. __B__

4. __A__

5. __C__

6. __D__

7. __A__

8. __B__

9. __B__

10. __B__

11. __D__

12. __D__

13. __B__

14. __B__

15. __A__

16. __C__

17. __C__

18. __D__

19. __D__

20. __C__

Bonus: __D__

Glencoe Division, Macmillan/McGraw-Hill

1. __10.8 m__

2. $2\vec{r} - \vec{s}$

3. $k = -3$

4. __18.36__

5. __4.12__

6. $11\vec{i} - 4\vec{j} + 4\vec{k}$

7. $(2, -15, 2)$

8. $(-33, 10)$

9. $(3, -13)$

10. $(-1, 7, 0)$

11. $(-6, -36, 20)$

12. $(7, 68, -30)$

13. __-27; no__

14. __0; yes__

15. $(-41, -61, 18)$

16. $(38, -52, 79)$

17. **Sample answer:** $(-1, 4, -2)$

18. **20.2 N; 11°24' above west**

19. __120.2 lb__

20. $x = t; y = -3t + 4$

21. $x = t; y = \frac{5}{3}t - \frac{1}{3}$

22. $y = x + 6$

23. $y = \frac{1}{2}x - 5$

24. __79.7 ft__

25. __64.9 ft__

Bonus: $x = t; y = 3t - 4$

1. **2.4 yd**

2. $\vec{s} - 4\vec{r}$

3. $k = -4$

4. **10.82**

5. **7.35**

6. $-9\vec{i} - 5\vec{j} - 2\vec{k}$

7. **(−7, 10, −7)**

8. **(7, −21)**

9. **(−5, 23)**

10. **(−3, 3, −3)**

11. **(41, −25, 21)**

12. **(57, −33, 27)**

13. **−12; no**

14. **6; no**

15. **(18, 48, 28)**

16. **(−10, 24, 47)**

17. **Sample answer: (1, 3, −2)**

18. **17.5 N; 70°14' below east**

19. **91.5 lb**

20. $x = t;\ y = -t + 3$

21. $x = t;\ y = -\frac{1}{2}t + \frac{5}{4}$

22. $y = -2x + 8$

23. $y = -2x - 8$

24. **23.8 ft**

25. **6.2 ft**

Bonus: $x = t;\ y = -4t + 6$

1. horiz. = 1.36 mm; vert. = 12.93 mm

2. 12.6 m

3. 2.06 miles

4. ≈ 6.1 cm

5. (−7, −5)

6. $2\sqrt{13}$ or 7.21

7. $-15\vec{i} + 5\vec{j}$

8. (−15, 20)

9. (21, −24)

10. (6, −10)

1. (1, −12, 0)

2. 18.14

3. $10\vec{i} + 3\vec{j} - 9\vec{k}$

4. (62, −12, 3)

5. (37, 6, −27)

6. 41; no

7. 9; no

8. (−11, 0, −33)

9. (18, 38, 25)

10. Sample answer: (−2, 2, −3)

1. 11.4 N; 50°44'

2. 19.15 N; 16.07 N

3. $x = t; y = 6t - 2$

4. $y = -\dfrac{1}{6}x + \dfrac{16}{3}$

5. $y = -\dfrac{4}{3}x - \dfrac{34}{3}$

1. 44.0 ft

2. 19.8 ft

3. 2.65 s

4. at about the 30-yard line the opposite side of the field, or about 45 yards (134 ft) down the field

5. 28.1 ft

1. vert. = 7.05 in.; horiz. = 9.71 in.

2. 39.6 cm

3. 6.71 miles

4. ≈ 7.1 cm

5. (−5, 1, −13)

6. 10

7. 11.05

8. 17.55

9. $5\vec{i} + 3\vec{j} - 4\vec{k}$

10. (−12, −30, −72)

11. (8, 4)

12. (11, 8)

13. (12, −1, 24)

14. (7, −29, −30)

15. (29, 16)

16. −4; no

17. 0; yes

18. (5, −45, 21)

19. (14, 16, 10)

20. Sample answer: (1, 0, −3)

1. C

2. D

3. A

4. C

5. B

6. D

7. B

8. A

9. C

10. D

Answers, Unit 2 Test

1. true

2. 81 cm²

3. $\dfrac{5x}{\sqrt{26}} + \dfrac{y}{\sqrt{26}} - \dfrac{2}{\sqrt{26}} = 0$

4. See students' graphs.

5. 5π inches

6. v: 11.3 cm; h: 14.4 cm

7. $x = t,$ $y = 5t - 2$

8. $\dfrac{\pi}{6}$

9. no solution

10. $\dfrac{\sqrt{6} + \sqrt{2}}{4}$

11. 7.6 units

12. −2; no

13. $\dfrac{2\sqrt{13}}{13}$

14. $270° + 360k°$

15. See students' graphs.

16. (−18, 12)

17. $-20\vec{i} - 3\vec{j} + 19\vec{k}$

18. 40.9°

19. $\dfrac{2\sqrt{7}}{7}$

20. 270°

21. $\beta = \arctan \dfrac{\sqrt{3}}{3}$

22. See students' work.

23. (7, 22, 2); yes

24. 96.2 cm

25. $-\dfrac{24}{7}$

26. See students' graphs.

27. 140°

28. 28.2 N; 10.3 N

29. 2, 360°, 0°

30. $\dfrac{4\sqrt{65}}{65}$

31. 335.4 feet

32. 30°

33. $a = 96.2,$ $B = 22°$ $C = 32°$

34. $y = \dfrac{1}{3}x + \dfrac{10}{3}$

35. See students' work.

36. $y = \text{Arccos } x;$ See students' graphs.

37. $\dfrac{1}{4}$

38. 83.8 cm²

39. 40°

40. yes

Answers, Chapter 9 Test Form 1A & 1B

1. B

2. D

3. B

4. A

5. A

6. C

7. B

8. B

9. D

10. B

11. B

12. A

13. C

14. D

15. C

16. A

17. B

18. D

19. C

20. C

Bonus: A

1. D

2. A

3. D

4. B

5. B

6. B

7. C

8. A

9. D

10. B

11. A

12. A

13. C

14. C

15. B

16. A

17. C

18. A

19. D

20. C

Bonus: A

Glencoe Division, Macmillan/McGraw-Hill

1. See students' graphs.

2. Sample answer: $\left(-6, \dfrac{-7\pi}{6}\right)$

3. See students' graphs.

4. See students' graphs; cardioid

5. $\left(2, \dfrac{3\pi}{4}\right)$

6. $(-0.35, -3.98)$

7. $r = 3 \sec \theta$

8. $x^2 + y^2 = 5$

9. See students' graphs.

10. $1 = r \cos (\theta - 37°)$

11. -7

12. $17 - 7i$

13. 49

14. $3 + 2i$

15. $8(\cos \pi + i \sin \pi)$

16. $-3.27 - 3.78i$

17. $-4i$

18. $-\dfrac{4}{9}$

19. 1

20. $2i$

Bonus: $2\sqrt{3}(\cos 330° + i \sin 330°)$

1. See students' graphs.

2. Sample answer: (1.5, 210°)

3. See students' graphs.

4. See students' graphs. $r = a\theta$

5. $\left(1, \dfrac{5\pi}{6}\right)$

6. $\left(-2, 2\sqrt{3}\right)$

7. $r \sin \theta = 3$

8. $x = 0$

9. See students' graphs.

10. $\dfrac{4\sqrt{5}}{5} = r \cos (\theta - 63°)$

11. $-2i$

12. $2\sqrt{6} - 2i$

13. $13 - 11i$

14. $\dfrac{18 - 13i}{29}$

15. $\sqrt{2}\left(\cos \dfrac{\pi}{4} + i \sin \dfrac{\pi}{4}\right)$

16. $\sqrt{2} - i\sqrt{2}$

17. $12\sqrt{3} - 12i$

18. $-3\sqrt{3} - 3i$

19. $-8 - 8\sqrt{3}i$

20. $\sqrt{2} + i\sqrt{2}$

Bonus: $2\sqrt{2}(\cos 315° + i \sin 315°)$

1. See students' graphs.
2. Sample answers: (4, 285°); (−4, −255°); (−4, 105°)
3. See students' graphs.
4. See students' graphs.
5. rose

1. $4i + 5$
2. 3
3. $−13 + 8i\sqrt{3}$
4. $\dfrac{−7 − i}{4}$
5. $5 − 2j$
6. $20.69 + 8.28j$
7. $8(\cos 150° + i \sin 150°)$
8. $\sqrt{5}(\cos − 0.46 + i \sin − 0.46)$
9. $−1.98 + 0.28i$
10. $−5\sqrt{2} + 5\sqrt{2}i$

1. $(−3, 135°)$
2. $(0, 3)$
3. $x^2 + y^2 = 4$
4. See students' graphs.
5. $2\sqrt{2} = r \cos (\theta − 45°)$

1. $−4 + 4i$
2. $\dfrac{2i + 3}{2}$
3. $6 − 6i$
4. $2i$
5a. 4
5b. $1 + i, 1 − i$

1. **Sample answers:
(−25, 150°), (−25, 510°),
(25, −30°), (25, 330°)**

2. **Sample answers: $\left(-2, \frac{4\pi}{3}\right)$,
$\left(2, \frac{-5\pi}{3}\right)$, $\left(-2, -\frac{2\pi}{3}\right)$, $\left(2, \frac{7\pi}{3}\right)$**

3. **See students'
graphs.**

4. **See students'
graphs.**

5. **See students'
graphs.**

6. **See students'
graphs.**

7. **limaçon**

8. **spiral of
Archimedes**

9. **Sample answer: $\left(4, \frac{4\pi}{3}\right)$**

10. **Sample answer: $\left(2, \frac{4\pi}{3}\right)$**

11. **$\left(\frac{-3\sqrt{3}}{2}, \frac{3}{2}\right)$**

12. **$\left(-1, -\sqrt{3}\right)$**

13. **$r = -3 \csc \theta$**

14. **$y = -4$**

15. **See students'
graphs.**

16. **See students'
graphs.**

1. **D**
2. **B**
3. **A**
4. **C**
5. **A**
6. **B**
7. **D**
8. **C**
9. **C**

Answers, Chapter 10 Test Form 1A & 1B

1. __C__		1. __B__	
2. __B__	12. __C__	2. __C__	12. __B__
3. __A__	13. __D__	3. __A__	13. __C__
4. __C__	14. __D__	4. __D__	14. __D__
5. __C__	15. __A__	5. __B__	15. __D__
6. __B__	16. __C__	6. __B__	16. __D__
7. __B__	17. __B__	7. __B__	17. __A__
8. __D__	18. __A__	8. __B__	18. __D__
9. __A__	19. __B__	9. __B__	19. __C__
10. __C__	20. __B__	10. __B__	20. __B__
11. __A__	Bonus: __C__	11. __A__	Bonus: __B__

Glencoe Division, Macmillan/McGraw-Hill

1. __parabola__

2. $(-2.2, -3.4);$ $(1.4, 3.8)$

3. __no solution__

4. $(x + 1)^2 +$ $(y - 1)^2 = 4$

5. __See students' work.__

6. $(1, 2); (1, 2 \pm 3\sqrt{2});$ $(1, 5), (1, -1);$ $y - 2 = \pm(x - 1)$

7. __See students' work.__

8. $\dfrac{\sqrt{7}}{4}$

9. $y = 8;$ $x = -1$

10. __hyperbola; 19°__

11. $(y - 2)^2 =$ $-6\left(x - \frac{1}{2}\right)$

12. __See students' work.__

13. $x^2 + 2\sqrt{3}xy -$ $y^2 + 32 = 0$

14. $(y - 2)^2 =$ $4(4)(x - 1); (5, 2);$ $(1, 2); x = -3; y = 2$

15. $\dfrac{x^2}{55} + \dfrac{y^2}{64} = 1$

16. $(1, 0); (1 \pm \sqrt{5}, 0);$ $(4, 0), (-2, 0), (1, \pm 2)$

17. __See students' work.__

18. $\sqrt{70}$

19. $\dfrac{(x - 2)^2}{36} - \dfrac{(y + 2)^2}{36} = 1$

20. __See students' work.__

Bonus: $(1,3)$

Glencoe Division, Macmillan/McGraw-Hill

1. **ellipse**

2. **(2.3, –1.6); (0.5, 2.0)**

3. **no solution**

4. $(x + 1)^2 + (y - 2)^2 = 4$

5. **See students' work.**

6. $(-1, 0); (-1 \pm \sqrt{2}, 0); (0, 0), (-2, 0); y = \pm(x + 1)$

7. **See students' work.**

8. $\dfrac{5}{4}$

9. $x + y - 14 = 0; x - y - 2 = 0$

10. **hyperbola, 333°**

11. $(x - 1)^2 = 4(3)(y + 2)$

12. **See students' work.**

13. $21x^2 + 10\sqrt{3}xy + 31y^2 = 144$

14. $(x - 2)^2 = 4(4)(y - 1); (2, 5); (2, 1); y = -3; x = 2$

15. $\dfrac{(x - 2)^2}{55} + \dfrac{y^2}{64} = 1$

16. $(1, 0); (1, \pm\sqrt{5}); (1, 3), (1, -3), (3, 0), (-2, 0)$

17. **See students' work.**

18. **4**

19. $\dfrac{(x - 1)^2}{16} - \dfrac{(y + 2)^2}{16} = 1$

20. **See students' work.**

Bonus: **(1, –2)**

Answers, Chapter 10 Quizzes

1. $(x + 2)^2 + (y - 2)^2 = 24$

2. $(x + 3)^2 + (y - 4)^2 = 117$

3. $(x - 2)^2 = 4(-2)(y + 1)$ $(2, -3)$; $(2, -1)$; $y = 1$; $x = 2$

4. $(y - 3)^2 = 4(-3)(x - 1)$; See students' work.

5. $(x + 2)^2 + (y - 3)^2 = 25$

1. $(-2, 1)$; $(-2 \pm \sqrt{5}, 1)$; $(1, 1)$, $(-5, 1)$, $(-2, 3)$, $(-2, -1)$; See students' work.

2. $\dfrac{(x - 2)^2}{36} + \dfrac{(y + 2)^2}{20} = 1$

3. See students' work

4. $\dfrac{(x + 2)^2}{4} - \dfrac{(y - 3)^2}{5} = 1$

5. an ellipse

1. $\sqrt{5}$

2. ellipse; $\dfrac{(x - 1)^2}{9} + \dfrac{(y + 2)^2}{1} = 1$

3. $\dfrac{(y - 4)^2}{9} - \dfrac{x^2}{16} = 1$; See students' graphs.

4. $(x - 1)^2 = 4\left(\dfrac{1}{6}\right)(y + 2)$

5. $xy = -8$

1. See students' work.

2. $(3, 0.3)$; $(-3, -0.3)$; $(0.3, 3)$; $(-0.3, -3)$

3. $2x + 3y - 13 = 0$; $3x - 2y = 0$

4. $\sqrt{11}$

5. $y = \pm 2$

Glencoe Division, Macmillan/McGraw-Hill

1. $\dfrac{(x+1)^2}{16}+\dfrac{(y+2)^2}{4}=1$
   See students' graphs.

2. $(x-1)^2+$ $(y-3)^2=37$

3. $\dfrac{x^2}{4}+\dfrac{y^2}{13}=1$

4. $(y+3)^2=$ $4(-3)(x-3)$; $(0,-3)$; $(3,-3)$; $x=6$; $y=-3$
   See students' graphs.

5. an ellipse

6. $(0,1)$; $(\pm\sqrt{5},1)$; $(\pm1,1)$; $y=\pm2x+1$; See students' work.

7. $\dfrac{(x+1)^2}{16}-\dfrac{(y-3)^2}{9}=1$

8. $(x+2)^2=$ $4(-3)(y-6)$

9. $(-1,-1)$; $(-1\pm\sqrt{5}, -1)$; $(2,-1)$, $(-4,-1)$, $(-1,1)$, $(-1,-3)$; See students' work.

10. $(x-1)^2+(y-2)^2=16$

1. **C**

2. **B**

3. **A**

4. **A**

5. **D**

6. **B**

7. **A**

8. **C**

9. **A**

10. **D**

11. **A**

12. **A**

Glencoe Division, Macmillan/McGraw-Hill

Answers, Chapter 11 Test Form 1A & 1B

1. **A**

2. **B**

3. **A**

4. **D**

5. **B**

6. **C**

7. **C**

8. **A**

9. **B**

10. **C**

11. **B**

12. **D**

13. **C**

14. **C**

15. **A**

16. **D**

17. **B**

18. **C**

19. **B**

20. **A**

Bonus: **A**

1. **D**

2. **B**

3. **A**

4. **B**

5. **D**

6. **A**

7. **C**

8. **D**

9. **D**

10. **A**

11. **B**

12. **C**

13. **D**

14. **B**

15. **C**

16. **A**

17. **C**

18. **D**

19. **D**

20. **B**

Bonus: **B**

Glencoe Division, Macmillan/McGraw-Hill

1. $\dfrac{3}{2}$

2. $7^{\frac{1}{3}} x^2 y^5$

3. $\sqrt[7]{a^2 b^3 c}$

4. 11.6648

5. 0.2798

6. See students' graphs.

7. See students' graphs.

8. 4.4817

9. 0.6 million ft^3

10. $9397

11. $\log_{27} 3 = \dfrac{1}{3}$

12. $2^3 = x^2 - 1$

13. $\dfrac{5}{2}$

14. 4

15. See students' graphs.

16. −1.3686

17. 2.2756

18. 3.2863

19. $x \le 3.40$

20. 99.49

21. 1.9843

22. −1.9849

23. 0.3679

24. 141.7959

25. 4.6836

Bonus: See students' graphs; 3 points

Answers, Chapter 11 Test Form 2B

1. $\dfrac{1}{2}$

2. $2b^{\frac{2}{3}}$

3. $|x|\sqrt[4]{2x}$

4. 5.4622

5. 3.7263

6. **See students' graphs.**

7. **See students' graphs.**

8. 0.6420

9. $201°F$

10. $\$3111$

11. $\log_{0.2} 0.008 = 3$

12. $7^3 = \left(\sqrt{7}\right)^6$

13. $\dfrac{4}{3}$

14. -3

15. **See students' graphs.**

16. -2.7447

17. $145{,}881$

18. 2.9154

19. -1.5283

20. $x > 1.2325$

21. ± 126.5030

22. 29.3121

23. -1.5041

24. 15.85

25. 0.5493

Bonus: **See students' graphs;** $x = 0$

1. $\dfrac{1}{2}$

2. $35^{\frac{1}{4}} a^{\frac{1}{4}} b^5$

3. $\sqrt[3]{a^2 b}$

4. 451.8079

5. See students' graphs.

1. 0.4973

2. $717

3. $\log_4 \dfrac{1}{16} = -2$

4. 6

5. See students' graphs.

1. 2.8775
2. −1.6635

3. 0.48
4. 1.01

5. 2.87

6. 2.3652
7. $x > 2.3010$

8. −0.6984
9. $x < 2.4265$

10. 2.1534

1. 3.7656

2. 0.9861

3. 0.87

4. 91.97

5. 50%

1. **1**

2. **49**

3. $-3x^2 y^{\frac{3}{5}}$

4. $\sqrt[4]{v^3}$

5. $a^4 \sqrt[3]{b^2 c^2}$

6. **50.4525**

7. **See students' graphs.**

8. **8.8022**

9. **10.5850**

10. **$2210**

11. **$1080**

12. $\log_{10} 100{,}000 = 5$

13. $9x^2 = 24$

14. **12**

15. **−4**

1. **D**

2. **A**

3. **D**

4. **B**

5. **B**

6. **C**

7. **A**

8. **B**

9. **C**

10. **B**

Glencoe Division, Macmillan/McGraw-Hill

1. $\dfrac{1}{2}$

2. ellipse

3. $\left(-\dfrac{1}{2}, \dfrac{5}{2}\right); x = -\dfrac{1}{2}$

4. $r = \pm\sqrt{6}$

5. $\dfrac{1}{13} - \dfrac{5}{13}i$

6. See students' graphs.

7. 8.9588

8. $\dfrac{1}{4913}$

9. $\dfrac{\sqrt{13}}{7}$

10. 2.26

11. $4\sqrt{3} + 4i$

12. cardioid

13. $(x + 3)^2 + (y + 1)^2 = 34$

14. See students' graphs.

15. 0.338

16. $\sqrt{3} + i$

17. 3 units

18. $\dfrac{x^2}{1} + \dfrac{y^2}{4} = 1$

19. $4012

20. 3.5807

21. See students' graphs.

22. ellipse; $\dfrac{(x+3)^2}{64} + \dfrac{(y+1)^2}{5} = 1$ See students' graphs.

23. $(-15.32, 12.86)$

24. $y = \pm\sqrt{3}$

25. -64

26. $2ay^{\frac{5}{3}}$

27. $-8i$

28. See students' graphs; $(3, 1), (-3, -1), (1, 3), (-1, -3)$

29. $8\left(\cos\dfrac{\pi}{2} + i\sin\dfrac{\pi}{2}\right)$

30. 18.7043

31. hyperbola; $\dfrac{(x-5)^2}{25} - \dfrac{(y+2)^2}{4} = 1$

32. $\sqrt{2}x - \sqrt{2}y - 6 = 0$

33. false

34. 2.2335

35. $y\sqrt[3]{x^2 y^2 z}$

36. $(343)^{\frac{1}{3}} = 7$

37. $(x - 8)^2 + (y - 8)^2 = 64;$ $(8, 8); 8$

38. 0.9522

39. 136.0665

40. $\dfrac{1}{4} + \dfrac{i\sqrt{3}}{4}$

41. $(3, 4); x = -1$

42. $x > 1.82$

43. $1 - i\sqrt{3}$

44. ellipse

45. See students' graphs.

46. $y = x$

47. 11.0232

48. $\log_2 64 = 6$

49. $16 - 11i$

50. $C(-1, 0);$ $F(-1 \pm \sqrt{10}, 0)$ $V(-1 \pm \sqrt{2}, 0)$

Glencoe Division, Macmillan/McGraw-Hill

Answers, Chapter 12 Test Form 1A & 1B

1. __A__

2. __D__

3. __B__

4. __A__

5. __C__

6. __A__

7. __B__

8. __D__

9. __A__

10. __D__

11. __A__

12. __C__

13. __D__

14. __D__

15. __C__

16. __D__

17. __A__

18. __B__

19. __B__

20. __C__

Bonus: __C__

1. __B__

2. __C__

3. __B__

4. __C__

5. __B__

6. __A__

7. __D__

8. __D__

9. __C__

10. __B__

11. __A__

12. __C__

13. __D__

14. __C__

15. __A__

16. __B__

17. __A__

18. __C__

19. __A__

20. __A__

Bonus: __B__

Glencoe Division, Macmillan/McGraw-Hill

1. -81

2. $\dfrac{1}{3}$

3. **does not exist**

4. $\dfrac{37}{99}$

5. Sample answer:

$$\sum_{k=1}^{\infty} 2 \cdot 10^{1-2k}$$

6. **does not exist**

7. $\dfrac{33}{25}$

8. $-3 + 4\sqrt{3}$

9. $\dfrac{422}{243}$

10. 396

11. $-7\dfrac{511}{512}$

12. **12.84**

13. $5 + \dfrac{10}{7} + \dfrac{20}{49} ; \dfrac{335}{49}$

14. $16x^4 - 32\sqrt{2}x^3 + 48x^2 - 16\sqrt{2}x + 4$

15. See students' work.

16. **convergent**

17. **divergent**

18. Sample answer:

$$\sum_{k=2}^{10} \dfrac{k^2 - 1}{k}$$

19. $i\pi + 2.5416$

20. $2e^{\frac{11\pi i}{6}}$

Bonus: 64

11. $344,064\, x^3y^6$

1. -250

12. 17.72

13. $1 \cdot 2 + 2 \cdot 3 + 3 \cdot 4 + 4 \cdot 5; 40$

2. 1

14. $8x^3 + 12\sqrt{3}x^2 + 18x + 3\sqrt{3}$

3. does not exist

4. $\dfrac{98}{99}$

15. See students' work.

Sample answer:

5. $\displaystyle\sum_{k=1}^{\infty} 35 \cdot 10^{-2k}$

16. convergent

6. $\dfrac{6}{5}$

17. divergent

7. does not exist

18. $\displaystyle\sum_{k=2}^{11} \dfrac{(k-1)(k-2)}{k}$

8. $8 + 8\sqrt{3}$

19. $i\pi + 2.5953$

9. $\dfrac{422}{405}$

20. $4\sqrt{2}e^{\frac{7\pi i}{4}}$

Bonus: 128

10. 1045

1. $\underline{\qquad 7.7 \qquad}$

2. $\dfrac{1}{3}, \pm\dfrac{\sqrt{5}}{9}, \dfrac{5}{27}, \cdots$

3. $\underline{\qquad 20.78125 \qquad}$

4. $\underline{\qquad 9\sqrt{5} \qquad}$

5. $\underline{-44\left(\sqrt{3} + \sqrt{5}\right)}$

1. $2 + \dfrac{1}{2} + 4 + \dfrac{1}{2} + 8 + \dfrac{1}{2}; \; 15\dfrac{1}{2}$

2. $81a^4 - 108a^3d + 54a^2d^2 - 12ad^3 + d^4$

3. $6{,}928{,}416\sqrt{2}\,a^7$

4. Sample answer:
$\displaystyle\sum_{k=1}^{\infty} \dfrac{16}{81}\left(\dfrac{3}{2}\right)k^{-1}$

5. $\underline{\qquad 35 \qquad}$

1. **does not exist**

2. $\underline{\qquad 1 \qquad}$

3. $-\dfrac{25}{24}$

4. **does not exist**

5. **divergent**

1. $\underline{\qquad 36.77 \qquad}$

2. **See students' work.**

3. $i\pi - 1.001$

4. $2e^{\frac{2\pi j}{3}}$

5. **See students' work.**

Answers, Chapter 12 Mid-Chapter Test, Standardized Test

1. $\frac{\sqrt{2}}{16}$
2. 9
3. 0
4. $-\frac{9310}{729}$
5. convergent
6. 50,500
7. divergent
8. $-3 + 37\sqrt{11}$
9. $\frac{72}{5}$
10. does not exist

1. C
2. B
3. C
4. C
5. B
6. A
7. A
8. D
9. B
10. D
11. B
12. B
13. D
14. A

Answers, Chapter 13 Test Form 1A & 1B

1. __B__

2. __D__

3. __A__

4. __D__

5. __C__

6. __D__

7. __B__

8. __A__

9. __D__

10. __C__

11. __B__

12. __A__

13. __C__

14. __C__

15. __D__

Bonus: __B__

1. __A__

2. __C__

3. __A__

4. __A__

5. __B__

6. __B__

7. __A__

8. __D__

9. __B__

10. __C__

11. __D__

12. __D__

13. __B__

14. __B__

15. __C__

Bonus: __C__

Glencoe Division, Macmillan/McGraw-Hill

1. $-\dfrac{1}{9}, -\dfrac{1}{81}, -\dfrac{1}{6561}$

2. 0.42

3. See students' graphs.

4. See students' graphs.

5. $m = 0.3$; staircase in

6. $(-5, -5)$

7. attractor

8. attractor

9. $(0.5, 0.3)$

10. $(-1, -1)$

11. period -2 attractor

12. $z_1 = 7 + 3i$, $z_2 = 22 + 9i$, $z_3 = 67 + 27i$,

13. $2 + i, 4 + 5i$ $-8 + 41i$

14. escape set

15. disconnected

16. outside

17. yellow

18. orange

19. orange

20. $4761, $5037.14, $5329.29

Bonus: Answers will vary.

1. $-3, -15, -255$

2. 28.23

3. See students' graphs.

4. See students' graphs.

5. $m = -4$; spiral out

6. $(0.5, 0.5)$

7. repeller

8. repeller

9. $(0.5, 0.1)$

10. $\left(\dfrac{1}{6}, \dfrac{1}{6}\right)$

11. period-3 attractor

12. $2 - i,$ $1 - 0.5i,$ $0.5 - 0.25i$

13. $i, -1 + i, -i$

14. escape set

15. connected

16. outside

17. orange

18. orange

19. light blue

20. $346.13, $368.62, $392.58

Bonus: Answers will vary.

1. -10.3, -1081.4

2. $2.8, -6.3$

3. See students' graphs; spiral in

4. staircase out

5. repeller

1. $\left(\dfrac{7}{12}, \dfrac{7}{12}\right); (0, 0)$

2. $\left(\dfrac{4}{9}, \dfrac{4}{9}\right); (0, 0)$

3. $(0.5, -0.075)$

4. period-2 attractor

5. fixed point attractor

1. $6 - i, 12 - i, 24 - i$

2. $-1 + 2i$ $-4 - 2i, 11 + 18i$

3. $5 - 3i, 6 - 5i, 7 - 7i, 8 - 9i$

4. See students' graphs.

1. escape set

2. disconnected

3. outside

4. no

5. It escapes.

1. 4, 16, 256

2. 0.84, 0.19, 0.97

3. See students' graphs; 2; staircase out

4. See students' graphs; $-\frac{1}{2}$; spiral in

5. $\left(\frac{5}{3}, \frac{5}{3}\right)$; repeller

6. $\left(\frac{1}{3}, \frac{1}{3}\right)$; attractor

7. $\left(\frac{1}{2}, \frac{7}{20}\right)$

8. $\left(\frac{1}{2}, \frac{1}{5}\right)$

9. fixed-point attractor

10. period-2 attractor

1. B

2. C

3. A

4. C

5. B

6. B

7. D

8. B

9. A

Answers, Chapter 14 Test Form 1A & 1B

1. __C__

2. __B__

3. __B__

4. __A__

5. __D__

6. __C__

7. __B__

8. __A__

9. __A__

10. __A__

11. __D__

12. __B__

13. __A__

14. __C__

15. __A__

16. __D__

17. __B__

18. __A__

19. __C__

20. __D__

Bonus: __B__

1. __D__

2. __A__

3. __B__

4. __D__

5. __C__

6. __D__

7. __D__

8. __B__

9. __B__

10. __A__

11. __C__

12. __B__

13. __A__

14. __A__

15. __D__

16. __C__

17. __B__

18. __B__

19. __C__

20. __D__

Bonus: __A__

Glencoe Division, Macmillan/McGraw-Hill

Answers, Chapter 14 Test Form 2A

1. **24**

2. **5040**

3. **420**

4. **6**

5. **2520**

6. **792**

7. **9**

8. $\dfrac{7}{22}$

9. $\dfrac{1}{4}$

10. $\dfrac{7}{40}$

11. $\dfrac{16}{49}$

12. $\dfrac{36}{65}$

13. $\dfrac{11}{32}$

14. $\dfrac{10}{11}$

15. $\dfrac{2}{15}$

16. $\dfrac{4}{7}$

17. $\dfrac{1}{4}$

18. $\dfrac{1}{256}$

19. $\dfrac{3087}{10,000}$

20. $\dfrac{7}{432}$

Bonus: $\dfrac{1}{2}$

1. _____ **840** _____

2. _____ **362,880** _____

3. _____ **120** _____

4. _____ **60** _____

5. _____ **780** _____

6. _____ **45** _____

7. _____ $\dfrac{4}{7}$ _____

8. _____ $\dfrac{1}{35}$ _____

9. _____ $\dfrac{1}{19}$ _____

10. _____ $\dfrac{15}{196}$ _____

11. _____ $\dfrac{1}{8}$ _____

12. _____ $\dfrac{11}{30}$ _____

13. _____ $\dfrac{2}{27}$ _____

14. _____ **0** _____

15. _____ $\dfrac{1}{3}$ _____

16. _____ $\dfrac{1}{2}$ _____

17. _____ $\dfrac{7}{32}$ _____

18. _____ $\dfrac{5}{16}$ _____

19. _____ $\dfrac{8}{9}$ _____

20. _____ $\dfrac{6561}{10,000}$ _____

Bonus: _____ **86,400** _____

Answers, Chapter 14 Quizzes

1. _____ **24** _____

2. _____ **24** _____

3. _____ **4200** _____

4. _____ **720** _____

5. _____ **360** _____

1. _____ $\dfrac{1}{1000}$ _____

2. _____ $\dfrac{7}{50}$ or 14% _____

3. _____ $\dfrac{1}{12}$ _____

4. _____ $\dfrac{63}{221}$ _____

5. _____ $\dfrac{15}{34}$ _____

1. _____ **1120** _____

2. _____ **12** _____

3. _____ **210** _____

4. _____ $\dfrac{9}{20}$ _____

5. _____ $\dfrac{33}{62}$ _____

1. _____ $\dfrac{1}{2}$ _____

2. _____ $\dfrac{3}{10}$ _____

3. _____ $\dfrac{1}{9}$ _____

4. _____ $\dfrac{1}{32}$ _____

5. _____ $\dfrac{9}{256}$ _____

Answers, Chapter 14 Mid-Chapter Test, Standardized Test

1. **16**

2. **210**

3. **8**

4. **72**

5. **12**

6. **10**

7. **_C_(16, 9)**

8. **420**

9. **$\dfrac{2}{5}$**

10. **$\dfrac{858}{19{,}967}$**

1. **C**

2. **A**

3. **B**

4. **D**

5. **B**

6. **A**

7. **A**

8. **C**

9. **D**

10. **B**

Glencoe Division, Macmillan/McGraw-Hill

Answers, Chapter 15 Test Form 1A & 1B

1. __B__

2. __C__

3. __B__

4. __D__

5. __A__

6. __A__

7. __D__

8. __B__

9. __D__

10. __A__

11. __D__

12. __C__

13. __A__

14. __C__

15. __B__

16. __D__

17. __A__

18. __A__

19. __C__

20. __A__

Bonus: __B__

1. __B__

2. __C__

3. __B__

4. __C__

5. __C__

6. __D__

7. __C__

8. __A__

9. __B__

10. __A__

11. __C__

12. __C__

13. __D__

14. __A__

15. __B__

16. __B__

17. __C__

18. __A__

19. __D__

20. __C__

Bonus: __A__

Glencoe Division, Macmillan/McGraw-Hill

1. See students' work.

2. 1940, 1960

3. 1980

4. 21

5. 85

6. 87

7. 15

8. 9.1

9. 78, 87, 91.5

10. 13.5

11. See students' work.

12. 38.3%

13. 95%

14. 379 to 421

15. 0.053

16. 5.1205−5.2795

17. 5.7%

18. See students' work.

19. $y = 5.57 + 1.2x$

20. strongly positive

Bonus: 22 or 23

1. See students' work.

2. See students' work.

3. 6%

4. 42%

5. 44

6. 53 and 57

7. 5

8. 4.0%

9. 1.25%

10. See students' work. 9.2

11. 95.5%

12. 107 and 133

13. 86.6%

14. 0.025

15. 2.5355−2.6645

16. 2.57−2.63

17. 0.9999

18. See students' work

19. −0.9955734335

20. strongly negative

Bonus: $y = 34.4 - 2x$

Glencoe Division, Macmillan/McGraw-Hill

1. See students' work.

2. 1990

3. 24.1

4. 2

5. 4.8

1. 56

2. 6.2

3. 13.5

4. 7.0

5. See students' work.

1. 95.5%

2. 615

3. 122

4. 6.7%

5. 136.8–163.2

1. 0.11

2. 5.984–6.416

3. 0.632

4. See students' work.

5. $y = 0.56 + 0.08x$

Answers, Chapter 15 Mid-Chapter Test, Standardized Test

1. See students' work.
2. See students' work.
3. See students' work.
4. $4785
5. $4600
6. $4600 and $5200
7. $1550
8. $950
9. $1233
10. $3552-$6018

1. B
2. A
3. D
4. A
5. C
6. B
7. C
8. A
9. B
10. C

Answers, Chapter 16 Test Form 1A & 1B

9. __B__

1. __B__

10. __C__

11. __A__

2. __D__

3. __C__

12. __D__

4. __D__

5. __D__

13. __D__

6. __D__

14. __A__

15. __D__

7. __D__

8. __B__

Bonus: __A__

1. __D__

9. __A__

2. __A__

10. __C__

3. __B__

11. __D__

4. __C__

12. __A__

5. __A__

13. __C__

6. __A__

14. __B__

15. __C__

7. __B__

8. __B__

Bonus: __B__

Glencoe Division, Macmillan/McGraw-Hill

1. **false**

2. **See students' graphs.**

3. **190**

4. **yes**

5. **path**

6. **no**

7. **no**

8. **Sample answer: *a, b, e, f, g, c, d, h, i***

9. **No, no vertices have an odd degree.**

10. **6; one path is *A, O, E, F, G, H, Z.***

11. ***A, H, F, Z;* 8**

12. **Sample answer: *a, b, c, i, k, e***

13. **11**

14.
$$\begin{array}{c} \quad A\ B\ C\ D \\ \begin{array}{c} A \\ B \\ C \\ D \end{array} \left[\begin{array}{cccc} 0 & 0 & 0 & 1 \\ 3 & 0 & 0 & 0 \\ 0 & 1 & 0 & 0 \\ 0 & 0 & 1 & 1 \end{array} \right] \end{array}$$

15. **See students' graphs.**

Bonus: **See students' graphs.**

Answers, Chapter 16 Test Form 2B

1. **true**

2. **See students' graphs.**

3. **55**

4. **no**

5. **cycle**

6. **yes**

7. **yes**

8. **Yes; it is connected and each vertex has an even degree.**

9. Sample answer: **a, b, f, e, g, c, d**

10. **5; one path is A, P, Q, T, S, Z.**

11. **A, B, F, Z; 5**

12. Sample answer: **b, c, i, h, f**

13. **17**

14.

$$\begin{array}{c c} & \begin{array}{cccc} A & B & C & D \end{array} \\ \begin{array}{c} A \\ B \\ C \\ D \end{array} & \left[\begin{array}{cccc} 1 & 1 & 0 & 0 \\ 0 & 0 & 0 & 1 \\ 0 & 1 & 0 & 0 \\ 0 & 0 & 1 & 0 \end{array} \right] \end{array}$$

15. **See students' graphs.**

Bonus: **See students' graphs.**

1. **See students' graphs.**

2. **See students' graphs.**

3. **no**

4. **Sample answer: *d, e, f, g***

5. **Yes; it is complete.**

1. **3; one path is *A, S, T, Z*.**

2. **3; the path is *A, N, T, Z*.**

3. **None; *A* and *Z* are not connected.**

4. ***A, B, I, D, Z*; 8**

5. ***A, M, N, D, Q, Z*; 11**

1. **yes**

2. **no**

3. **yes**

4. **No; each vertex does not have an even degree.**

5. **No; all vertices have an odd degree.**

1. **yes**

2. **Sample answer: *c, b, a, j, i, h, g, f, e***

3. **16**

4.
$$
\begin{array}{c}
 \begin{array}{cccc} U & V & W & X \end{array} \\
\begin{array}{c} U \\ V \\ W \\ X \end{array}
\left[
\begin{array}{cccc}
0 & 1 & 1 & 1 \\
0 & 0 & 0 & 1 \\
0 & 0 & 0 & 1 \\
0 & 0 & 0 & 0
\end{array}
\right]
\end{array}
$$

5. **See students' graphs.**

Answers, Chapter 16 Mid-Chapter Test, Standardized Test

1. **true**

2. **c, d, and e**

3. **See students' graphs.**

4. **28**

5. **yes**

6. **a, j**

7. **circuit**

8. **Sample answer: d, b, c, g, h**

9. **yes**

10. **No; it is not connected.**

ͻs.

1. **B**

2. **D**

3. **A**

4. **C**

5. **A**

6. **B**

7. **A**

8. **B**

9. **A**

10. **C**

Glencoe Division, Macmillan/McGraw-Hill

1. connected

2. 49.65%

3. no

4. 128

5. $\dfrac{1}{21}$

6. $\sqrt{2}e^{i\frac{\pi}{4}}$

7. (0.5, 0.475)

8. true

9. 7; *A, G, E, Z*

10. See students' graphs; spiral out

11. See students' graphs; significantly positive

12. 10,080

13. convergent

14. $-1, -i, -1 - 2i$

15. 91

16. $\dfrac{64}{125}$

17. $x^3 - 6x^2y + 12xy^2 - 8y^3$

18. Sample answer: *a, b, k, l, d, n, g, f*

19. −2; attractor

20. 20

21. 10; 20.5, 30.5, 40.5, 50.5, 60.5

22. 15

23. 2, 2, 2

24. circuit

25. does not exist

26. $\dfrac{3}{5}$

27.
	U	V	W	X
U	1	1	0	0
V	1	0	2	0
W	0	2	0	2
X	0	0	2	0

28. true

29.
4	2
5	1 3 3 9
6	1
7	5
8	
9	
10	0 4|2 = 42

30. mean: 61.75; median: 56; mode: 53

31. $\dfrac{1}{221}$

32. $\dfrac{4}{11}$

33. 15.85%

34. no; contai cycles

35. 149

36. $\dfrac{3}{10}$

37. 0.36; 35.07 36.93

38. true

39. no

40. 125.48 − 1

Answers, Chapter 17 Test Form 1A & 1B

1. C

2. B

3. D

4. A

5. C

6. C

7. B

8. C

9. D

10. A

11. C

12. B

13. C

14. B

15. D

Bonus: B

1. B

2. D

3. A

4. B

5. A

6. C

7. D

8. C

9. D

10. D

11. B

12. C

13. D

14. A

15. C

Bonus: C

Glencoe Division, Macmillan/McGraw-Hill

1. 72

2. 1

3. -1

4. -9

5. 81

6. $25x^4 - 16x^3 - 9x^2$

7. $24x^2$

8. $14x^6 - 24x^3$

9. $\dfrac{\sqrt{3x}}{2x}$

10. $\dfrac{5x^2 - 1}{4x^2}$

11. $\dfrac{1}{5}$ sq units

12. $\dfrac{32}{3}$ sq units

13. $\dfrac{81}{4}$ sq units

14. $\dfrac{9}{2}$ sq. units

15. $\dfrac{1}{3}$ sq. units

16. $15x + C$

17. $x^3 + 2x^2 - x + C$

18. $\dfrac{7x^4}{4} + \pi x + C$

19. $\dfrac{3x^6}{2} + C$

20. $g(x) = 3x^2 + \dfrac{162}{x} + C$

21. $\dfrac{2}{3}$

22. 0

23. $-\dfrac{4}{3}$

24. $\dfrac{16}{3}$ sq. units

25. $\dfrac{157}{12}$ sq. units

Bonus: $\dfrac{2}{\sqrt{x}} - \dfrac{5}{2x\sqrt{x}}$ or $\dfrac{4x\sqrt{x} - 5\sqrt{x}}{2x^2}$

Glencoe Division, Macmillan/McGraw-Hill

1. 5

2. $-\dfrac{4}{3}$

3. 3

4. -8

5. $\dfrac{1}{4}$

6. $6x^5 + 8x^3 + 6x$

7. 3

8. $\dfrac{x+3}{\sqrt{x^2+6x+4}}$

9. $7x^6 + 20x^4$

10. $-\dfrac{16}{x^5}$

11. $\dfrac{64}{3}$ sq. units

12. $\dfrac{32}{5}$ sq. units

13. $\dfrac{16}{3}$ sq. units

14. $\dfrac{1}{3}$ sq. units

15. $3.2\sqrt{2}$ sq. units

16. $25x^4 + C$

17. $\dfrac{(x-7)^{11}}{11} + C$

18. $-3x^3 + 2x^2 + C$

19. $-\dfrac{1}{3x^3} - \dfrac{x^3}{3} + C$

20. $h(t) = -5t^2 + 30t + C$

21. $\dfrac{16}{3}$

22. 12

23. $\dfrac{125}{6}$

24. $\dfrac{49}{4}$ sq. units

25. 8 sq. units

Bonus: $-\dfrac{\sqrt{5}}{25}$

1. 3
2. -4
3. 10

4. -13
5. 0
6. 0
7. $3x^2 - 2$
8. $8x^3 - 4x$
9. $\dfrac{\sqrt{x}}{2x}$
10. $\dfrac{3}{2\sqrt{3x+4}}$

1. $-5x + C$
2. $\dfrac{x^4}{12} - \dfrac{2x^3}{3} + 10x + C$
3. $-2\sqrt{1 + x^2} + C$
4. $\dfrac{5x\sqrt[5]{x}}{2} + C$
5. $v(t) = 3t^2 - 6t + C$

1. 72 sq. units
2. $\dfrac{1}{2}$ sq. units
3. $\dfrac{a^5}{5}$ sq. units
4. $\dfrac{7}{6}$ sq. units
5. $\dfrac{4}{3}$ sq. units

1. $\dfrac{9}{2}$
2. $\dfrac{9}{2}$
3. 66
4. 8 sq. units
5. $\dfrac{32}{3}$ sq. units

1. 3

2. 1

3. $\dfrac{1}{6}$

4. 2

5. -25

6. -7

7. $12x$

8. -10

9. $\dfrac{-\sqrt[3]{x^2}}{3x^2}$

10. $9x^2 - 8x$

11. $45x^2 - 12x$

12. $9x^2(x^3 - 6)^2$

13. $\dfrac{-2\sqrt{x}}{x^2}$

14. $\dfrac{4x^2 + 16x + 1}{x^2 + 4x + 4}$

15. $\dfrac{81}{4}$ sq. units

16. 39 sq. units

17. 9 sq. units

18. 120 feet

19. $\dfrac{1}{6}$ sq. unit

20. $\dfrac{3}{4}$ sq. unit

---

1. **B**

2. **B**

3. **A**

4. **C**

5. **C**

6. **A**

7. **D**

8. **C**

9. **C**

10. **B**

Glencoe Division, Macmillan/McGraw-Hill

Answers, Semester 1 Test (3 multiple choice pages)

1. D

2. B

3. B

4. A

5. B

6. A

7. C

8. C

9. B

10. D

11. C

12. D

13. B

14. A

15. B

16. A

17. A

18. D

19. C

20. D

21. A

22. C

23. B

24. A

25. D

Glencoe Division, Macmillan/McGraw-Hill

Answers, Semester 1 Test (2 free-response pages)

26. $f(x) = x - 3$

27. $y = -\frac{3}{2}x - \frac{5}{2}$

28. $0°, 120°$

29. $\begin{bmatrix} 10 & -6 \\ -6 & 10 \end{bmatrix}$

30. $12.86, -15.32$

31. $y = x + 1$

32. $\dfrac{-5 \pm \sqrt{10}}{5}$

33. $y = \cot x$;
See students' graphs.

34. 1.0098

35. $y = -\frac{1}{3}x + \frac{7}{3}$

36. 5.864 cm

37. $(-13, 13)$

38. infinite discontinuity

39. 3.2 units

40. $-2, -0.5, 4$

41. $4; 360°$

42. See students' graphs; $(-2, 1)$, $(0.5, 1)$, $(3, 6)$; min: -10; max: 0

43. yes

44. Sample answer: $y = -5 \cos \dfrac{\pi t}{3}$

45. $\dfrac{6\sqrt{2} - \sqrt{7}}{12}$

46. 1.5

47. $(8, -7, -9)$

48. $A = 10.89°$
$B = 49.10°$
$c = 45.83$

49. translated 1 unit to the right

50. $\begin{bmatrix} -\frac{5}{2} & \frac{3}{2} \\ -2 & 1 \end{bmatrix}$

Glencoe Division, Macmillan/McGraw-Hill

Answers, Semester 2 Test (3 multiple choice pages)

1. C

2. A

3. C

4. C

5. A

6. A

7. B

8. D

9. D

10. B

11. A

12. D

13. A

14. B

15. C

16. A

17. B

18. A

19. B

20. D

21. B

22. A

23. D

24. A

25. B

26. yes

27. 4; one path is A, D, E, F, Z.

28. 1.20

29. $\dfrac{7}{32}$

30. (−15.32, 12.86)

31. $\lim\limits_{n \to \infty} \sum\limits_{i=1}^{n} \left(\dfrac{3i}{n}\right)^2 \left(\dfrac{3}{n}\right)$
9 sq. units

32. $\dfrac{1}{4}, \dfrac{1}{2}, 1, 2$

33. Sample answer:
$3x - 10y = -80$

34. $y = -x^2 + 2x + 3$

35. period-2 attractor

36. $\dfrac{(x-2)^{11}}{11} + C$

37. $\dfrac{3}{13}$

38. 1287

39. false

40. $\dfrac{1}{4} + \dfrac{i\sqrt{3}}{4}$

41. 360

42. outside

43. −117

44. $2\sqrt{3} + 2i$

45. Euler path

46. 8.69

47. Sample answer:
50,000, 70,000,
90,000, 110,000,
130,000, 150,000

48. 14.4 feet

49. $\dfrac{5}{4}$

50. See students' graphs.

Glencoe Division, Macmillan/McGraw-Hill

Answers, Final Test (2 multiple choice pages)

1. __B__

2. __A__

3. __A__

4. __A__

5. __C__

6. __D__

7. __D__

8. __A__

9. __D__

10. __D__

11. __D__

12. __D__

13. __A__

14. __D__

Glencoe Division, Macmillan/McGraw-Hill

Answers, Final Test (2 multiple choice pages)

15. __C__

16. __B__

17. __B__

18. __B__

19. __B__

20. __A__

21. __A__

22. __D__

23. __B__

24. __B__

25. __D__

26. __B__

27. __B__

28. __A__

29. __C__

30. __C__

31. **does not exist**

32. **271.4 cm^2**

33. **outside**

34. $\left(\dfrac{20}{7}, \dfrac{6}{7}\right)$

35. **3; 135°**

36. **$579.36 - $620.64**

37. **See students' graphs.**

38. $\dfrac{(x-5)^2}{25} + \dfrac{(y+3)^2}{9} = 1$

39. $\dfrac{500}{3}$ **units^2**

40. **true**

41. $\dfrac{1}{8}$

42. **0 or 2; 1; 1, 2, −5**

43. **14 years**

44. **17.2 feet**

45. **false**

46. **Sample answers: (−8, 60°), (8, −120°), (8, 240°), (−8 ,420°)**

47. **$2\sqrt{13}$**

48. **−1.7434**

49. **0 - 25**

50. **$16y^2 - 9x^2 = 144$**

51. **45°, 135°**

52. $\dfrac{255}{4}$ **units^2**

Glencoe Division, Macmillan/McGraw-Hill

53. $x \to \infty, f(x) \to -\infty;$ $x \to -\infty, f(x) \to -\infty.$

54. alternate optimal solutions

55. $-\dfrac{1}{2}$

56. 362,880

57. $\sqrt{2}e^{i\left(\frac{5\pi}{4}\right)}$

58. $-3i + 2, -4i + 4, -5i + 6$

59. (5.4, 5.9)

60. no real solution

61. Sample answer: $y = \pm 4 \sin \frac{4}{3}\theta$

62. See students' graphs; (0, –3), (1.6, 3.4)

63. (0, 0), (1, 0.5), (1, –0.5), (2, 1), (2, –1); no

64. $-6\vec{i} + 2\vec{j} + 3\vec{k}$

65. See students' work.

66. (2, –1, 3)

67. $\dfrac{55}{221}$

68. trail

69. 2.17

70. csc x

71. $h(t) = 1600t - 16t^2$

72. (4, –3)

73. 16,384

74. $-\tan 45°$

75. $m > 1$

Glencoe Division, Macmillan/McGraw-Hill